Flame Emission and Atomic Absorption Spectrometry

VOLUME 1 — *THEORY*

Flame Emission and Atomic Absorption Spectrometry

EDITED BY

John A. Dean

DEPARTMENT OF CHEMISTRY
UNIVERSITY OF TENNESSEE
KNOXVILLE, TENNESSEE

AND

Theodore C. Rains

ANALYTICAL CHEMISTRY DIVISION
NATIONAL BUREAU OF STANDARDS
WASHINGTON, D. C.

VOLUME 1 *THEORY*

M A R C E L   D E K K E R   *New York and London*   *1969*

CHEMISTRY

MARCEL DEKKER, INC.
95 *Madison Avenue, New York, New York* 10016

UNITED KINGDOM EDITION

Published by

MARCEL DEKKER LTD.
14 *Craufurd Rise, Maidenhead, Berkshire, England*

LIBRARY OF CONGRESS CATALOG CARD NUMBER 76-78830

PRINTED IN THE UNITED STATES OF AMERICA

Preface

The Editors are bringing together in a treatise of three volumes the various aspects of flame emission, atomic-absorption, and atomic-fluorescence spectrometric methods. These volumes provide a source of theoretical and practical analytical information for all inquisitive persons who are either engaged in or considering the use of these flame spectrometric methods, both the novice and the experienced. We were fortunate to enlist the aid of a considerable number of authorities from all areas of the world. These authors accepted the invitation to participate and to discuss criticaliy the theory or state of the art as it pertains to their assigned topics.

Volume 1 is devoted to the theoretical aspects of the several flame methods. It commences with a general historical survey and inter-comparison of the methods with each other and with other competitive analytical methods. This is followed by chapters that discuss excitation mechanisms, flames, flame emission spectra, species in existence in flame gases, interferences of all types, accuracy and precision, and interrelationships among operational parameters and spectral features. From these chapters the reader will achieve a better understanding of the numerous problems facing a flame photometrist. A knowledge of the limitations of a particular flame method is a *sine qua non* for the person concerned with wrestling quantitative data from an observed spectra.

Volume 2 considers instrumentation and operational techniques. There are chapters on the optical train, light sources for atomic absorption and atomic fluorescence, electronic equipment, burners and nebulizers, and a description of all available commercial instruments. The chapters on instrumentation will provide the reader with a better perspective of equipment available and perhaps the insight necessary to assemble his own experimental arrangements from individual components. The sections on general operations and techniques provide detailed suggestions, beginning with the dissolution of the sample, intermediate steps such as removal or sequestering interferences, measurement of the emission or absorption signal, and continuing through the evaluation of the data secured. Tables of analytical wavelengths arranged by elements and by wavelengths conclude this volume.

Volume 3 is devoted to the consideration of the individual elements that either can be excited to emit radiation in a flame or in their atomic state can absorb radiation transmitted through the flame gases. The nature of the spectrum and the optimum excitation or absorption conditions for each element are considered; and spectral, chemical, and physical interferences from other cations and anions are discussed. The more important sample matrices are treated in the final chapters of this volume.

Although the editors have made a conscientious effort to unify the material in the several volumes, it is obviously impossible to eliminate a certain amount of duplication. However, overlapping presented by different authors can provide stimulating and, sometimes, controversial viewpoints. The symbols have been standardized throughout the volumes, and a List of Symbols used is given on p. xiii.

March, 1969.   JOHN A. DEAN
                                                        THEODORE C. RAINS

Contributors to Volume 1

C. Th. J. Alkemade, *Fysisch Laboratorium, Rijks-Universiteit, Utrecht, The Netherlands*

B. E. Buell, *Union Oil Company of California, Brea, California*

I. Cornides, *Department of Analytical Chemistry, University of Chemica Industries, Veszprém, Hungary*

A. N. Hambly, *Chemistry Department, Australian National University, Canberra, Australia*

D. R. Jenkins, *Shell Research Ltd., Thornton Research Centre, Chester, U.K.*

Richard N. Kniseley, *Institute of Atomic Research, Department of Chemistry, Iowa State University, Ames, Iowa*

S. R. Koirtyohann, *University of Missouri, Columbia, Missouri*

Robert L. Mitchell, *Macaulay Institute for Soil Research, Craigiebuckler, Aberdeen, Scotland*

E. Pungor, *Department of Analytical Chemistry, University of Chemical Industries, Veszprém, Hungary*

Theodore C. Rains, *Analytical Chemistry Division, National Bureau of Standards, Washington, D.C.*

Juan Ramirez-Muñoz, *Beckman Instruments, Inc., Fullerton, California*

C. S. Rann, *Chemistry Department, Australian National University, Canberra, Australia*

Ivan Rubeška, *Geological Survey of Czechoslovakia, Prague, Czechoslovakia*

R. K. Skogerboe, *Department of Chemistry, Cornell University, Ithaca, New York*

W. Snelleman, *Fysisch Laboratorium, Rijks-Universiteit, Utrecht, The Netherlands*

T. M. Sugden, *Shell Research Ltd, Thornton Research Centre, Chester, U.K.*

Contents

List of Symbols

A	Surface area; rate of spontaneous emission	f	Focal length; oscillator strength
A_{nm}	transition probability of spontaneous emission ($m{\rightarrow}n$ energy level)	$f(u)$	Velocity distribution function
		G^0	Gibb's free energy
		g_0, g_n	Statistical weight of lower energy state
A_{rot}	Rotational transition probability	g_i, g_m	Statistical weight of upper energy state
a	Transmission factor of apparatus	H	Slit height
B	Rotational constant	ΔH	Enthalpy change
B_{mn}	Transition probability of absorption ($n{\rightarrow}m$ energy level)	h	Planck's constant
		I	Intensity; moment of inertia
B_{nm}	Transition probability of induced or stimulated emission ($m{\rightarrow}n$ energy level)	I_λ	Number of photons cm^{-2} $ster^{-1}$ and per unit wavelength
C	Concentration	$I(v)$	Spectral intensity
$\bar{C}$	Average concentration	i	Current
C_p	Specific heat at constant pressure	J	Rotational quantum number
		j	Inner quantum number
c	Speed of light in a vacuum	K	General equilibrium constant
D	Angular dispersion	K_p^d	Equilibrium constant (dissociation reaction)
D_g	Diffusion coefficient (gas)		
D_0	Dissociation energy	K_p^i	Equilibrium constant (ionization reaction)
d	Particle diameter; path length; distance		
E_i	Ionization energy	k	Boltzmann constant; general rate constant
E_m, E_n	Energy of upper and lower electronic state		
		$k(v)$	Absorption coefficient
E_p	Excitation potential	L	Specific heat of vaporization
E_r	Rotational energy	$\mathbf{L}$	Resultant angular momentum
E_{rms}	Root-mean-square voltage signal (noise)	$\mathbf{l}_i$	Orbital angular momentum
		M	Metal atom (symbol)
E_v	Excitation potential	M	Gram atomic or gram molecular weight
e^-	Electron (symbol)	M^*	Atom in excited state
F	Flux transmitting power	m	Mass
		N_m	Population of state m
ΔF	Band width or band pass	N_n	Population of initial state of the atom

m_e	Mass of an electron	Z	Nuclear charge; number of collisions per second
N_i	Number of particles in ith energy level	Z	Collisional partner
N_0	Total number of particles	Z_{mn}	Number of absorbed quanta
n	Number of . . .	Z_{nm}	Number of emitted quanta
n_r	Radial quantum number		
n_ϕ	Azimuthal quantum number	α	Decay rate of recombination reactions
P	Pressure (total); number of photons per second	α_d	Degree of dissociation
p	Partial pressure; ratio of chemical de-excitation to collisional de-excitation at full equilibrium	α_i	Degree of ionization
		β	Radiation coefficient
		δ	Correction terms
P_s	Saturation pressure of vapor at particle surface	η	Viscosity; efficiency of photodetector
Pr	Prandtl number	ι	Capillary length
Q	Partition function	Λ	Projection of resultant angular momentum
q	Charge		
R	Resistance; total rate of recombination	λ	Wavelength; thermal conductivity of gas
R	Rydberg constant	$\Delta\lambda$	Width of absorption line
R_H	Rydberg constant for hydrogen atom	μ	Reduced mass; "true" value (statistics)
$\mathscr{R}$	Gas constant	μ_g	Coefficient of gas viscosity
Re	Reynolds number	ω	Angular momentum
r	Radius	ϕ	Mixture strength (flame gases); ratio of compound formation to total present
S	Spin number; cross-section values; effective area of dispersing element	ϕ_e	Efficiency of photocathode
		ϕ_f	Yield factor
$\mathbf{S}$	Resultant spin	ρ	Density
ΔS	Entropy change	ρ_e	Spectral volume density (at equilibrium)
s	Spin quantum number		
s_t	Standard deviation	$\rho(\nu), \rho(\lambda)$	Spectral density of radiation field
s^2	Variance		
T	Temperature	$\rho_{\Delta\lambda}$	Spectral volume density of radiation field
T_b	Temperature at boiling point		
T_E	Excitation temperature	π	Pi (3.1416)
T_R	Radiation temperature	Ψ	Amplitude of wave associated with moving particle
t	Time		
U_λ	Radiation density	σ	Standard deviation; surface tension
u	Radial velocity		
V	Potential energy	ν	Frequency
V_air	Volume of air	$\bar{\nu}$	Wave number
V	Volume of liquid	τ	Mean lifetime; relaxation time
v	Vibrational quatum number	υ	Velocity
w	Weight	$[\ ]$	Molar concentration (solution); moles cm^{-3} (gases)
X	Negative portion of metal compound (symbol)	∇^2	Laplacian function

Flame Emission and Atomic Absorption Spectrometry

VOLUME 1 — *THEORY*

1 Flame Methods: Their Development and Application

Robert L. Mitchell

MACAULAY INSTITUTE FOR SOIL RESEARCH
CRAIGIEBUCKLER
ABERDEEN, SCOTLAND

I. The Birth of Flame Methods

In 1752 a 26-year-old Glasgow scientist, Thomas Melvill (*1*), described his examination of flames produced by spirits mixed with nitre, sea salt, or other materials by means of a prism illuminated through a round aperture. After giving details of his findings, which included the observation

1

of a preponderance of a bright yellow light, Melvill wrote: "Because the hole appears thro' the prism quite circular and uniform in colour; the bright yellow which prevails so much over the other colours, must be of one determined degree of refrangibility; and the transition from it to the fainter colour adjoining, not gradual, but immediate." Had he employed a slit aperture and had he not died in the following year, the discovery of spectral lines in the emission from flames might have come much earlier than it did, as he had proposed to apply himself to the further illustration of the theories of light and color. These had been left uninvestigated following Newton, who had indeed himself shown little interest in flames.

The first signs of recognition of the possible implications of spectral differences came in the early 19th century. In 1802 Wollaston (2) reported what were almost certainly the Fraunhofer lines, now known to be due to atomic absorption, some 12 years before Fraunhofer (3) carried out the work published in 1817 in which he also reported the construction of the first spectroscope and the recognition of the doublet nature of the D line. Wollaston's observation arose from an examination of daylight by means of a prism. When he looked at candlelight he noted a bright yellow line as well as a series of five broad, distinct images of different colors—in other words, the yellow Na doublet and the Swan C_2 bands. Wollaston was aware that the spectrum extended into the ultraviolet and that this could be observed by the effect on silver chloride, an effect independently reported by Ritter (4) in 1801. Thus, both flame emission and atomic absorption studies can be considered to have originated by 1802, although the significance of the findings was certainly not appreciated.

The spectral diagrams obtained from different salts in an alcohol flame, which Herschel (5) reported in 1822, provide the earliest intensity representations of flame spectra. That for muriate of strontium is particularly interesting as it includes what would now be identified as the unresolved Na yellow doublet at 5890/6 Å and the narrow orange–yellow SrOH band at 6050 Å, as well as the diffuse band in the red. Herschel noted that the yellow line could be removed from the spectrum, leaving the orange–yellow band, by inserting a bright red glass into the beam and thereby took the first step toward filter flame photometry.

In 1826 Talbot (6) came close to relating the yellow monochromatic flame of various solutions to the presence of sodium, but he did not appreciate that the test was so sensitive that the occurrence of the same radiation with alcoholic solutions or with sulfur could be explained by the presence of trace amounts of sodium. He did confirm the identity of the radiations from sulfur and from salt-loaded alcoholic flames by placing one source behind the other and observing not two yellow lines but one of increased brilliance. Perhaps an early inkling of quantitative significance could have been drawn from this observation. Discussing the light from the Brewster (7) alcohol flame, Talbot wrote: "But the most remarkable quality of this light is its homogeneity, which is perfect as far as I have been able to ascertain. I speak of the yellow rays which form the mass of the light and quite overpower the feeble effect of the blue and green. The origin of this homogeneous light appears to be difficult to explain. I have found that the same effect takes place whether the wick of the lamp is steeped in the muriate, sulphate, or carbonate of *soda*, while the nitrate, chlorate, sulphate, and carbonate of *potash* agree in giving a blueish-white tinge to the flame. Hence the yellow rays may indicate the presence of *soda*, but they, nevertheless, frequently appear where no soda can be supposed to be present." It would be interesting to know the significance Talbot attached to the word "supposed." Talbot concluded his paper by discussing the attribution of an orange ray to strontia—"If this opinion should be correct and applicable to other definite rays, a glance at the prismatic spectrum of a flame may show it to contain substances, which it would otherwise require a laborious chemical analysis to detect." No better justification of the use of flame methods could be put forward today.

Although photographic spectra of the light of the sun were made around 1840 following the production of daguerreotype and silver chloride photographic papers, no significant progress in flame spectroscopy came until 1860 when Kirchhoff and Bunsen (8) definitely correlated spectral lines with specific elements, using in their flame studies introduction of solutions into a Bunsen burner by means of a platinum wire or a hydrogen spray. This immediately pointed the way to chemical analysis by spectral observation of the flame, and soon other workers were reporting practical applications. For instance, in the following year, Simmler (9) published details of investigations on the alkali and alkaline earth metals present in Swiss rocks, minerals, waters, and wine, illustrated by some colored spectra (dated 1860) drawn from his observations. He added a request for samples for examination to be sent to him at the Kantonsschule in Chur. The potential widespread application of flame emission methods to chemical analysis was quickly appreciated once the initial breakthrough had been made.

II. The Development of Flame Emission Methods

Ten years later, attempts were being made to develop quantitative flame emission methods by Janssen (10) and by Champion, Pellet, and Grenier

(*11*), who claimed to determine Na over the range 0.05–1.0 % NaO (*sic*) in solution by visual comparison, using neutral wedges, of Na *D* line intensities in two flames fed, respectively, by constant and variable levels of Na, the latter consisting of standard or analysis samples introduced on platinum wire. An accuracy of 2–5 % was claimed for the determination of Na in plant ashes.

A. SAMPLE INTRODUCTION

The method of introduction of the sample into the flame was the least reproducible feature of early techniques. The first pneumatic aspirator used in flame photometry was that developed by Gouy (*12*). This nebulizer charged the air supply to the burner with droplets of the sample solution which could be recirculated continuously through the aspirator. This is the prototype of the indirect aspiration techniques which are still widely employed. Gouy introduced regulators into the air and gas supplies and assessed the emission from the flame by means of a photometric ocular.

Attempts to improve mechanical processes of introduction were made by Mitscherlich (*13*) using bundles of platinum or asbestos threads, Eder and Valenta (*14*) using a rotating platinum mesh, and Gooch and Hart (*15*) using a platinum spiral. Electrolytic sprays were tried by Beckmann (*16*) and Klemperer (*17*).

In the meantime, the introduction of dry plates about 1880 had led to the design of practical spectrographs, but the various analytical flame techniques proposed all had considerable limitations and were restricted to the alkali and alkaline earth metals. Little real progress was made until Lundegårdh (*18–22*), from 1928 onward, developed the first method of quantitative spectrochemical analysis to be widely adopted. It is still employed without substantial modification in some laboratories. Lundegårdh introduced several improved designs of nebulizers, burners, and gas control devices, and employed a microphotometer to measure spectral line density, so that serial analyses became practicable. An air–acetylene flame took the place of earlier air–coal gas flames, and the number of elements whose assessment was possible rose to 40. Photographic recording enabled ultraviolet lines such as those of Cu and Mg to be utilized.

B. MICROPHOTOMETRY

Lundegårdh appears to have been the first to appreciate fully the value of objective measurement of spectral line density by means of microphotometry. This had been employed in recording form by Koch (23) using a photoelectric cell, and developed by Moll (24) and Harrison (25) using thermoelectric devices, but few of the spectrochemical analysts working in the 1920's recognized its significance. Gerlach and Schweitzer (26), writing in 1929, discuss microphotometers but say that "in many cases a simple visual photometer designed on the principle devised by Hartmann will suffice, especially when it is practicable to employ sufficiently broad spectrum lines."

The method of evaluation used by Lundegårdh (21), taking the ratio of the galvanometer deflections for line plus background and background, compensated for variation in background density and would appear to be the first attempt to make such allowance. The process is applicable in practice at the low densities normally employed in flame work, although, as he pointed out, it is unsound at higher densities.

C. Early Photometers

The earliest photoelectric flame photometer is also attributable to Lundegårdh (20). This instrument, using a vacuum photocell, suffered from the rudimentary electronic amplification then available, and stability was difficult to achieve. Active research in the early 1930's, directed toward the sound-film industry and the use of electronics in communications and defense projects, soon led to the availability of improved photocell and amplifier designs that were subsequently applied in flame photometry.

During the next 10 years many workers, notably in Germany, employed equipment based on Lundegårdh's design. Jansen, with Heyes and Richter (27–30), used spectrographic and flame photometric methods to determine alkali and alkaline earth metals. They found that when extraneous elements were present a monochromator was preferable to filters, which were now being tried out. Waibel (31) described new nebulizer and burner designs. From 1937 onward, selenium barrier-layer cells became widely used in flame photometry in conjunction with multiple filters capable of isolating narrow spectral bands (Schuhknecht, 32; Goy, 33; Giesecke and Rathje, 34), and commercial instruments became available from German manufacturers. Such early filter flame photometers were used chiefly for potassium. Their use for sodium and other elements was restricted by the lack of suitable filters until the introduction of interference filters (Pratt and Larson, 35), which are now used extensively in commercial instruments covering all the alkali and alkaline earth metals.

D. Multichannel Photometers

The early flame photometers were all single-channel instruments, although there was no obvious difficulty in arranging a number of filter photometers around a single flame, as was later done by several workers including Leyton (*36*) and Ivanov (*37*). Ivanov made provision for internal standard or background correction. The first multielement direct-reading instrument was in fact based on a spectrographic process. This was the Lundegårdh Robot (*38*), built in 1940, in which the camera head carried 35-mm film. The film was automatically developed and scanned in a simple, built-in recording microphotometer which produced an intensity trace, also on film. This instrument went further in mechanization than most modern direct readers, as it incorporated a conveyer-belt sample feed. In 1949 Mitchell (*39*) described a three-channel instrument, built by A. M. Ure, using a spectrometer with separate photomultipliers for sodium and calcium; and for potassium, a filter, an image converter, and a photomultiplier.

While spectrographic methods were widely used before 1945, only in continental Europe were flame photometric techniques being applied. The filter instrument of Barnes, Richardson, Berry, and Hood (*40*) was the first reported in the United States; it was subsequently modified to a two-channel system with internal standard measurement by Berry, Chappell, and Barnes (*41*) and was produced commercially by Perkin-Elmer. Later models substituted a double prism for the filters. The introduction of an internal standard permitted correction for interferences which affected internal standard and analysis elements equally, but this technique has generally proved to be less advantageous in flame than in arc or spark emission work because of the inherent stability of the flame source. In 1956 Vallee and Margoshes (*42*) described a multichannel grating flame photometer for Na, K, Ca, Mg, and Sr.

E. Burner and Nebulizer Design

Up to this time, burners and nebulizers had followed the basic Lundegårdh design more or less closely, but Barnes et al. (*40*) used a Meker-type burner with indirect sample introduction. Total consumption, direct-injection burners based on the design suggested by Baum (*43*) were adopted, however, for several of the commercial instruments becoming available at this time. These included the Weichselbaum–Varney, Zeiss, and Beckman flame photometers. The Beckman burner has been further developed by

Gilbert (44, 45) to incorporate a sample pump and to provide sheathed flames suitable for the fuel-rich conditions in which certain metals normally occurring as oxides are reduced. Reducing flames were pioneered by several workers including Knutson (46), Allan (47) (in absorption), and Fassel, Curry, and Kniseley (48). The related effect of chemiluminescence has been discussed by Gilbert (49). A much earlier attempt to extend the range of elements determinable in the flame was the spark-in-flame source of Lundegårdh and Philipson (50).

Direct injection burners enable separate nebulizers and mixing chambers to be dispensed with, thus reducing the size of the equipment, but they give less scope for adjustment of burner parameters and, by introducing the whole of the aspirated sample into the flame, make it more difficult to control clotlet size. It was realized very early that expansion chambers and baffles removed large droplets and so reduced interference due to compound formation. A baffle directly in front of the aspirator nozzle was introduced by Rauterberg and Knippenberg (51) and is now widely used in flame photometry and atomic absorption. Warren (52) has used a direct injection burner designed for operation with small volumes in a recording flame spectrophotometer which scanned only over the wavelength regions in which a line occurred.

Various devices to replace pneumatic nebulizers have been tried in the past few years. Straubel (53) has employed an electrostatic nebulizer, and Dunken, Pforr, Mikkeleit, and Geller (54) have developed an ultrasonic aerosol generator. The latter has been used with considerable success by Pforr and Klostermann (55) and others in combination with a plasma torch burner.

F. SOLID SAMPLES

The requirement for adequate nebulization in the flame, to ensure the presence of a large and reproducible supply of uncombined atoms of the elements being determined, has largely limited the application of flame methods to solution samples, but several attempts have been made to devise methods of introduction employing solid samples. Ramage (56) developed a semiquantitative technique employing filter paper spills, a method adapted to quantitative measurements by Steward and Harrison (57). A related technique, extended to microlevels by integrating flame photometry, is that of Ramsay, Falloon, and Machin (58), who dried a measured drop on a platinum loop and burned it off completely. These methods depended on the use of small or well-dispersed solution residues on a suitable carrier and did not differ significantly from solution injection apart from the localized nature of the introduction. Attempts to use powder samples by blowing them directly into the flame have been less successful but are reported by Rusanov (59), among others. Particles of minerals or other insoluble materials are generally too stable to be broken up in the relatively cool flames used for flame emission work, as Lundegårdh (21) appreciated when he used an acetylene–oxygen flame in an attempt to analyze ores carried on an asbestos disk. Gilbert (60) has described a method involving the suspension of fine powder in a liquid of suitable viscosity which is introduced into a Beckman nebulizer-burner.

G. INTERELEMENT INTERFERENCE

The first report of interelement interference would appear to be Gouy's findings (61) that the phosphates of Ca and Sr gave very weak spectra compared with those with other anions. The effect of Al on Ca, which is even more marked, was observed by Mitchell and Robertson (62), who overcame it by the addition of an excess of Sr, which removes sufficient Al from association with Ca to enable accurate determinations to be made. It has been shown that La fulfils a similar function (Yofe and Finkelstein, 63) and that some protection can also be given to Ca by substances such as EDTA which form soluble complexes with it and prevent the formation of compounds which are not broken up readily in the flame. Huldt (64) and other workers have studied interferences due to compound formation in some detail. Such effects are generally greatest in low-temperature flames and disappear in hot sources such as the cyanogen–oxygen flame of Fuwa, Thiers, and Vallee (65). This flame is a further example of the investigation into source parameters carried out in the 1950's to extend the range of flame methods. Such high-temperature flames increase interelement interference arising from the ionization effects described by Smit, Alkemade, and Hattinga-Verschure (66). These tend to be smaller in total consumption burners.

H. ORGANIC SOLVENTS

Another approach to increased sensitivity introduced at this stage was the use of organic solvents, first suggested by Smit et al. (66). Greater intensification is found with organic solvents alone than with water-organic solvent mixtures, but even the latter often provide several-fold enhancement. As pointed out by Dean (*67*), in whose laboratory much of the work on organic solvents has been carried out, the use of a suitable organic solvent for selective extraction from aqueous solution of the elements to be determined can give a many-fold increase in emission as well as reducing interferences due to extraneous elements which are not extracted. The effect can be attributed to increased aspiration rate, decreased spray droplet size and variation in flame dimensions and temperature; in addition, protective complexation of the analysis element may reduce interelement effects.

I. SUMMARY

At their fullest development some 10 years ago, the most widespread use of flame photometry, and of flame emission methods in general, was in the biological and agricultural sciences. This was because it is largely for the alkali and alkaline earth metals that sensitivities of the levels required are available, although good sensitivity (<1 μg/ml) is also available in the air–acetylene flame for Ag, Cu, Mn, and Tl and reasonable sensitivity (~ 10 μg/ml) for Fe, Co, Ni, Cr, Au, and Pb. In many agricultural laboratoties the basic Lundegårdh design of burner and aspirator has been employed for K, Na, Ca, and, to a limited extent, Mg determinations by spectrographic and flame photometric methods. At the Macaulay Institute for Soil Research it has been in use for some 30 years, during which period nearly a million determinations have been made.

III. The Introduction of Atomic Absorption Methods

Such was the general position in flame work when in 1955 Walsh (*68*) and Alkemade and Milatz (*69*) independently realized the analytical potentialities of absorption by neutral atoms in the flame. This process had already been applied by Woodson (*70*) to determine mercury in air, but the breakthrough came when it was appreciated that most elements present as free atoms in flames could be assessed by this method, provided sources of high intensity and narrow line-width were available. Walsh pointed out that these were provided by hollow cathode lamps. Soon methods had been established for many elements that cannot be assessed by flame emission, largely because the flame does not provide energy adequate for emission of lines much shorter than Mg 2852 Å. In atomic absorption, on the other hand, excellent sensitivity is obtained with the Zn resonance line at 2138 Å.

A. THE ESTABLISHMENT OF THE METHOD

The analytical development of atomic absorption has been due almost entirely to Walsh and his colleagues in the CSIRO Division of Chemical Physics, Melbourne, Australia. In 1957, Russell, Shelton, and Walsh (71) described a practical atomic absorption spectrophotometer. This used modulated hollow cathode radiation to enable absorption in the flame to be measured without interference from flame emission, and a double-beam system with ratio-recorder to enable percent absorption to be recorded directly. These authors also pointed out the utility of a multiple-pass flame. Subsequent papers from this laboratory have announced practically all the major developments in atomic absorption instrumentation. These have included the introduction of high-intensity hollow cathode lamps (Sullivan and Walsh, 72) and nitrous oxide–acetylene flames (Willis, 73). The high-intensity lamp, in addition to increased emission, gives a spectrum that consists essentially of resonance lines, so that interference from non-resonance lines with elements such as Ni and Co is eliminated. The nitrous oxide–acetylene flame provides a high-temperature source in which the oxides of many elements which are stable in the air–acetylene flame are reduced, and so enables their determination to be carried out. Examples of sensitivities reported by Willis are 0.03 μg/ml Be, 1.0 μg/ml Al, and 5.0 μg/ml Si. A further development has been the introduction by Sullivan and Walsh (74) of the resonance detector, a device consisting essentially of a hollow cathode lamp in which the atomic vapor picks up the radiation from a high-intensity lamp after it has passed through the analytical flame. The resultant resonance radiation, which is emitted in all directions, is measured at right angles to the optical axis, there being no necessity for any other form of monochromator. Versions of this equipment for several elements are produced by Techtron, who have pioneered the commercial intro-duction of most of the aforementioned developments.

Many of the early applications of atomic absorption were made for agricultural and biological purposes from 1958 onward by David (75) in Australia and Allan (47, 76) in New Zealand, and some useful advances were made in their laboratories in the course of such applications. David (77) pointed out the advantage of a reducing flame for molybdenum. Clinton (78) suggested the use of a long, cooled, slot-type burner giving an increased path length, and demonstrated the effect of burner rotation on sensitivity. Such devices have been widely used in commercial instruments, although Hilger initially employed a burner with parallel rows of holes instead of a slot. Parallel slots are now being used.

The available flame path length and thereby the sensitivity have been increased by Robinson (79), Fuwa and Vallee (80), and Koirtyohann and Feldman (81), by directing the flame through a horizontal tube in the optical axis. Robinson used a T-shaped flame tube while the others introduced the flame at one end of a 40-cm-long tube. For specialized purposes, the tube technique can provide greatly increased sensitivity.

B. INTERFERENCE EFFECTS

It was soon apparant that chemical interferences such as those of Al or P on Ca or Mg were as serious in atomic absorption as in flame emission and that they could be overcome by similar methods. In addition, a light loss due to particle scattering or molecular absorption has been shown to be significant at certain wavelengths (David, 77; Capacho-Delgado and Sprague, 82). Interferences due to interatom energy transfer are of much less significance than in emission, while effects due to radiation from the flame can be eliminated by using a modulated source and tuned receiver. Thus, the conditions prevailing in a flame have proved relatively favorable for atomic absorption, particularly if a high-temperature flame is used when oxide or other compound formation is liable to occur. Several further methods of overcoming compound formation and increasing sensitivity have been suggested; for instance, the use of preheated gases by Rawson (83) and heated nebulizer chambers by Hell (84). The former in particular appears to reduce the size of droplets and thus clotlets very considerably.

C. CURRENT APPLICATIONS

The earliest commercial atomic absorption spectrophotometers were based on standard spectrophotometers and flame photometers, but more specialized equipment has become available from numerous manufacturers. There are too many to mention other than some of the earliest in the field, such as Hilger, Techtron, Perkin-Elmer, Jarrell-Ash, and Optica-Milan. Some, notably Perkin-Elmer, who pioneered a commercial double-beam system, have sponsored a considerable amount of research and development of methods and published the findings in their house journals. Many instruments now provide facilities for several types of flame, involving the use of acetylene, butane, or town gas as fuel and air or nitrous oxide as oxidant, and give quick change between conventional and high-intensity hollow cathode lamps, with recorder or digital read-out.

The popularity of atomic absorption methods in the 1960's has been due to its applicability to elements, including many industrially important metals, which were not readily determined by flame emission. The technique is, to a greater extent than flame emission photometry, essentially a single-element process, and multielement determinations in the same solution generally require repetition of the analytical procedure. Multielement hollow cathode lamps have been made by Jones and Walsh (85), and lamps have been used in tandem by Butler and Strasheim (86). Some workers, e.g., Strasheim and Butler (87), have used demountable lamps with inter-changeable cathodes. The use of continuous sources has been proposed by Allan (88) and Gibson, Grossman, and Cooke (89), but this requires a high-intensity source and very high resolving power. Several multichannel spectrophotometers have been described, such as that of Butler and Strasheim (86). A two-channel resonance detector for Ca and Mg, using different flame paths, is available from Techtron.

Apart from its widespread use in biological work, atomic absorption is now used for many industrial applications, such as mineral analysis, lubricating oil and catalyst testing, and precious metal assay, in addition to the examination of solutions of metals and alloys. Many elements that could be determined equally well by flame emission photometry, such as K, Na, and often Ca, are being determined by atomic absorption, but the trend may be reversing again, as at least one manufacturer now provides a flame emission attachment for an atomic absorption spectrophotometer.

In addition to flame sources, various attempts have been made to use other high-temperature devices in atomic absorption. These have been based mainly on the furnace devised by L'vov (90). Although there are sound reasons for using sources other than flames, no satisfactory substitute has yet been found.

IV. The Beginnings of Atomic Fluorescence Methods

The early reports, for instance that of Nichols and Howes (91), of the fluorescence of atoms in flames were concerned with studies of excitation conditions rather than with analytical possibilities. The first to consider the latter appears to have been Robinson (92), following his observation of the fluorescence of Mg 2852 Å in an oxyhydrogen flame. But interest in the subject was not aroused until Alkemade (*93*) discussed resonance fluorescence in the course of a consideration of excitation and related phenomena in flames. Thereupon Winefordner and his colleagues investigated the theoretical (Winefordner and Vickers, *94*) and practical (Winefordner and Staab, *95, 96*) aspects. Metal vapor discharge lamps were used to excite Hg, Zn, Cd, and Tl, and sensitivities better than 1 μg/ml were obtained in an acetylene–oxygen flame, using a Beckman-type burner. For Zn the limit of detection was as low as 0.005 μg/ml. For this technique, unlike atomic absorption, spectral purity of the source used to flood the flame with energizing light is not required, and any high-intensity source without self-reversal is suitable. With appropriate optics a continuous source can be employed, and Veillon, Mansfield, Parsons, and Winefordner (*97*), using a 150-W xenon arc source, have reported limits of detection varying from 0.08 to 20 μg/ml for 13 elements (Cu, Ag, Au, Pb, Bi, Mg, Zn, Cd, Tl, Ca, Ba, Ga, and Ni) in a hydrogen–oxygen flame.

Another suitable source is the microwave-excited, electrodeless discharge tube which has been studied by West and his colleagues. Dagnall, Thompson, and West (*98–100*) have prepared tubes for over 30 elements and report limits of determination as low as 0.25 and 0.12 μg/ml for Se and Te, respectively, in a propane flame, which is considered superior to hydrogen or acetylene flames. Ellis and Demers (*101*), using a 450-W xenon arc, report improved sensitivity for Mg and Co in an argon (entrained-air)–hydrogen flame, in line with the findings of Veillon et al. (*97*).

Some work on interelement interferences has been carried out by Goodfellow (*102*), who reports that the technique appears to be at least as interference-free as atomic absorption. The lack of effects due to alkali metals is considered noteworthy.

Atomic fluorescence methods are still at an early stage of development, and the full potentialities have not yet been realized. Most work has so far been carried out with modified spectrophotometers or flame photometers. Once appropriate conditions have been established and commercial equipment, possibly in conjunction with atomic absorption, becomes available, considerable advances are probable. In the meantime, excitation sources and flame conditions both appear to require further development.

V. Comparison of Flame Methods with Other Techniques

The choice of an analytical technique to meet a specific requirement depends on at least four factors—the type of sample to be examined, the elements to be determined, the number of samples involved, and the funds available. Flame methods are essentially methods for the serial analysis of solution samples in which only a few elements have to be determined. The initial cost of the equipment is relatively low compared with other types of physicochemical apparatus for chemical analysis, maintenance is simple, and operation is not difficult.

No technique is capable of determining all elements simultaneously at trace levels; spark-source mass spectroscopy probably comes nearest but has limitations as far as speed, and possibly accuracy, are concerned. The sensitivity is very good, but the initial cost is high and the operational requirements are considerable, so that it should not be considered as a primary tool for the serial analysis of a restricted number of elements that can readily be determined by other methods. The limitations of X-ray fluorescence lie almost entirely in its somewhat restricted sensitivity. Now that means of making allowance for matrix effects are available, it is probably the preferred method for the determination of major constituents in powder samples. The initial cost is once again high. Related methods such as the electron probe are specialized techniques dealing with variations in composition within a material and are not directly comparable with flame methods. Neutron activation can provide information on a limited number of samples, but is very expensive unless activation facilities are readily available.

The standard processes of analytical chemistry can now be highly mechanized by equipment such as the Technicon Autoanalyser. Such automatic methods are most applicable to the estimation of elements including nonmetals that can be determined by colorimetric or fluorimetric methods, although equipment for other methods of measurement is available. They must be considered for some applications; the decision may depend to some extent on the laboratory facilities available and on the other types of work being carried out. The cost of such equipment, with several analytical channels and provision for various methods of assessment, will generally be considerably greater than that for flame equipment.

For certain purposes an electroanalytical technique may be appropriate, but the versatility of the various methods of this type, such as polarography, coulometry, and potentiometric analysis, is much less than that of the other general methods being reviewed. Such methods, like automatic analysis, can sometimes be used for the determination of some organic constituents as well as for elemental analysis. For specialized determinations specific ion electrodes may provide a suitable analytical tool. The cost of equipment for electroanalysis generally falls into the same price range as flame equipment.

For the determination of trace elements in solid samples, the use of spectrographic or direct-reading methods, with direct current arc excitation, must be considered, particularly if the analysis can be carried out without any form of pretreatment. Preliminary concentration may be worthwhile if several elements can thereby be determined simultaneously, as is the case for trace elements in plant materials. This process can eliminate interfering constituents and extend the range for some elements down to the part per hundred million level. The accuracy of dc arc methods is not as poor as some authors make it out to be. In biological work the determination of the composition of extracts of organs, plants, or soils often requires a concentration technique prior to arc excitation, which can deal with ashed, precipitated concentrates weighing 20 mg or less. On the other hand, it is probably impracticable to use volumes of less than 1 ml in solution analysis on a routine scale, and therefore there can be an advantage of at least 50-fold by concentrating into solid rather than solution.

Porous cup, vacuum cup, rotating disk, and impregnated electrodes can all be used for solution work with some form of spark or arc excitation and can have advantages over flame methods, particularly for multielement determinations using a direct reader. For certain applications it may be advantageous to dissolve metals or alloys and determine the desired constituent by a flame technique, but generally a direct-reading spectrometer with spark or arc excitation will be preferred for such work. The cost of direct-reading spectrometers is very much greater than that of flame equipment. Spectrographic apparatus is not appreciably dearer and is much more versatile, but it requires greater operator skill and experience.

VI. Selection of the Appropriate Flame Method

Flame methods can be grouped into three broad categories, namely, flame emission techniques, atomic absorption spectrometry, and atomic fluorescence spectrometry. No one technique is better than the others in all circumstances. Each can deal with some problems more effectively than the others can, and generally an instrument chosen to cover several requirements will be a compromise.

A. ANALYTICAL APPLICATIONS

In flame work the use of spectrographic methods has been largely abandoned during the past 20 years, but there are circumstances in which a spectrogram can give information more quickly or more reliably than direct reading, for instance, for multielement determinations or where the elimination of spectral interferences and background effects is necessary. A modern recording or display microphotometer would be a desirable accessory in flame spectrographic work. Where a number of elements have to be determined in a limited number of samples, it may well be that the advantages of flame photometry have been overemphasized, particularly if only a single-channel instrument is available. If serial analyses of materials are required in order to check the contents of a few specific constituents, then a flame photometric method will generally be preferable, but if the requirement is for some diagnostic investigation, the elements involved may not all be known or it may be tedious to determine them all. In such a case a spectrographic or other record may be advantageous as it will quickly make any abnormality obvious. The initial indication that soil infertility due to nickel excess occurred in some areas in northeast Scotland came from Lundegårdh flame spectrograms of soil extracts being examined for K content.

The simplest flame technique is flame photometry. A relatively inexperienced assistant can carry out all the necessary operations at a speed which cannot be approached by the other flame methods. With a three-channel instrument, meters for each channel, and provision for taking the aspirator tube to the sample container, it is possible in 1 hr to carry out 240 determinations of K, Na, and Ca in 80 samples. Standard solutions are readily prepared and the necessary precautions to take account of interferences are well understood and easily applied.

The sample is almost always presented to the flame in the form of a solution spray. Aqueous solutions are used unless circumstances preclude their use. Solutions are generally slightly acid in order to hold dissolved salts in solution, and the total solid content must not be so high as to affect aspiration or flame conditions. Viscosity, specific gravity, and surface tension may all affect the behavior of solutions in the nebulizer, changing the amount sprayed and the droplet size. Only if there is a requirement for increased sensitivity or removal of interfering constituents are organic solvents employed. It should be pointed out that with organic solvents it is often unnecessary to make time-consuming manipulations, as it may be possible, without further separation, to sample the organic layer directly from the vessel in which the extraction is carried out. Volume requirements are generally of the order of 1 ml/min for all forms of flame work. Standard solutions should be run frequently during the course of a series of analyses to check instrumental adjustment.

Flame photometry depends on a single emission measurement, as background can generally be ignored and an internal standard is seldom necessary because of the reproducibility of the source. Multichannel flame photometers are available or readily constructed. With the development of recently introduced flame sources such as nitrous oxide–acetylene, the number of elements that can be determined by flame photometry has increased and the use of multichannel direct-reading instruments appears even more attractive.

Atomic absorption is essentially a method for the determination of one element at a time, and the time factor and sufficiency of the solution sample must be taken into account if the determination of a number of elements is required in each sample. It involves a difference measurement, and determinations cannot be made as quickly as by flame photometry. There are many parameters that have to be considered if the optimum sensitivity is to be obtained for all of some 70 elements now claimed to be determinable by atomic absorption. These include hollow cathode lamp characteristics, flame composition and shape, sample solvent, and nebulizer design. The optimum conditions vary for different elements.

The sensitivity provided by atomic absorption is almost always greater than that by flame photometry. The difference may amount to 10–100 times. There are indications that atomic fluorescence may provide determinations at even lower contents.

B. Operational Requirements

No great demands on operator skill or experience are made by flame methods, although some preliminary instruction in the observation of possible causes of error is essential. The somewhat more elaborate method of assessment inevitable with a difference technique means that there is more possibility of errors arising with atomic absorption, and the occurrence of instrumental maladjustment is generally more quickly detected by a more experienced or more highly qualified operator. The responsibility for errors arising from interference effects must lie not with the operator but with the supervisor. There is less requirement for operational dexterity with flame methods than with most other types of spectroscopic source, particularly with arc methods in which electrode preparation and the maintenance of the physical and electrical excitation parameters throughout the period of the burn are directly under the operator's control.

Hazards to the operator exist with both flame and electrical excitation.

More positive measures to eliminate them can be taken with electrical excitation, and flame operators must be fully briefed in the risks of explosion and fire and in the methods of avoiding them.

The instrumental precision of photometric flame methods is of the order of 1–2%, and with spectrographic recording, about 3%. This compares with a precision of better than 1% for most direct-reading spectrometers. The analytical accuracy can be as good as 2%, but this depends to a considerable extent on the level being determined, on the closeness of correspondence between analysis samples and standards, and on the efficiency of means of overcoming interferences. Near the limits of determination, errors can rise above 10%.

C. Costs

Flame photometry can generally compete very favorably with all other instrumental methods as regards cost. A simple filter flame photometer can be obtained in Britain for as little as £100 ($250). More elaborate instruments with prism or grating dispersion can cost at least 10 times this amount. The cheapest commercial atomic absorption equipment costs over £600 ($1500), and the range of price up to the most expensive is at least fivefold. Commercial atomic fluorescence apparatus is not yet available, but there seems no reason why the prices should differ much from atomic absorption equipment. A combined absorption-fluorescence facility would inevitably raise the total price somewhat. Sophisticated read-out devices and built-in electronic computation can increase the cost of all spectrometric equipment far beyond that of the basic instrument, and its justification must depend on the projected utilization.

In selecting any form of flame equipment, attention should be given to future development possibilities and modifications in techniques, unless only a restricted, short-term requirement is envisaged. It would seem reasonable for atomic absorption apparatus capable of adaption to fluorescence to be preferred by a laboratory whose future requirements might lead in this direction.

The cost of maintenance of flame emission methods is minimal, while that of atomic absorption can be significant. The life of hollow cathode lamps is not unlimited, and indeed, in the author's experience, seldom exceeds several hundred hours. Such lamps cost £25–70 ($60–160), and the expense involved in the provision of lamps, which are not included in the basic price of an instrument, and in their regular replacement, can be considerable, particularly as they may have a limited shelf life and as it is desirable to have at least two lamps for each element whose determination is regularly required. For this reason, laboratories with occasional requirement for a considerable number of different elements may prefer to use demountable lamps. Hollow cathode life and reliability are aspects of atomic absorption analysis that might demand further improvement.

All flame methods require the provision of air and fuel gases; the cost of these has not been taken into account in any of the figures quoted. Nitrous oxide is a rather expensive gas if it is available only in the medical grade.

D. SUMMARY

To sum up, flame methods are capable of providing analytical facilities which can meet the requirements of many industrial or research laboratories. They are relatively inexpensive and staffing is not a serious problem. They complement other spectrochemical techniques in laboratories which demand a wide coverage of elements. They are most appropriately employed in serial analysis of a few elements in a considerable number of samples, although the number of elements that can be determined is quite large. The fact that many laboratories have adopted flame emission and atomic absorption methods is proof of their value. The wide acceptance of atomic absorption methods in the past 10 years is in fact one of the success stories of analytical chemistry.

REFERENCES

1. T. Melvill, Observations on light and colours, *Essays and Observations, Physical and Literary, Edinburgh*, **2**, 12–90 (1756).
2. W. H. Wollaston, A method of examining refractive and dispersive powers, *Phil. Trans.*, **92**, 365–380 (1802).
3. J. Fraunhofer, Determination of refractive and dispersive power of various glasses . . ., *Ann. Physik (Gilbert's Ann.)*, **56**, 264–313 (1817).
4. J. W. Ritter, Untitled note in *Ann. Physik (Gilbert's Ann.)*, **7**, 527 (1801).
5. J. F. W. Herschel, On the absorption of light by coloured media . . ., *Trans. Roy. Soc. (Edinburgh)*, **9**, 445–460 (1823).
6. H. F. Talbot, Some experiments on coloured flames, *Edinburgh J. Sci. (Brewster's)*, **5**, 77–81 (1826).
7. D. Brewster, Description of a monochromatic lamp . . ., *Trans. Roy. Soc. (Edinburgh)*, **9**, 433–444 (1823).

8. G. Kirchhoff and R. Bunsen, Chemical analyses by means of spectral observations, *Ann. Physik (Poggendorf's Ann.*), **110**, 161–189 (1860).

9. R. T. Simmler, Chemical–physical reports from the laboratory of the Cantonal School in Chur, II, *Jahresber. d. Naturforsch. Ges. Graubündens (1859–1860)*, N.F. **6**, 194–218 (1861).

10. M. J. Janssen, On quantitative spectral analysis, *Compt. Rend.*, **71**, 626–629 (1870).

11. P. Champion, H. Pellet, and M. Grenier, On spectrometry; the spectronatrometer, *Compt. Rend.*, **76**, 707–711 (1873).

12. A. Gouy, Photometric investigations on coloured flames, *Ann. Chim. Phys.* (5), **18**, 5–101 (1879).

13. A. Mitscherlich, Contributions to spectral analysis, *Ann. Physik (Poggendorf's Ann.*), **116**, 499–507 (1862).

14. J. M. Eder and E. Valenta, On the process of bunsen-type flame reactions in the ultraviolet spectrum . . ., *Wiener Denkschr.*, **60**, 467–476 (1893).

15. F. A. Gooch and T. S. Hart, The detection and determination of potassium spectroscopically, *Am. J. Sci.* (3), **42**, 448–459 (1891).

16. E. Beckmann, Quoted from a note in *Z. Elektrochem.*, **5**, 327 (1899).

17. R. I. Klemperer, On quantitative spectral analysis, Thesis, University of Dresden, 1910; quoted from Lundegårdh (19).

18. H. Lundegårdh, Investigations on quantitative spectral analysis, I, *Arkiv. Kemi. Min. Geol.*, **10A**, No. 1 (1928).

19. H. Lundegårdh, *Die Quantitative Spektralanalyse der Elemente [The Quantitative Spectral Analysis of the Elements]*, Gustav Fischer, Jena, 1929.

20. H. Lundegårdh, New contributions to the technique of quantitative chemical spectral analysis, *Z. Physik*, **66**, 109–118 (1930).

21. H. Lundegårdh, *Die Quantitative Spektralanalyse der Elemente, II [The Quantitative Spectral Analysis of the Elements, II]*, Gustav Fischer, Jena, 1934.

22. H. Lundegårdh, Investigations into the quantitative emission spectral analysis of inorganic elements in solutions, *Lantbruks-Högsk. Ann.*, **3**, 49–97 (1936).

23. P. P. Koch, On a recording microphotometer, *Ann. Phys. (Paris)*, IV, **39**, 705–751 (1912).

24. W. J. H. Moll, A new registering microphotometer, *Proc. Phys. Soc.*, **33**, 207–215 (1921).

25. G. R. Harrison, Precision densitometers for photographic photometry, *J. Opt. Soc. Am.*, **10**, 157–167 (1925).

26. W. Gerlach and E. Schweitzer, *Die Chemische Emissionsspektralanalyse*, Voss, Leipzig, 1930 (Transl. anon., *Chemical Emission Spectral Analysis*, Hilger, London, 1931).

27. W. H. Jansen and J. Heyes, The application of spectral analysis to the quantitative determination of alkalis and alkaline earths, I, *Z. Physiol. Chem. (Hoppe-Seyler's*), **211**, 75–87 (1932).

28. W. H. Jansen and J. Heyes, The application of spectral analysis to the quantitative determination of alkalis and alkaline earths, II, *Z. Physik. Chem. (Leipzig*), **168A**, 257–266 (1934).

29. W. H. Jansen, J. Heyes, and C. Richter, The application of spectral analysis to the quantitative determination of alkalis and alkaline earths, IV, *Z. Physik. Chem. (Leipzig*), **171A**, 268–280 (1934).

30. W. H. Jansen, J. Heyes, and C. Richter, The application of spectral analysis to the quantitative determination of alkalis and alkaline earths, V, *Z. Physik. Chem. (Leipzig)*, **174A**, 291–300 (1935).

31. F. Waibel, Quantitative flame spectral analysis, *Wiss. Veroffentl. Siemens-Werken*, **14**, 32–40 (1935).

32. W. Schuhknecht, Spectral analytical determination of potassium, *Angew. Chem.*, **50**, 299–301 (1937).

33. S. Goy, On a very simple process for the quantitative determination of potassium by photometry, *Angew. Chem.*, **50**, 301–302 (1937).

34. F. Giesecke and W. Rathje, Report on the findings with the Siemens and Zeiss equipment for the flame photometric determination of potassium in plant ash, *Bodenk. Pflanz.*, **9–10**, 776–779 (1938).

35. P. F. Pratt and W. E. Larson, Use of interference filters in the reduction of error due to calcium in the flame photometric determination of sodium, *Anal. Chem.*, **21**, 1296 (1949).

36. L. Leyton, An improved flame photometer, *Analyst*, **76**, 723–728 (1951).

37. D. N. Ivanov, The use of interference filters in the determination of sodium and potassium in soils, *Pochvovedenie*, **1953**, No. 1, 61–66.

38. H. Lundegårdh, *Die Blattanalyse*, Gustav Fischer, Jena, 1945 (Transl. by R. L. Mitchell, *Leaf Analysis*, Hilger, London, 1951).

39. R. L. Mitchell, Flame photometry, *Spectrochim. Acta*, **4**, 62–63 (1950).

40. R. B. Barnes, D. Richardson, J. W. Berry, and R. L. Hood, Flame photometry, a rapid analytical procedure, *Ind. Eng. Chem., Anal. Ed.*, **17**, 605–611 (1945).

41. J. W. Berry, D. G. Chappell, and R. B. Barnes, Improved method of flame photometry, *Ind. Eng. Chem., Anal. Ed.*, **18**, 19–24 (1946).

42. B. L. Vallee and M. Margoshes, Instrumentation and principles of flame spectrometry: multichannel flame spectrometer, *Anal. Chem.*, **28**, 175–179 (1956).

43. E. Baum, A new light source for thermal excitation, *Ann. Physik*, (5), **34**, 377–388 (1939).

44. P. T. Gilbert, Analytical flame photometry: new developments, *Am. Soc. Testing Materials, Spec. Tech. Publ. 269*, 73–156 (1960).

45. P. T. Gilbert, New horizons in flame spectrophotometry, *Analyzer, Beckman Instruments*, **2**, No. 4, 3–6 (1961).

46. K. E. Knutson, Flame-photometric determination of magnesium in plant material: a study of the emission of magnesium in a highly reducing oxygen-acetylene flame, *Analyst*, **82**, 241–254 (1957).

47. J. E. Allan, Atomic absorption spectrophotometry with special reference to the determination of magnesium, *Analyst*, **83**, 466–471 (1958).

48. V. A. Fassell, R. H. Curry, and R. N. Kniseley, Flame spectra of the rare-earth elements, *Spectrochim. Acta*, **18**, 1127–1153 (1962).

49. P. T. Gilbert, Chemiluminiscent flame spectrophotometry, *Proceedings Xth Colloquium Spectroscopicum Internationale*, Spartan, Washington, D.C. (1963), 171–215.

50. H. Lundegårdh and H. Philipson, The spark-in-flame method for spectral analysis, *Lantbruks-Högsk. Ann.*, **5**, 249–260 (1938).

51. E. Rauterberg and E. Knippenberg, Potassium determination by flame photometry, *Angew. Chem.*, **53**, 477–479 (1940).

52. R. L. Warren, A versatile micro-sample flame spectrophotometer, *Proceedings VIIIth Colloquium Spectroscopicum Internationale, Luzern, 1959*, 213–215 (1960).

53. H. Straubel, Electrostatic nebulization of liquids, *Naturwissenschaften*, **40**, 337 (1953).

54. H. Dunken, G. Pforr, W. Mikkeleit, and K. Geller, Different methods of atomization in flame photometry, *Spectrochim. Acta*, **20**, 1531–1542 (1964).

55. G. Pforr and K. Klostermann, On the use of a contamination-free plasma burner as excitation source for ultrasonically nebulized aqueous $MnCl_2$ solutions, *Z. Chem.*, **5**, 354–355 (1965).

56. H. Ramage, Spectrographic chemical analysis, *Nature*, **123**, 601–602 (1929).

57. F. C. Steward and J. A. Harrison, The absorption and accumulation of salts by living plant cells, IX, *Ann. Botany (London)*, [N.S.] **3**, 427–454 (1939).

58. J. A. Ramsay, S. W. H. W. Falloon, and K. E. Machin, An integrating flame photometer for small quantities, *J. Sci. Instr.*, **28**, 75–80 (1951).

59. A. K. Rusanov, Spectroscopic analysis of minerals with the help of the acetylene: air burner, *Z. Anorg. Allgem. Chem.*, **214**, 77–80 (1933).

60. P. T. Gilbert, Direct flame-photometric analysis of powdered minerals, *Anal. Chem.*, **34**, 1025–1026 (1962).

61. A. Gouy, Photometric investigations on coloured flames, *Compt. Rend.*, **85**, 70–72 (1877).

62. R. L. Mitchell and I. M. Robertson, The effect of aluminium on the flame spectra of the alkaline earths: a method for the determination of aluminium, *J. Soc. Chem. Ind. (London)*, **55**, 269T–272T (1936).

63. J. Yofe and R. Finkelstein, Elimination of anionic interference in flame photometric determination of calcium in the presence of phosphate and sulphate, *Anal. Chim. Acta*, **19**, 166–173 (1958).

64. L. Huldt, On the influence of foreign elements on the intensity of spectrum lines in the flame of acetylene, *Arkiv Mat. Astron. Fysik*, **33A**, No. 5 (1946).

65. K. Fuwa, R. E. Thiers, and B. L. Vallee, A burner for cyanogen flame spectroscopy, *Anal. Chem.*, **31**, 1419–1421 (1959).

66. J. Smit, C. T. J. Alkemade, and J. C. M. Hattinga-Verschure, A contribution to the development of the flame-photometric determination of sodium and potassium in blood serum, *Biochim. Biophys. Acta*, **6**, 508–523 (1951).

67. J. A. Dean, *Flame Photometry*, McGraw-Hill, New York, 1960.

68. A. Walsh, The application of atomic absorption spectra to chemical analysis, *Spectrochim. Acta*, **7**, 108–117 (1955).

69. C. T. J. Alkemade and J. M. W. Milatz, Double-beam method of spectral selection with flames, *J. Opt. Soc. Am.*, **45**, 583–584 (1955).

70. T. T. Woodson, A new mercury vapour detector, *Rev. Sci. Instr.*, **10**, 308–311 (1939).

71. B. J. Russell, J. P. Shelton, and A. Walsh, An atomic-absorption spectrophotometer and its application to the analysis of solutions, *Spectrochim. Acta*, **8**, 317–328 (1957).

72. J. V. Sullivan and A. Walsh, High intensity hollow-cathode lamps, *Spectrochim. Acta*, **21**, 721–726 (1965).

73. J. B. Willis, Nitrous oxide-acetylene flame in atomic absorption spectroscopy, *Nature*, **207**, 715–716 (1965).

74. J. V. Sullivan and A. Walsh, Resonance radiation from atomic vapours, *Spectrochim. Acta*, **21**, 727–730 (1965).

75. D. J. David, Determination of zinc and other elements in plants by atomic absorption spectroscopy, *Analyst*, **83**, 655–661 (1958).

76. J. E. Allan, The determination of iron and manganese by atomic absorption, *Spectrochim. Acta*, **15**, 800–806 (1959).

77. D. J. David, The determination of molybdenum by atomic-absorption spectrophotometry, *Analyst*, **86**, 730–740 (1961).

78. O. E. Clinton, A burner for atomic absorption spectrophotometry, *Spectrochim. Acta*, **16**, 985–988 (1960).

79. J. W. Robinson, Observations in atomic absorption spectroscopy, *Anal. Chim. Acta*, **27**, 465–469 (1962).

80. K. Fuwa and B. L. Vallee, The physical basis of analytical atomic absorption spectrometry. The pertinence of the Beer-Lambert law, *Anal. Chem.*, **35**, 942–946 (1963).

81. S. R. Koirtyohann and C. Feldman, Atomic absorption spectroscopy using long absorption path lengths and a demountable hollow cathode lamp, in *Developments in Applied Spectroscopy* (J. E. Forrette and E. Lanterman, eds.), Vol. 3, Plenum Press, New York, 1964, pp. 180–189.

82. L. Capacho-Delgado and S. Sprague, Calcium interference in atomic absorption analysis for barium, *Atomic Absorption Newsletter*, **4**, 363–364 (1965).

83. R. A. G. Rawson, Improvement in performance of a simple atomic absorptiometer by using pre-heated air and town-gas, *Analyst*, **91**, 630–637 (1966).

84. A. Hell, Advanced laminar flow burner for atomic absorption. Paper presented at the 5th Australian Spectroscopy Conference, Perth, June 1965.

85. W. G. Jones and A. Walsh, Hollow-cathode discharges—the construction and characteristics of sealed-off tubes for use as spectroscopic light sources, *Spectrochim. Acta*, **16**, 249–254 (1960).

86. L. R. P. Butler and A. Strasheim, Multiple element atomic absorption analysis, *Spectrochim. Acta*, **21**, 1207–1216 (1965).

87. A. Strasheim and L. R. P. Butler, A versatile hollow cathode lamp for atomic-absorption spectroscopy, *Appl. Spectry.*, **16**, 109–110 (1962).

88. J. E. Allan, Atomic absorption spectrophotometry absorption lines and detection limits in the air-acetylene flame, *Spectrochim. Acta*, **18**, 259–263 (1962).

89. J. H. Gibson, W. E. L. Grossman, and W. D. Cooke, The use of continuous sources in atomic absorption spectroscopy, in *Analytical Chemistry 1962* (P. W. West, A. M. G. Macdonald, and T. S. West, eds.), Elsevier, Amsterdam, 1963, pp. 288–290.

90. B. V. L'vov, The analytical use of atomic absorption spectra, *Spectrochim. Acta*, **17**, 761–770 (1961).

91. E. L. Nichols and H. L. Howes, The photoluminescence of flames, II, *Phys. Rev.* (2), **23**, 472–477 (1924).

92. J. W. Robinson, Mechanism of elemental spectral excitation in flame photometry, *Anal. Chim. Acta*, **24**, 254–262 (1961).

93. C. T. J. Alkemade, Excitation and related phenomena in flames, *Proceedings Xth Colloquium Spectroscopicum Internationale*, Spartan, Washington, D.C. (1963), 143–170.

94. J. D. Winefordner and T. J. Vickers, Atomic fluorescence spectrometry as a means of chemical analysis, *Anal. Chem.*, **36,** 161–165 (1964).

95. J. D. Winefordner and R. A. Staab, Determination of zinc, cadmium, and mercury by atomic fluorescence flame spectrometry, *Anal. Chem.*, **36,** 165–168 (1964).

96. J. D. Winefordner and R. A. Staab, Study of experimental parameters in atomic fluorescence flame spectrometry, *Anal. Chem.*, **36,** 1367–1369 (1964).

97. C. Veillon, J. M. Mansfield, M. L. Parsons, and J. D. Winefordner, Use of a continuous source in flame fluorescence spectrometry, *Anal. Chem.*, **38,** 205–208 (1966).

98. R. M. Dagnall, K. C. Thompson, and T. S. West, An investigation of some experimental parameters in atomic fluorescence spectrophotometry, *Anal. Chim. Acta*, **36,** 269–277 (1966).

99. R. M. Dagnall, K. C. Thompson, and T. S. West, Studies in atomic-fluorescence spectroscopy, III, Microwave-excited electrodeless discharge tubes as spectral sources for atomic-fluorescence and atomic-absorption spectroscopy, *Talanta*, **14,** 551–555 (1967).

100. R. M. Dagnall, K. C. Thompson, and T. S. West, Studies in atomic-fluorescence spectrocopy, IV. The atomic-fluorescence spectroscopic determination of selenium and tellurium, *Talanta*, **14,** 557–563 (1967).

101. D. W. Ellis and D. R. Demers, Use of the hydrogen-entrained-air flame in atomic-fluorescence flame spectroscopy, *Anal. Chem.*, **38,** 1943–1945 (1966).

102. G. I. Goodfellow, Some experimental observations on interelement effects in atomic fluorescence spectroscopy, *Anal. Chim. Acta*, **36,** 132–134 (1966).

2 Basic Principles of Flame Emission, Atomic Absorption, and Fluorescence Methods

Juan Ramírez-Muñoz

BECKMAN INSTRUMENTS, INC.
FULLERTON, CALIFORNIA

I. Introduction

In the following paragraphs some basic ideas are included on the production of active entities in the flame to show the important role played by the flame in this process. Spraying and atomization are differentiated and briefly discussed.

In a following section, some fundamental processes are pointed out with special attention to the direct emission process, the atomic-fluorescence process, and the atomic-absorption process, that is, those processes which are the basis of the three fields of major interest among flame methods. Instrumentation and differences in operating techniques are also considered in some detail.

Finally, a section on terminology in flame methods has been added. This section is more informative than critical, as definitive decisions about recommended terms should result from work of nomenclature committees. In this transitional period, until a definitive terminology is established, flame photometrists should take into consideration the general terms already recommended for spectral methods which may be applied and utilized in the flame field.

II. Role of the Flame in the Production of Active Entities in Flame Methods

Flame methods are distinctively characterized among other spectral methods by the use of flames as a means of converting samples and standards into appropriate media which can produce measurable emissions or absorptions. In other words, the flame transforms the analytes existing in samples and standards into active entities. These may emit or absorb radiation at definite and characteristic wavelengths; the intensity of the corresponding emission or absorption, as measured by the instrument, can then be related to the concentration of the analytes in the samples and standards (numerically or graphically). Therefore, those values can be related to the concentration in the original samples.

Flame systems used for these purposes should have these characteristics:

1. Adequate temperature to form active entities.
2. Sufficient stability to provide an emitting or absorbing medium of constant qualitative and quantitative composition to allow reliable correlation between measurement and sample concentration.
3. Appropriate flame composition (a function of combustion gases) to produce the necessary temperature and reducing characteristics and to maintain or produce the active entities involved in the process.
4. Appropriate geometry, a factor which is important according to the function of the flame, as participant in the emitting source or as participant in the absorbing medium. Geometry of the flame (shape and dimensions) is a function of burner geometry and feed-rate of gases and analyte.

5. Sufficient adjustment versatility, depending principally on the versatility in the adjustment of gas flows and pressures. This provides freedom in changing flame characteristics for a given gas mixture to adapt the operating conditions to a given analyte and thus to allow changes in sensitivity and concentration range.
6. Appropriate mechanical versatility, provided by the mechanical devices attached to the burner which allows alignment, focusing, rotation (in long slot burners), and variation of burner elevation. As a result of this versatility, the operator will be able to optimize the flame for viewing the optimum zone of the flame or, if necessary, to cut down sensitivity for dealing with higher concentrations—burner rotation techniques.

In flame methods the flame plays a dual role: (1) It is involved in the thermal processes necessary to convert the test portion of the sample into active entities and to maintain them in this status as long as possible, and (2) in emission techniques, it is involved in the spectrochemical processes that bring the active entities to higher energy levels—the excitation process. Afterwards, the active entities will emit characteristic radiation when returning to lower energy levels.

Once the test portion of the original sample has been divided into small particles by sprayers, nebulizers, or similar devices, and these particles are introduced into the flame, the solvent is evaporated and the analyte is vaporized and at least partly dissociated in order to release neutral atoms. In some cases the analyte retains its status as diatomic or polyatomic compounds, not dissociated, but as compounds which may still participate in absorption and emission processes. Furthermore, the atoms of the analyte may be associated with other atoms existing in the environment. At this juncture the potential emitting species can be excited as a consequence of the thermal energy of the flame or they can be excited by some particular process (chemiluminescence or overexcitation) (*1*). On emission there is a spontaneous return of these entities to lower energy levels (ground state or intermediate states).

In the case of metallic analytes the neutral atoms play the most important role. When excited, they emit characteristic radiation which may be recognized as discrete lines. In atomic-absorption methods neutral atoms also are the entities which absorb characteristic radiation and may be recognized as a decrease of luminosity or absorption at selectable wavelengths. The fact that these emissions and absorptions are correlated with the concentration of neutral atoms involved in the phenomenon permits a further correlation with the concentration in the original samples. Similarly, in atomic-fluorescence methods, the neutral atoms are involved in the emission of fluorescence spectra and are also able to be selected and measured. At the same time, some of the atoms can be ionized. These ionized species can also be excited and will emit radiations at wavelengths different from neutral atoms of the same element. By this process ionized lines arise in flame spectra (*2, 18*).

When diatomic or polyatomic species are formed or remain in the flame, they can give rise to molecular band spectra. These spectra are much more complicated than line spectra because the electronic transitions corresponding to different electronic excitation levels have superimposed on them the vibrational energies. Degraded asymmetrical bands can spread over considerable regions of the spectrum. The locations of these bands are qualitatively characteristic of the analyte involved, and some of them are quantitatively measurable in emission spectra. Molecular entities may be also responsible for molecular absorption (*3*).

In considering the phenomena involved in the analytical use of flames, flame methods can be grouped operationally as shown in Table 1.

TABLE 1

Flame Methods

Emission methods	
Direct emission	
Atomic and molecular emission processes	
Photographic recording:	Atomic-emission flame spectrography
	Molecular-emission flame spectrography
Direct measurement:	Atomic-emission flame photometry
	Molecular-emission flame photometry
Fluorescence emission	
Atomic processes:	Atomic-fluorescence flame photometry
Absorption methods	
Atomic and molecular processes:	Atomic-absorption flame photometry
	Molecular-absorption flame photometry

Emission spectra are not as simple as might be supposed since they involve more than the emission produced by the analyte. In complex matrices the spectra (discrete or continuous) of concomitant components also appear, plus the emission characteristics of the flame used—OH bands, and in acetylene flames, CH and C_2 bands, and continua caused by CO molecules.

In absorption work, concomitants can be responsible for anomalous absorptions associated with spectral matrix effects (4).

A. SPRAYING AND ATOMIZATION

These two processes are at present not considered as being synonymous, but rather a sequence involving first, a means to divide finely a sample fed into the instrument (spraying or nebulization); and, subsequently, the liberation in the flame of the active entities so far as the association and thermal dissociation equilibria allow.

In some systems, such as a spray chamber plus premix burner, the two processes appear far apart, being carried out in two different sections; in others (sprayer–burners) they seem to overlap, but even in turbulent flame operation there is some sequence for the two processes along the time scale. Short delays are also observed in those devices designed to deal with solid samples such as jet fuel methods, furnaces, graphite cells, and sputtering chambers.

In the most popular systems, in which the sample is provided in the form of a solution or a suspension of finely powdered sample, the sprayer acts simply as a sample-size reduction device. A further sample-size reduction can be achieved during the step known as drop selection (spoilers, dispersal ball, dispersal plate, baffle, condensing chamber, reflux chamber, traps). In fact, the transformation of a spray into a mist and ultimately a nebula brings about a dilution or reduction of the analyte concentration in the aerosol going to the flame. In order to avoid this dilution and, even more, to achieve a relative concentration of the analyte in the aerosol, heated-chamber units have been designed (5–9). The spray undergoes a vaporization phase, then the heated spray is directed through a condensing chamber in which part of the solvent can be condensed and drained away. The support gas brings toward the premixing section of the burner a mixture of very fine and concentrated solution droplets, solvent vapor, and finely divided solid particles or clotlets. On the solid particles a partial condensation of the solvent can also take place.

A completely different picture is presented in sprayer–burners. In these a heterogeneous (in dropsize) spray is fed directly into the flame. Spot vaporization of the solvent is left to the flame itself. Part of the spray passes on through the flame.

Spraying, and the consequent formation of liquid-gas aerosol and/or solid-gas aerosol, is a common process for all flame methods, involving the use of solutions or suspensions. Atomization is a necessity when atomic processes have to be studied.

In considering the thermal effects of the flame in the atomization step, it is natural to think of the use of organic solvents (as an additive or as the main solvent) and of high-temperature flames in order to help the dissociation process and to avoid, as far as possible, any regression by association processes. At the same time, the utilization of highly reducing flames helps to avoid the formation of nonabsorbing or low-emitting entities, especially oxide types. The acetylene flame has been used to solve or decrease many of these problems, in part associated with what is designated in the literature as condensed phase chemical interferences. It is important to remember that excessively hot flames can lead to ionization processes, a phenomenon easily seen in the determination of alkali and alkaline earths metals. Counter-interferents to prevent ionization can be added to the sample and standard solutions to minimize, as far as possible, the interferences by shifting the equilibrium pattern of the flame (2).

III. Fundamental Processes in Flame Methods

A. DIRECT EMISSION PROCESS

Some of the atomic and molecular entities liberated or formed in the flame at the atomization stage are excited by the thermal energy of the flame; the flame can also produce ionization at the same time in part of the active entities. These entities can only be in specific levels of internal energy. When excited and brought to higher levels and when emitting luminous radiation and returned to lower levels, they follow definite energy changes. The radiation emitted corresponds to a frequency v given by the well-known equation

$$E_2 - E_1 = hv \tag{1}$$

where h is Planck's constant. The radiation can be located at a wavelength λ given by the relationship

$$\lambda = c/v \tag{2}$$

Multiple radiations identified for an analyte in emission flame instruments correspond to transitions between different energy levels. If energy changes other than electronic energy are involved (vibrational and rotational energy), bands and continuous background will also be detected.

If a sufficient number of entities of the same kind of analyte are involved, one can expect to find radiations corresponding to all energy transitions involved and represented in the spectrum. The intensity of each radiation will be a function of the total concentration of analyte in the flame and the transitional probability.

The thermal energy of the flame is very limited in comparison with other spectral excitation sources. Only a small fraction of all available analyte entities are excited, and only lines of low excitation potential should be expected to be observed in flame spectra. This explains the traditional statement that flame spectra are simple and consist only of a few characteristic lines. This is clearly shown in spectra obtained by means of low-temperature flames (air–natural gas, air–coal gas, or air–propane flames).

The electron spin, which is associated with orbital motion, gives rise to the production of doublets (from atoms with a single outer electron), triplets (two outer electrons), or multiplets. Sometimes it is difficult to detect these lines separately, even by using instruments with high resolution.

Lines corresponding to ionic spectra (observed for the alkaline earth metals) should be expected when using high-temperature flames which provide enough energy to release electrons from the atom. Singly ionized atomic spectra can be detected under these circumstances.

Some well-defined bands, detected as envelopes of the vibrational pattern, have been, and still are, the basis of some emission flame-photometric determinations.

Unfortunately, most line and band spectra appear in the emission flame spectrum superimposed upon a continuous background, especially when the analyte is fed into the flame in large concentrations. This background is a consequence of unquantized transitions. These may be transitions to unstable states or equilibria between positive ions and free electrons.

In the emission process, two analytical variables are involved: (1) the *qualitative variable* (wavelength characteristic to the analyte) and (2) the *quantitative variable* (radiation intensity, as a function of the analyte concentration in the flame). Emission flame photometry can take advantage of both of them for identification and determination purposes. Step by step identification or continuous identification by scanning are used in the qualitative analysis of unknowns. Sufficiently rapid scannings at constant operating conditions in comparison with reference solutions has given rise to the so-called semiquantitative emission flame photometric analysis. Some idea about the order of magnitude of concentrations of the analytes can be achieved in this way by following similar steps as those used in semiquantitative emission spectrographic analysis.

Quantitative analysis is usually performed at a fixed wavelength (a wavelength corresponding to the analyte emission) or by scanning and recording a limited wavelength interval. Standards are necessary for instrument calibration at frequent intervals.

Only a fraction of the total amount of analyte in the sample solution acts actively to produce radiation. The numerical or graphical correlation established between the radiation emitted and the concentration of the analyte in the solution involves a series of coefficients which can be considered as efficiency coefficients. These coefficients have to be considered:

(1)   the efficiency coefficient of the sprayer;
(2)   the efficiency coefficient of the spray chamber (if any);
(3)   the efficiency coefficient of the condensing chamber (if any);
(4)   the efficiency coefficient of the burner; and
(5)   the efficiency coefficient of the flame.

In the last one a series of equilibria should be included, each one governed in its turn by a different coefficient; namely the evaporation, dissociation, ionization, excitation, and self-absorption equilibria. Besides the excitation equilibria, the probability of transition toward the lower state should also be considered. The emitted radiation is also a function of energy of the light quantum. The influence of some of these equilibria, for instance, ionization and self-absorption equilibria, can cause variations in shape and curvature of the calibration curves.

The radiation intensity is highly dependent on the temperature and varies exponentially with the absolute temperature. High-temperature flames are necessary to obtain lines which correspond to high energy levels. This also explains the dependence of emission flame-photometric results on flame temperature variations and the imperative need of maintaining all flame parameters constant during experimental work. Temperature also favors the dissociation equilibrium, but a compromise is reached when ionization phenomena also can be observed. Low total efficiency, temperature dependence, and spectral interferences have been the main limiting factors when comparing emission flame photometry with atomic-absorption flame photometry.

B. ATOMIC-FLUORESCENCE PROCESS

If a population of atoms receives radiation, some can be excited and afterwards release energy in the form of radiation of characteristic wavelength and intensity which may be related to the analyte concentration in the sample used to produce the active atom population. In spite of the fact that the basis of the atomic-fluorescence process has been known for many years, its use in chemical analysis did not become widespread until 1964 (*9a*). Since then, a series of papers has been published on fundamentals and applications.

Atomic-fluorescence processes can be grouped in four main categories:

(1) Resonance fluorescence. Atoms in the ground state are excited and re-emit the same energy absorbed when returning to the ground state. This process has been recently used in atomic absorption to simplify the instrumental systems by the use of resonance lamp detectors.

(2) Direct-line fluorescence. Atoms excited to upper energy states can drop to lower but intermediate energy levels relative to the ground state.

(3) Stepwise-line fluorescence. The atoms may be excited to high energy states and then deactivated by steps; a first step is a radiationless transition followed by a fluorescence transition down to the ground state.

(4) Sensitized fluorescence. Donor entities are excited by means of a radiation source and transfer their energy to acceptor entities—analyte atoms. The analyte atoms emit the fluorescence radiation when deactivated.

The radiation coming from illuminating sources is absorbed at wavelengths corresponding to atomic-absorption lines. The radiation emitted is qualitatively characteristic of the analyte. The intensity of the atomic-fluorescence radiation depends on many factors: intensity of the light output of the illuminating source, the geometry of the absorption–emission cell, geometry of the light beams involved, characteristic wavelengths, and a series of efficiency coefficients related to the conversion of absorbed energy into fluorescence energy and other parameters of spectral nature.

The atomic-absorption process is not greatly disturbed by changes in temperature, as fluorescence emission depends on a fraction of the atoms existing initially at lower energy states, and not on atoms excited by thermal effects. As the atom population generally is generated by spraying a sample solution into a flame, physical properties, chemical composition, sprayer characteristics, gas flows, and all related factors in spraying processes will have effects similar to those in other flame methods. Considerations related to turbulent flame sprayer–burners (total consumption burners) should be applied here, as most workers prefer to use this type of device for producing the aerosol.

Sources should be intense, but it is not necessary that they emit lines as narrow as those in atomic absorption. Vapor discharge lamps have been used for this purpose and are satisfactory unless they present excessive self-reversal. Electrodeless discharge tubes can be utilized in atomic-fluorescence methods if enough light output is obtained. Work has also been done with hollow-cathode lamps (normal and high-intensity) and with continuum sources such as a xenon arc. Low light output and the need of high resolution are limiting factors in the use of continuum sources. Detectability can be improved by using more intense illuminating sources. Source fluctuation is not as serious as in atomic-absorption work. Large dynamic ranges of analyte concentration can be handled and good linearity is obtained in the analytical working curves.

Scattering effects have been found to be a major source of interferences in atomic-fluorescence work. Physical and chemical interferences are comparable to those found in atomic-absorption methods.

The method has, really, enough fundamental and experimental potentialities to compete with other flame methods in most of the well-known applications as soon as some of the limiting features can be solved and overcome.

C. ATOMIC-ABSORPTION PROCESS

If a population of atoms in the ground state is illuminated by a source, the atoms absorb the resonant radiation at a wavelength qualitatively characteristic of the analyte forming that atom population. Since the source is practically constant, the decrease of radiation energy resulting from exciting the ground state atoms to bring them to upper states of energy can be measured. This measurement can be quantitatively related, either numerically or graphically, to the concentration of analyte atoms in the absorbing medium or to the concentration of analyte in the sample used to prepare that absorbing medium.

Although several devices have been proposed to convert a sample into its constituent atoms, the flame seems to be one of the more reliable ways, especially when the sample is supplied in the form of a solution. The atomization system should consist of a sprayer section coupled to a burner section, either functioning as sprayer–burner (turbulent flame operation) or as a sprayer connected via a spray chamber (and condensing chamber) to a premix laminar flow burner. The use of flames characterizes the field of atomic-absorption spectroscopy known as *atomic-absorption flame photometry*.

The atomic-absorption process has been known for many years but did not become popular as a chemical analysis method until 1955. Since that time, an enormous number of reviews have discussed fundamental principles and applications, and an increasing number of research papers are appearing in the literature.

The outstanding characteristics of absorption methods, which are the basis for this widespread acceptance, are the capabilities to determine analytes difficult to determine by emission flame photometry and the high sensitivity achieved with a considerable number of elements, plus the practical freedom from many spectral interferences. Physical and chemical interferences have to be considered in atomic-absorption work as in other flame methods.

The atomic-absorption process is not greatly affected by temperature changes, another advantage over emission flame photometry. Of course temperature is an imperative factor in the atomization process (atomization of species difficult to dissociate, for instance) prior to the absorption process. All factors influencing the atomization process should be considered, plus the need to use discrete narrow line sources of high intensity and good stability. Fluctuation of the source will affect experimental results. The use of continuum sources is limited by the resolution attainable with most of the available monochromators.

Atomic absorption is a quantitative method. It is difficult to think of qualitative analysis or rapid semiquantitative analysis as can be done in emission work. Element by element examination is necessary for identification or semiquantitative purposes. Quantitative analysis is performed, as in other flame methods, at a fixed wavelength, according to the analyte determined, and by measurement and comparison of the absorption produced by standards and samples. Standards are necessary. As recommended in all flame methods, the calibration should be repeated at frequent intervals. Only a fraction of the atom population existing in the absorbing cell acts in the absorption process. A series of efficiency coefficients should also be considered in this process.

Measured absorptions should be converted into absorbances to obtain a linear relationship with concentration of the solutions fed into the instrument. Lack of linearity is observed in some cases, due principally to source (background or proximity of nonabsorbing source lines) and to concomitant ionization interferences.

As sources, vapor discharge lamps and hollow-cathode lamps have been widely used, and some efforts have also been directed to studies using continuum sources. Recently, the selection step has been simplified by the elimination of monochromators and substitution of resonance lamp detectors—a modification of the selection system which can be of considerable interest in routine determination of given analytes under the same operating conditions and within given concentration ranges.

The element by element type of determination is being supplemented in routine analysis by the use of multielement lamps and instruments, which are also appropriate for routine analysis for a given set of analytes determined under fixed conditions and concentration range. Routine determinations by atomic-absorption methods are being made easier by automatization leading to semiautomatic working conditions including the use of round-table samplers and coupled digital displays and/or printers. The latter gives printed sample number sequence plus the direct concentration reading of the sample measured.

IV. Instrumental Systems

Instrumental systems used in flame methods have many points in common. All of them deal with radiation that either comes from a flame or passes through a flame from a constant emitting source. All of them are prepared to receive samples and standards in the form of solutions—sometimes as suspensions—and must bring these solutions in finely divided form into a flame. All of them must perform some selection step in order to isolate qualitatively single radiations from more or less complicated spectra received at the entrance slit. Finally, all of them have to measure the intensity of the original emission or residual absorption intensity of the selected radiation; the measurement provides numerical values which can be correlated with concentration of the analyte in the test solutions.

The modular components for the several flame methods are outlined in Table 2. Subsequent chapters in these volumes will expand on the details. Strip-chart recorders, printers, punch-tape devices, digital displays, and other means of presenting numerical information can be connected to the electrical output of the photometric system. The selection and photometric systems accomplish exactly the same functions for any one of the methods. Drastic differences are found in the first two systems. For this reason some significant differences are found in the arrangement of the components, as shown schematically in Fig. 1. The source in the atomic-fluorescence method should be placed at an angle (generally 90°) with respect to the general optical axis of the atomization system and selection system.

Emission flame photometry requires in some cases higher resolution than the other methods, as it has to face the problem of selecting some emission lines from among very complicated spectra, often accompanied by some background. Atomic-fluorescence flame photometry, and definitely atomic-absorption flame photometry, deal with less complicated

TABLE 2

Instrumental Components for the Various Flame Methods

Module	Method		
	Emission flame photometry	Atomic-fluorescence flame photometry	Atomic-absorption flame photometry
Emission system	The flame and coupled sprayer section accomplish the functions of both systems: spraying, atomization, and emission	Constant source emission	Constant source emission
Atomization system		Spraying, atomization, and fluorescence emission	Spraying, atomization, and atomic absorption
Selection system	Selection of emitted radiations at analytical wavelengths	Selection of emitted fluorescence radiations at analytical wavelengths	Selection of emitted radiations from the source at analytical wavelengths
Photometric system	Measurement of emitted and selected radiations [Numerical information]	Measurement of emitted and selected radiations [Numerical information]	Measurement of residual emitted and selected radiations [Numerical information]

spectra; instruments need to perform only the second step of spectral selection (2). However, good resolution in the selection system helps in atomic-absorption for cases in which the emitting source produces a line-rich spectrum and when the analytical line lies very close to other analyte lines.

Sufficient available energy allows the flame photometrist to use narrow slits, thus achieving better resolution; and, although gain suffers, one often observes an improved signal-to-noise ratio. High-intensity lamps as the

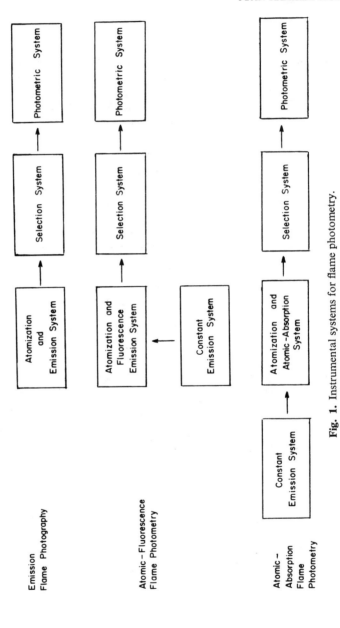

Fig. 1. Instrumental systems for flame photometry.

source will improve operating conditions in atomic-absorption flame photometry. Lamp stability is another important requirement. Monitoring of the source by splitting the original beam into a working beam and a reference beam improves unfavorable conditions due to lamp instability but at the price of a decrease in available energy.

Operating techniques follow very similar series of steps in all methods:

(1) Preliminary preparation of the sample—dissolution, extraction, separation;
(2) secondary preparation of the sample—additions, final dilution;
(3) introduction of the samples in the instrument and simultaneous recording of numerical data; and
(4) calculations.

The calculation step can be speeded up, when necessary, by means of a laboratory computer or by feeding data into more sophisticated electronic computers (*10, 11, 12*).

In step (3) all variable parameters should be set according to previous experience with known samples containing the same analyte or analytes. From this preliminary study the necessary steps for (1) and (2) can be planned. Variable parameters, as a general rule, should be maintained constant or practically constant during the measurement period. Any change of parameters requires a new calibration. Thus, new working curves are needed for determinations made under different operating conditions.

As no one method can be considered the universal solution for all problems involving all types of analytes, the choice of one or the utilization of two or even all three methods should be left to the decision of the flame photometrist. This is the reason why some instruments include capabilities for working either with atomic-absorption flame photometry or emission flame photometry (multipurpose instruments) and why attachments are available to incorporate emission or atomic-fluorescence capabilities in instruments primarily designed for the atomic-absorption method.

V. Terminology

Very few new terms have actually been proposed for flame methods. Most terms which have become popular and widely employed throughout the flame literature are modifications or adaptations of previously used terms, perhaps with the addition of some distinctive auxiliary adjectives (*long-tube* adapter, *sheathed* burner, *premix* burner, *laminar flow* burner, *nitrous oxide-acetylene* burner, *percentual* and *fluctuational* sensitivity). Terms used in flame methods, and also commonly used in other branches of science, have been borrowed from three main sources:

(1) Errors theory. This is the origin of the expressions: accuracy, precision, standard deviation, absolute and relative errors, relative standard deviation (lately accepted instead of coefficient of variation, so popular for many years in English printed literature), and other similar or related terms which so often appear in the quantitative consideration of the analytical behavior of flame methods.

(2) Classical analytical chemistry. From this source come most of the sensitivity terms, concentration and dilution expressions, concentration units, names for sample and standards solutions and other solutions such as blanks and unknowns, preparative operations such as extractions and separations, and even the recent term analyte.

(3) Spectral methods (absorption and emission) and other instrumental methods. Actually, flame methods embrace both. It is logical to find in their terminology terms profusely used in other instrumental methods, especially those devoted to spectral analysis.

In this section the author does not intend to present a compilation of all terms used in flame methods. They have already been listed in a recent publication (*13*) with the aim of establishing correlation between English and Spanish nomenclature. Only some special cases will be mentioned and discussed, especially when synonymous expressions are currently in use.

It is necessary to emphasize the desirability of having some unified accepted nomenclature. Unification helps enormously in the classification, indexing, and retrieval of flame literature and information, a more difficult task every day for the flame photometrist.

A. NOMENCLATURE OF FLAME METHODS

For direct emission methods, these names have been proposed:

(1) emission flame spectrometry (. . . photometry, spectrophotometry, spectroscopy, or spectography); and

(2) flame emission spectrometry (. . . photometry, spectrophotometry, spectroscopy, or spectrography).

When distinguishing flame methods from among other emission methods, such as arc or spark, it seems logical to place "flame" first. However, when all methods considered are flame methods, it seems more realistic to attach the word "flame" to the distinctive name of the particular method, preceded by the appropriate descriptive adjective (emission in this case) to distinguish it from absorption or fluorescence methods. Thus, emission flame spectrometry would be preferred. The name "photometry" has become popular for brevity; it was the expression used by early workers and consequently has become emplanted in many textbooks and papers. According to some authors the terms "photometry" and "spectrophotometry" should be considered synonymous in flame applications. In fact, most of the so-called photometers and spectrophotometers render direct measurement on a meter scale or on a digital display. Insofar as the output of the instrument is received by a recorder and graphical recording is obtained at a fixed or variable wavelength, the term "spectrograph" might also be used. Tradition has reserved the term "spectrography," however, for those cases in which a photographic plate is used for permanent recording.

A similar set of names might be used to describe atomic-fluorescence methods; atomic-fluorescence flame spectrometry seems suitable.

For atomic-absorption methods, a question arises concerning the use of the hyphen. It seems convenient to use it to form compound adjectives (*2, 14*). The hyphen might or might not be used when mentioning only atomic absorption as the generic name for the whole field. Names which have been employed are: atomic-absorption spectrophotometry, atomic-absorption spectroscopy, atomic-absorption flame photometry, atomic-absorption flame spectrophotometry, and absorption flame photometry.

If atomic is deleted, the name is converted into a general name covering both atomic and molecular absorption. The word "atomic" should appear, therefore, when mentioning phenomena really atomic. *Atomic-absorption spectroscopy* seems to be the most accepted expression to cover all atomic-absorption methods (flame, furnace, sputtering chamber). But if the flame is involved, the word "flame" should be included. For parallelism with emission nomenclature, *atomic-absorption flame photometry* and *atomic-absorption flame spectrometry* may be used.

B. Methods, Techniques, Procedures, Processes, and Operations

In the flame literature there appears also the same confusion with regard to nomenclature as in other analytical fields. *Method* requires some methodology, well established, such as:

Use of flames, spectral selection, and emission processes—method of emission flame photometry.

Use of flames, spectral selection, and atomic-absorption processes—method of atomic-absorption flame photometry.

Traditionally, the word "method" has been used for many techniques: addition method, dilution method, indirect methods, calibration method, and many others. The only way to justify the use of "method" instead of "technique" is if it is considered from the viewpoint of a certain methodology applicable in general to many cases. In this category might be included the following methods:

single-standard	addition
two-standard (or bracketing)	dilution
indirect	calibration

The greatest variety of names has been employed for the addition method (2):

standard addition	incremental addition
standard additions	admixture
standard-addition evaluation	autostandardization
addition-standard	method of increments
mixture	method of additions

For brevity, self-description, and wide acceptance, *addition method* seems to be acceptable.

Other activities are more aptly called *techniques*, as they may be adjusted specifically to different problems even though certain methodology is also involved; these techniques are:

compensation	moderate addition
equalization	extraction
buffering	separation
massive addition	

The word "procedure" should be reserved for practical chemical or instrumental work with a definite problem, such as the determination of calcium in blood serum or determination of zinc in vegetable matter. Preparative recipes and operating instrumental conditions can be included in the complete procedure.

The word "process" should be reserved for those occasions in which a definite phenomenon is involved: emission process, absorption process, ionization process, vaporization process, atomization process.

Finally, the word "operation" should be only used for some particular operating conditions as single-pass operation, triple-pass operation, hot operation, cold operation.

A special word seems appropriate for the use of the expression *double-beam method*. In atomic-absorption flame methods, it is not practical to compensate for sample factors such as the flame. Instead, the optical system is designed to monitor lamp source variations. Thus, the expressions source-monitoring, source-monitoring system, and source-monitoring method might be used instead.

C. CONCENTRATION AND SENSITIVITY

When handling very dilute aqueous solutions, one often encounters the terms parts per million (ppm) or parts per billion (ppb). However, if understood as a weight/volume relationship, these terms lose some meaning if the density of the solution differs from unity. Therefore, the preferred expressions are $\mu g/ml$ or pg/ml (picograms per milliliter). Powers of 10 with equal magnitude units, for example 1.00×10^{-6} g/ml for 1.00 $\mu g/ml$, also are used.

From classical analytical chemistry, terms such as "concentration limit" and "dilution limit" can be extended to flame methods. Detectability, a specific aspect of sensitivity and referring only to detection of an analyte, might be expressed by the terms "detection limit" or "detectability limit," so far as they are distinguished as concentration detection limit and dilution detection limit. Expressions of limits on the basis of concentrations are more frequent.

Although sensitivity cannot be expressed in concentration units, it can be expressed by the functionally related limits. In atomic-absorption methods, tabulation of concentration limits obtained for a given per cent absorption (in most cases 1 unit of the reading scale, or 1 %) have frequently been used. This has led to the introduction of the terms "percentual sensitivity" and "percentual concentration limits," with distinction from fluctuational sensitivity and fluctuational concentration limits calculated from experimental fluctuations observed when only a blank is sprayed into the flame (*2, 15–17*). These expressions refer to qualitative values obtained for each analyte.

The introduction of *quantitative sensitivity* and *absolute sensitivity* and related limits correlates the most appropriate ranges for measurement with values which represent qualitative sensitivity, and tries to evaluate minimum amount of analyte identifiable or measurable, respectively.

D. Instrumental Modules

A flame photometer should be considered as an instrument consisting of different systems: (a) emission system, (b) nebulization and atomization system (considered as absorption system in atomic-absorption work), (c) selection system, (d) photometric system.

In emission, (a) and (b) coincide. The sprayer section and the burner section are included in the atomization system. Parts of the systems are recognized in flame photometers as sections, components, devices, accessories, mechanisms, or just parts. Among them, a few parts have received in the past and at present the most diverse names.

Sources producing continuum output have been designated as "continuous sources" and "continuum sources." The latter name seems to be more acceptable as it refers to the continuum radiation.

The sprayer section some time ago was called atomizer. This name appears in some classical flame photometry books (*18–20*) along with the corresponding term *atomization*. In view of the real meaning of atomization, especially in atomic-absorption methods, the use of the term sprayer or nebulizer is preferred (*13*). Thus, the term atomizer–burner should be changed into sprayer—or nebulizer—burner.

There still remains the fine distinction between *sprayer* and *nebulizer*, which goes along with the distinction between *spray* and *nebula*. In a broad sense the sprayer should be considered as a part inside the nebulizer section if the original spray is converted into a nebula by drop-size selection. The term "aspirator–burner" is appropriate when the component is designed to aspirate a solution, but its principal function is to spray a sample into the flame. Aspirator–burner is not self-explanatory for the principal processes involved in its use.

Chamber is a widely accepted word (spray chamber, condensing chamber, sputtering chamber) according to different functions. In spite of the fact that "spraying chamber" might be admitted, the term "spray chamber" seems to be more appropriate. Atomization chamber or atomizing chamber should be avoided if used in the sense of spray chambers. However, sputtering chambers, furnaces, and graphite cells can be considered as atomization or atomizing chambers.

Besides this discussion on spraying and aspirating, some mention seems warranted of the variety of names used to express the ratio of milliliters per minute or the rate at which the solution is introduced in the instruments. Velocity or speed, instead of rate, have not been frequently used.

The following expressions have been employed:

sample consumption	sample intake
sample consumption ratio or rate	sample intake ratio or rate
solution consumption ratio or rate	solution intake
sample flow rate	solution intake ratio or rate
solution flow rate	flow rate
sample flow	aspirating rate
solution flow	aspiration rate
feeding rate	spraying rate
feed rate	

Feeding rate or *feed rate* are recommended by the author.

No problems appear with the term "fuel gas" or "combustible gas." If a second gas is used, these terms are utilized: comburent gas, oxidizing gas, spraying gas, or support gas (supporting).

A support gas is involved in both main processes—supporting combustion and supporting spraying. Even if inert (argon, nitrogen), it still can be designated as support gas.

Not too many differences exist in naming flames. The terms, in the order support gas–fuel gas, have become common; thus, air–acetylene flame, nitrous oxide–acetylene flame, air–propane flame. Also adjectives such as reducing, high-temperature, fuel-rich, turbulent, and laminar are often used. The blue cone of flames from round-tip burners is still called blue cone in long-slot burners. It should be called blue zone or blue edge. The blue cone, zone, or edge becomes red or pink in nitrous oxide–acetylene flames.

The viewed zone of the flame, after appropriate selection, is called *selected zone* or *selection zone*, but if the selection is made by adjusting the elevation of the burner with respect to the optical axis of the spectrometer, the following expressions have been introduced:

observation height
height of the selection zone (selected zone)
height of the beam
height of the burner (burner height)
elevation of the burner (burner elevation)
height of the viewed zone over the burner

When the component moved is the burner (up and down), and its position is measured from a reference scale, then *burner elevation* is quite descriptive. The adjective *optimum* can be added when optimized.

E. Interferences

The interference problem has been for years, and still is, a matter of discussion and controversy. Flame photometrists have agreed to distinguish between (1) spectral interferences, (2) physical interferences, and (3) chemical interferences. Of course, different subclassifications have been proposed (2). Attention has been directed once again toward the concept of chemical interferences by Fassel and Becker (21), who considered the so-called "solute vaporization interferences"; these do not exist or are negligible when using appropriate high-temperature flames.

The term quenching effects does not enjoy current acceptance. Inter-element interferences, a completely acceptable term, has been profusely used in view of the singular absence in some cases of interelement effects in atomic-absorption methods. Actually, interelement interferences can be classified, according to the nature of the process, as either spectral or chemical interferences. *Instrumental interferences* can be cited when referring to disturbances introduced by some system or parts of the instrument.

The use of phrases such as "interferences *by* phosphate *on* calcium" or "phosphate interferences *on* calcium" is more descriptive than a variety of sentences which have been used for the same purpose. These expressions allow the indexing of any interference case as

> *calcium*, interferences by phosphate on;
> *phosphate* interferences on calcium;
> *interferences* by phosphates on calcium.

No clear distinction has been formulated for the use made of the terms: interferents, interferent components (interfering components), interferent matrix component, interferent matrix constituent, interferent major component, interferent partner, interfering ions (cations or anions), and interfering concomitants. All of them occur frequently in the literature.

No doubts appear in the use of *competing ion*, but some confusion appears in the use of *releasers* and *protectors*. Releasers actually help to free the analyte, but protectors protect it against the combination with interferent components. Special attention should be paid to the real chemical process involved.

There is such a variety of additions to be used in flame methods that it is difficult to suggest a definite terminology. Some attempts at concordant terminology have been published (2, 22).

F. Curves

Most papers on flame photometry attempt to illustrate by means of curves the behavior of analytes under different operating conditions. As percentual sensitivity can drastically change according to the operating conditions chosen, authors also try to show how the measured variable changes as a function of the concentration of the standard solutions utilized. These curves are named: calibration curves, analytical curves, standard curves, or working curves. Calibration curve, and even analytical calibration curve, are acceptable during verification of the analytical behavior of a given analyte in regard to variation of parameters and effect of concomitants. If the curve is used for quantitative determination of concentration of analyte, then the term *working curve* or analytical working curve may be used.

No confusion has yet been observed between *flame profiles* and *flame patterns*. Other curves are usually named according to the variables or phenomenon involved (absorbance vs. air pressure curves, interference curves, feeding rate curves).

There seems little doubt as to the adoption of the term *absorbance* in atomic-absorption methods in preference to the related terms: optical density, extinction, and absorbancy. Relative absorbance has often been used in papers to show relative values in per cent as a function of the variation of some parameters.

G. Conclusion

In spite of the comments and suggestions included in this section, the author wishes to emphasize the convenience of accepting national recommendations for nomenclature in flame methods when proposed by authorized committees.

REFERENCES

1. P. T. Gilbert, Jr., *Proceedings Xth Colloquium Spectroscopicum Internationale,* Spartan, Washington, D.C., 1963, p. 171.
2. J. Ramírez-Muñoz, *Atomic-Absorption Spectroscopy,* Elsevier, Amsterdam, 1968.
3. V. A. Fassel, R. N. Kniseley, R. H. Wendt, and J. Fiorino, *Pittsburgh Conf. on Anal. Chem. and Appl. Spectr.,* Pittsburgh, Pa., *February 1966.*
4. S. R. Koirtyohann and E. E. Pickett, *Anal. Chem.,* 37, 601 (1965).

5. A. Hell, *5th Australian Spectr. Conf., Perth, May 1965*.
6. A. Hell, J. Ramírez-Muñoz, and N. Shifrin, *4th Nat. Meeting of Soc. for Appl. Spectr., Denver, Colo., August 1965*.
7. A. Hell, J. Ramírez-Muñoz, and N. Shifrin, *Meeting on Inorg. and Anal. Chem. of Roy. Spanish Soc. for Phys. and Chem., Madrid, February 1966*.
8. A. Hell, J. Ramírez-Muñoz, and N. Shifrin, *Pittsburgh Conf. on Anal. Chem. and Appl. Spectr., Pittsburgh, Pa., February 1966*.
9. N. Shifrin, A. Hell, and J. Ramírez-Muñoz, *9th Rocky Mountain Spectry., Conf., Denver, Colo., August 1967*.
9a. J. D. Winefordner and T. J. Vickers, *Anal. Chem.*, **36**, 161 (1964).
10. J. Ramírez-Muñoz, J. L. Malakoff, and C. P. Aime, *Anal. Chim. Acta*, **36**, 328 (1966).
11. J. L. Malakoff, J. Ramírez-Muñoz, and C. P. Aime, *Anal. Chim. Acta*, **43**, 37 (1968).
12. J. L. Malakoff, J. Ramírez-Muñoz, and W. Z. Scott, *Anal. Chim. Acta*, **42**, 515 (1968).
13. J. Ramírez-Muñoz, *Inform. Quim. Anal.* (in press).
14. W. T. Elwell and J. A. F. Gidley, *Atomic-Absorption Spectrophotometry*, 2nd ed., Pergamon, Oxford, 1966.
15. J. Ramírez-Muñoz, *Talanta*, **13**, 87 (1966).
16. J. Ramírez-Muñoz, N. Shifrin, and A. Hell, *Microchem. J.*, **11**, 204 (1966).
17. J. Ramírez-Muñoz and W. F. Ulrich, *Flame Notes, Beckman*, **1**, 33 (1966).
18. J. A. Dean, *Flame Photometry*, McGraw-Hill, New York, 1960.
19. F. Burriel-Marti and J. Ramírez-Muñoz, *Fotometría de llama*, Vols. 1 and 2, Monografias de Ciencia Moderna del C.S.I.C., Madrid, 1955.
20. F. Burriel-Marti and J. Ramírez-Muñoz, *Flame Photometry: A Manual of Methods and Applications*, Elsevier, Amsterdam, 1960.
21. V. A. Fassel and D. A. Becker, *XIIIth Colloquium Spectroscopicum Internationale, Ottawa, June 1967*.
22. P. T. Gilbert, Jr., in *Analysis Instrumentation—1964* (L. Fowler, R. J. Harmon, and D. K. Roe, eds.), Plenum, New York, 1964, p. 193.

3 Emission Problems of Unsalted Flames

E. Pungor and I. Cornides

DEPARTMENT OF ANALYTICAL CHEMISTRY
UNIVERSITY OF CHEMICAL INDUSTRIES
VESZPRÉM, HUNGARY

I. Basic Principles of Electronic Spectra

A. Origin of Spectra and Basic Concepts

The origin of spectra may be illustrated by a simple scheme (Fig. 1). A body, the light source, transforms under appropriate conditions the input (thermal, electrical, light, chemical, or nuclear) energy into light energy whose distribution in different wavelength (its spectrum) can be visualized, recorded, and measured by a subsequent detector. The energy relations may be more complex in some cases. In flames, chemical energy is transformed to thermal energy, only a fraction of which is consumed to produce the emission observed from flame gases. A direct transformation of chemical energy to radiation may also take place; it is denoted as chemi-excitation. Involved are both chemical and physical processes. With flames, the combustion of a fuel and the excitation of atoms and molecules by thermal collisions with molecules of the burnt gases are the most significant.

The spectral distribution of the energy emitted from flames may be continuous or discontinuous. In the latter case, line and band spectra can be distinguished. Generally speaking, line and band spectra are emitted by relatively free individual atoms and molecules, respectively, and reflect

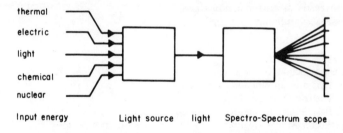

Fig. 1. Schematic diagram of the origin of a spectrum.

what atomic and molecular species are present in the light source. On the other hand, continuous spectra (if not emitted by hot solids such as carbon particles) may provide information concerning the nature of processes occurring in the source. There is also an absorption spectrum which is the spectral distribution of energy absorbed by a substance in the source. Either type of spectrum may reveal useful information on the chemical composition of the absorbing or emitting medium.

Spectral lines are characterized by their wavelength and intensity. The total spectral line energy is not confined to an infinitely sharp line. It has a distribution over a certain wavelength interval and thus a finite line width. The total intensity of a spectral line is defined by an integral of the distribution function over the line width; its wavelength as the point of maximum intensity.

Line energy distribution obtained experimentally, so-called line shapes or profiles, are markedly influenced by actual experimental conditions. This is also true of the intensity, even of relative intensities, within a spectrum. The wavelength may be considered to be the most stable characteristic of a spectral line although it exhibits some fluctuation with excitation conditions. Generally speaking, one can attain a close approach to the intrinsic properties of atoms and molecules through their spectra only if the ideal undisturbed state of the atomic and molecular entities is realized to a sufficient extent. This entails low pressure and low analyte density in the light source. Unfortunately, in practical work the selection of excitation conditions and other experimental arrangements is dictated by requirements which may demand quite different operating procedures for each analysis.

To establish the relationship between the spectra and structures of emitting atoms or molecules, a detailed theory of the emission mechanism is necessary. This theory was developed in two stages: first, the so-called "old quantum theory," followed by the modern wave theory or quantum mechanical model.

B. The Old Quantum Theory

The first investigations of regularities in atomic spectra date back to the last two decades of the 19th century. After some qualitative observations of different spectra were reported by Liveing and Dewar (1) and Hartley (2), Balmer (3) succeeded in describing the sequence of the visible hydrogen lines by an exact mathematic formula. Introducing the wave number in place of the wavelength, Rydberg (4) was able to reproduce Balmer's equation in the generalized form

$$\bar{v} = R\left[\frac{1}{(m+\delta_m)^2} - \frac{1}{(n+\delta_n)^2}\right] \tag{1}$$

where R is a universal constant, n and m are running indices which vary in integral steps, and δ_n and δ_m are correction terms characteristic of the element. By selecting the value of m, we get a definite series of spectrum lines, the individual lines of which are defined by the actual value of n. Equation (1) is applicable not only to all spectral lines of the hydrogen atom, but to spectra of the alkali atoms as well. Similar equations are valid for the spectra of singly ionized helium and the singly ionized alkaline earth atoms and, in fact, for all one-valence-electron atoms. The correction terms in Eq. (1) are zero for the hydrogen spectrum, but have nonzero values for the other elements.

   The form of the Rydberg–Balmer expression led Ritz (5) to the combination principle and to the suggestion of the empirical term system. Introducing the concept "term" by the relation

$$T = E/hc$$

the wave number of a spectral line is given by the corresponding term difference. Expressing any spectral line of an atom by the difference between two terms provides a systematic set of terms. Difficulties inherent

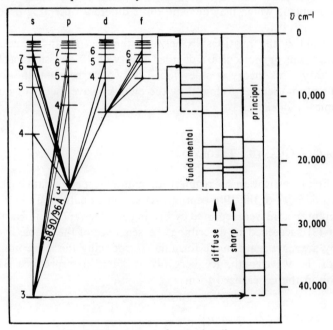

Fig. 2. Term system of neutral sodium atom.

in a systematic survey of the complex structure of spectra are thereby lessened. Its use has been extended to all atomic and molecular spectra.
   The term diagram of the sodium atom is represented in Fig. 2. On this figure the best-known term series have been indicated. The same wave number scale is used for the term values and the spectral lines. The terms are deduced from the spectral line series observed experimentally. Correlation between the term diagram and the spectrum (the system of the spectral lines) is apparent in the case of the spectral limits obtained for n infinite. In the diagram it is the term lower than all the others.

The correlation between the term and spectral systems is emphasized by the traditional designation of the first four term series. The running indices of the term combinations furnishing the wave numbers of the sharp series are called s-terms; the p-, d-, and f-terms are denoted as "principal," "diffuse," and "fundamental," respectively.

The existence and regularities of line spectra received a theoretical interpretation in Bohr's quantum theory. Introducing Planck's quantum concept into the classical mechanics of the atomic model developed by Rutherford (6), Bohr (7) succeeded in creating a theory capable of explaining the formation of discrete spectral lines.

The very essence of Bohr's theory may be stated as follows: The atom as a system of positive nucleus and negative electrons interacting by Coulomb forces can exist only in discrete, or quantized, energy states, the transitions between which constitute the emission or absorption of energy. The frequency of the light emitted or absorbed is determined by Bohr's frequency condition

$$\Delta E = E_1 - E_2 = h\nu \tag{2}$$

where E_1 and E_2 are the quantized energies of the atom in its initial and final states, respectively, and h is Planck's constant.

The possible energy states are defined by Bohr's quantum condition, the formulation of which requires a realization of the motion and energetic conditions within the atom. Classical mechanics demanded that the electrons follow circular or elliptical orbits around the nucleus. Bohr assumed that an electron in the field of a nucleus was not capable of moving along every one of the paths that were possible according to classical theory but was restricted to move along one of a discrete set of paths that fulfilled the quantum condition

$$\oint p_i \, dx_i = n_i h \tag{3}$$

$\oint$ meaning integration over a complete cycle and where $i = 1$ or 2 (a two-dimensional problem), x_i and p_i are generalized coordinates and momenta, respectively, and n_i is any positive integer—the quantum numbers. Supplementing the classical equations of motion with this condition, the possible quantized elliptic orbits of electrons can be calculated. Taking the radial and azimuthal coordinates for x_1 and x_2, respectively, we get for the half-axes

$$a = \frac{h^2}{4\pi^2 m_e Z e^2} \, (n_r + n_\phi)^2$$

$$b = a\left(\frac{n_\phi}{n_r+n_\phi}\right)$$

Here e is the electronic charge, Ze the charge of the nucleus, m_e the mass of the electron, and n_r, n_ϕ are the radial and azimuthal quantum numbers. The energy of the atom may be calculated from Eq. (4):

$$E = \frac{-2\pi^2 m_e Z^2 e^4}{h^2} \frac{1}{(n_r+n_\phi)^2} \tag{4}$$

The negative sign is due to the arbitrary choice of the zero energy level as the least energy required to ionize the atom by removal of the electron.

With the notations: $n_r+n_\phi = n$ and $n_\phi = k$, the energy as a function of the principal quantum number n is given as

$$E_n = \frac{-2\pi^2 m_e Z^2 e^4}{h^2}\left(\frac{1}{n^2}\right) \tag{5}$$

while the ratio of the two axes is given by $b/a = k/n$. The possible values of the quantum numbers are

$$n = 1, 2, 3, \ldots$$
$$k = 1, 2, 3, \ldots, n$$

For a transition: $E_n \to E_m$, emission of a spectral line occurs. Wave numbers may be written as a difference:

$$\bar{v} = \frac{E_n-E_m}{hc} = \frac{E_n}{hc} - \frac{E_m}{hc} \tag{6}$$

The spectral terms are thus proportional to the energy levels of the atom.

As the energy formula quoted does not contain δ corrections for the running index n, it can be valid in this form only for the hydrogen atom having a single series of terms. Taking $Z = 1$, therefore, the special Rydberg–Balmer formula furnishing the lines of the hydrogen spectrum is obtained,

$$\bar{v} = R_H\left[\frac{1}{m^2} - \frac{1}{n^2}\right] \tag{7}$$

with the Rydberg constant

$$R_H = \frac{2\pi^2 \mu e^4}{h^3 c}$$

expressed by universal constants where μ is the reduced mass of the electron.

The reliability of the Bohr theory was first demonstrated by the excellent agreement of the theoretical and the experimental values of R_H.

Equation (7), although derived for the hydrogen atom, applies equally well to the spectrum of ionized helium (with $Z = 2$ and taking into account the slight increase in the reduced mass) and, in fact, to all one-electron spectra.

In the case of the alkali atoms, however, it must be taken into consideration that they possess more than one electron. They represent many-body systems and the many-body problem of mechanics cannot be exactly solved. It is, therefore, impossible to derive exact formulas for the electron orbits or the energy levels. Nevertheless, the special structure of the electron configurations of the alkali atoms renders it possible to use a semiquantitative approximation.

The Bohr theory achieved its second great success by explaining the periodic system of elements. The periodic properties were shown to be related to the electron configurations, that is, to the distributions of the electrons in the different energy levels or orbits and governed by the Pauli exclusion principle in addition to the Bohr postulates. The electron configuration of the alkali atoms turned out to consist of an inner group of $Z - 1$ electrons which formed a nearly symmetrical cloud of negative charge around the nucleus and a single outer electron that revolved generally outside this cloud. This outer electron is responsible for the optical and chemical behavior of the atom. It is, therefore, sufficient to compute the energy of the atom associated with the position and motion of this electron (sometimes called the optical or valence electron).

Now, the conditions for the outer electron of an alkali atom are very similar to those existing in the hydrogen atom because the nucleus with its Ze positive charge and the inner electrons with their $(Z-1)e$ negative charge represent a net charge of $+e$ for the atomic volume. Motion and energetics of the outer electron are, therefore, expected to be "hydrogen-like." There are, however, two effects giving rise to deviations from the hydrogen-like behavior. The outer electron polarizes the nucleus-inner electron system, distorting thereby the Coulomb field presumed when calculations were made. This effect cannot be neglected for close orbits, that is, for small values of the quantum number n. Secondly, orbits of great eccentricity, corresponding to small values of the quantum number k, must partly penetrate into the cloud of the inner electrons, where the field is again not Coulomb-like. Both effects decrease the energy levels, which can be accounted for by a correction δ of the principal quantum number in the energy formula:

$$E_{n,k} = -hc \frac{R}{(n-\delta)^2} \qquad (8)$$

where the energy is a function of the azimuthal quantum number, as the δ-values decrease with increasing values of k.

The empirical terms: $R/(n-\delta)^2$ for the alkali atoms were explained, as was the existence of different term series, that is, different term values for the same principal quantum number, with disappearing differences as n increases. It is also evident that the s-terms, exhibiting the greatest decrease in energy (i.e., the greatest value of δ), correspond to $k = 1$ (orbits of greatest eccentricity), the p-terms to $k = 2$, etc.

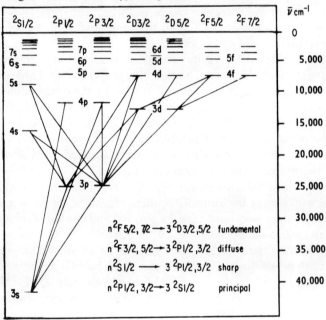

Fig. 3. Detailed term system of sodium atom.

The term system of the sodium atom is given in Fig. 3 with the conventional term notations and also in a more detailed form. Some features require additional explanation. Unlike the H-atom, the lowest term of the sodium atom belongs to $n = 3$. This is, nevertheless, easy to understand if one considers that the orbits of still lower energy content are occupied by the inner electrons. Similarly, the lowest term of the potassium atom belongs to $n = 4$, that of the rubidium atom to $n = 5$, etc., due to the increasing number of inner electrons.

It is far more difficult to explain the splitting observed for all except the *s*-terms, which brings about spectral terms grouped in multiplets. The multiplet concept was necessitated by observations of line doublets in the alkali (and other) spectra; an example is the well-known yellow doublet (the $D_1 - D_2$ lines) of the sodium spectrum.

An explanation involved the postulation that the electron rotates around itself while rotating around the nucleus. The spinning electron represents a small magnetic dipole which, in the magnetic field of the orbital motion of the electron, possesses some energy due to the dipole-field interaction. The magnitude of this small energy surplus depends on the relative position of the dipole (the magnetic moment) and the field, which, in turn, is determined by and may be expressed by the directions of the corresponding angular momentum vectors.

The orbital angular momentum, quantized in the Bohr theory, had possible values equal to $k(h/2\pi)$. This quantum property, extended logically to the resultant (orbital + spin) angular momentum of the electron, prevents the spin (more precisely the spin angular momentum) from acquiring any direction in the field. Agreement with the experimental findings necessitated assigning two possible directions (parallel or antiparallel) and the magnitude $h/4\pi$ to the spin vector. The spin angular momentum of the electron is $s(h/2\pi)$, where s, the spin quantum number, may have the value $+\frac{1}{2}$ or $-\frac{1}{2}$. Accordingly, there exist two energy levels for each pair of the quantum numbers n and k. By accepting the spin hypothesis, a reasonable explanation is provided for the splitting of the alkali terms.

Simultaneously, however, two new problems arose. One was the inconsistency connected with the lack of splitting of the *s*-terms. This and the existence of the electron spin can be made compatible only if the magnetic field is assumed to disappear for the lowest value of the azimuthal quantum number. Replacing k by a new azimuthal or orbital quantum number, $l = k - 1$, the possible values of l are

$$0, 1, 2, \ldots, n-1$$

Now the orbital angular momentum, $l(h/2\pi)$, and the proportional orbital magnetic momentum and field disappear for $l = 0$, i.e., for the *s*-terms when the electron trajectory is circular. For other values of l the trajectory is elliptic, the ellipse being more elongated as l is smaller.

A second problem arose when the relationship between the doublet terms and doublet lines was more carefully inspected. The line doublets of the principal and sharp series corresponded to transitions between two terms, one of which is a singlet, the other a doublet term. If, on the other hand, both the basic and the running terms are doublets, as in the case of the diffuse and fundamental series, four different transitions should be possible altogether and a quadruplet should arise (Fig. 4.). With spectroscopes of sufficiently high sensitivity, a very faint third line was actually observed. The fourth line, however, could not be observed; the transition indicated by dotted line in Fig. 4 seemed, for some reason, to be forbidden. The alkali spectra present even more conspicuous examples of such forbidden transitions; for example, a p-term may combine only with s- or d-terms, that is, with terms belonging to term series being in the immediate vicinity of the p-series, but cannot combine with an f- or another p-term.

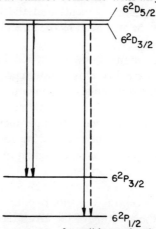

Fig. 4. Term system of possible quadruplet lines.

These observations show that definite selection rules are in operation for transitions from one energy state to another. The rule that the quantum number k or l may change by $+1$ or -1 only, i.e.,

$$\Delta l = \pm 1$$

expresses concisely the empirical fact that transitions occur only between neighboring term series.

This rule is, however, insufficient whenever one has to select the permitted transitions in cases of multiplet terms, as in Fig. 4. The necessary additional rule can be easily formulated by the use of the so-called inner quantum number j which takes one of the two values $l \pm s$, i.e., $l + \frac{1}{2}$ or $l - \frac{1}{2}$. Physically, j takes into account the resultant angular momentum of the electron and distinguishes the slightly different terms of doublets. The spectral terms are unambiguously characterized by the quantum numbers n, l, and j as manifested by the term notation, quite universally adopted, and used in Figs. 3 and 4. The term $3\,^2P_{3/2}$, for example, has the quantum numbers $n = 3$, $l = 1$ (expressed by the capital letter P). The right subscript indicates the value of j. The left superscript (called the term multiplicity) gives the value of the multiplicity of the term. Note that the s-terms, though being singlets, always possess the same multiplicity index as the p-, d-, etc. terms belonging to them.

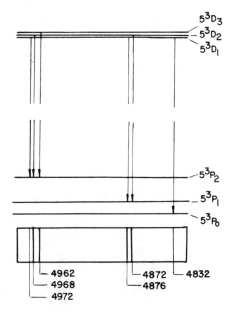

Fig. 5. Some term combinations of strontium atom.

The empirically ascertained selection rule for j is

$$\Delta j = 0,\ \pm 1 \quad (0 \rightarrow 0 \text{ excluded})$$

The multiplet character of the spectral terms and lines is referred to as their fine structure. The complexity increases as the number of the outer electrons increases. Atoms with two valence electrons, such as helium, the alkaline earth atoms, and mercury, have line series originating from combinations between terms of two triplet term series. All members of these series contain six lines; three more lines fall out due to the selection rule for j. As an example, the $5\,^3D \rightarrow 5\,^3P$ transitions and the corresponding spectral lines for the strontium atom are shown in Fig. 5.

Remarkably, the fine structure of the hydrogen lines, e.g., the Balmer lines, is more complex than that of the alkali "doublets." This can be explained as follows. Bohr's first calculations indicated that the energy levels of the hydrogen atom, with no inner electrons, were independent of the orbital quantum number. Although Sommerfeld's relativistic theory (8) revealed some small differences, the very slightly different $s, p, d \ldots$ terms of the hydrogen do not constitute separate term series, merely a splitting of the terms belonging to $n = 1, 2, 3 \ldots$ This splitting is superimposed on that caused by the spin-orbit interaction—more precisely, the interaction

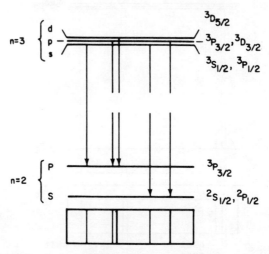

Fig. 6. Theoretical fine structure of H_α line ($n = 3 \to n = 2$) for atomic hydrogen.

between the electrons magnetic dipole and the magnetic field associated with orbital motion—producing thereby the complex multiplicity of the hydrogen terms.

In Fig. 6 the terms responsible for the H_α line are shown. There are two terms for $n = 2$ (S, P), and three for $n = 3$ (S, P, D); altogether five terms. In addition, the p- and d-terms are split due to the spin effect, which, however, does not increase the number of the terms, since three pairs practically coincide. (A difference of 0.03 cm^{-1} between the terms $2\,^2S_{1/2}$ and $2\,^2P_{1/2}$ could be detected with the help of a special microwave method.) The five possible transitions correspond to the fine structure observed and obey the selection rules.

Spectra obtained under high resolution revealed additional hyperfine line structures. Two nuclear phenomena are responsible—the nuclear spin and the isotope effect. Term splitting in magnetic and electric fields (the Zeeman and the Stark effects) are mainly of theoretical interest, but exemplified the validity of the quantum theory.

Now let us summarize the results of the Bohr quantum theory in the field of spectroscopy and also show its weak points. The Bohr theory proved to be of inestimable value in providing a physical model to deal with discrete line spectra. It gave a correct quantitative description of the one-valence-electron spectra, and it explained the normal Zeeman and the Stark effects. Nonetheless, the limitations of the theory soon became apparent. The weak points of the Bohr theory may be divided into two categories.

There are concrete discrepancies between theory and experimental data. For example, the Bohr theory completely fails in the case of the two-electron spectra (e.g., helium atom). The standard approximation methods of the three-body problem provide in this case completely incorrect results. In some cases only minor empirical modifications were necessary to obtain formulas which provided results compatible with experiments [e.g., replacing l^2 by $l(l+1)$]. No theoretical reasoning, however, justified these modifications.

Secondly, some problems of great importance for spectroscopy could not be handled in the framework of the Bohr theory. Its inability to determine the intensities of the spectral lines was a great deficiency. Generally speaking, any details of the transition process itself (transition probabilities or lifetime of excited states) are beyond the scope of Bohr's "old quantum theory."

From a purely methodological point of view, the theoretical foundation of the old quantum theory is highly objectionable. It was just an ad hoc mixture of classical mechanics with many arbitrarily accepted and rather extraneous principles, e.g., quantum rules.

All these deficiencies were overcome by the modern quantum mechanics developed independently and in different mathematical form by Schrö-dinger (9) (wave mechanics) and Heisenberg (10) (matrix mechanics). It seems, therefore, reasonable to discuss briefly the basic principles and conclusions of this theory before proceeding to the treatment of topics such as many-electron spectra, band spectra, and intensity relations.

C. Basic Principles and Results of Quantum Mechanics

Schrödinger's theory had its origin in the unusual idea of particle waves proposed by de Broglie (11). In this conception, moving particles behave like waves and their motion is to be treated accordingly. The adequate mathematical formulation is the famous Schrödinger wave equation

$$\nabla^2\Psi + \frac{8\pi^2 m}{h^2}(E-V)\Psi = 0 \tag{9}$$

where m is the mass of the particle, E and V its total and potential energy, respectively, h is Planck's constant, Ψ is the amplitude of the wave associated with the moving particle, and $\nabla^2\Psi$ stands for the Laplacian of Ψ. $\Psi = \Psi(x,y,z)$ is taken here as a function of the space coordinates only, that is, the Schrödinger equation in this form is only capable of describing stationary states, which are, however, just of prime necessity for the theory of spectra.

As a demonstrative example, the solution of the wave equation for the hydrogen atom will be given. Taking $V = -e^2/r$ (the Coulomb potential) and $m = \mu$ (the reduced mass of the electron and proton) we have

$$\nabla^2\Psi + \frac{8\pi^2 \mu}{h^2}\left(E + \frac{e^2}{r}\right)\Psi = 0 \tag{10}$$

Solution for Ψ is sought under the boundary conditions that Ψ and its derivative are everywhere continuous, finite, and single-valued. Mathematical considerations show that taking E negative (states inside ionization), solutions satisfying these conditions are possible only if E has one of the values

$$E = -\frac{2\pi^2 \mu e^4}{n^2 h^2}$$

the "eigenvalues" of Eq. (10), with the possible values of $n = 1, 2, 3 \ldots$ From the Schrödinger equation the discrete energy levels of the hydrogen atom and the quantum number n appear quite naturally as a consequence of the structure of the wave equation.

The corresponding solutions for Ψ, the "eigenfunctions" of the differential equation, constitute an expression of rather complex form. In addition to values of n, the eigenfunctions contain the quantum number l, the possible values of which are $l = 0, 1, 2, \ldots (n-1)$. The eigenfunctions contain also the so-called magnetic quantum number $m = 0, \pm 1, \pm 2, \ldots,$ $\pm l$ introduced by a separate quantum condition in the Bohr theory to explain the Zeeman effect.

Finally, computing the angular momentum we obtain

$$\sqrt{l(l+1)}\left(\frac{h}{2\pi}\right)$$

as its possible values. Here we see that the change of l^2 mentioned earlier is justified by quantum mechanics.

Having reproduced all results of the old theory (in corrected form, if it was necessary) for the H-atom, the question concerning the physical meaning of the eigenfunction $\Psi(x,y,z)$—the amplitude of the wave associated with the electron—will now be considered. $|\Psi(x,y,z)|^2$ determines the probability of the electron being present in a unit volume around the point (x,y,z). The discrete electron orbits of the Bohr–Sommerfeld theory are thereby replaced by continuous probability-density distributions. Like the old orbits, these are dependent on the specific values of the quantum numbers. This picture of the spatial motion of

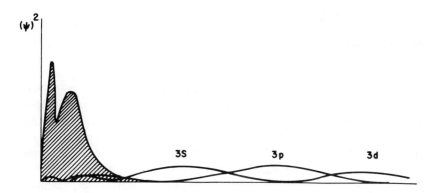

Fig. 7. Radial probability-density distribution functions of electrons of sodium atom.

the electron is rather strange for the classical mechanics. However, it avoids such awkward contradictions of the old theory as electron orbits for $l = 0$, which should have degenerated to straight lines through the nucleus.

For atomic systems with more than one electron, Ψ is a function of all coordinates. Consequently, the Schrödinger equation becomes more complex and calculations become exceedingly difficult. Only approximation methods are available. Often it is necessary to extrapolate from simple cases. For example, by means of his self-consistent field method and using successive approximations, Hartree and Hartree (*12*) were able to calculate the radial probability-density distributions for electrons of the alkali metals. In Fig. 7 these functions are shown for the sodium atom; the shaded curve presents the resultant for all inner or core electrons, the other curves represent the distribution functions of the valence electron in its ground state (3*s*) and two excited states (3*p*, 3*d*). In the 3*s* and 3*p* states, the valence electron spends some time inside the core, whereas in the 3*d* state it does not. This is in agreement with the old theory insofar as the first two of the corresponding orbits penetrate the core but the third does not.

The terms corresponding to the nonpenetrating orbits are hydrogen-like, apart from small differences due to a polarization effect of the core by the valence electron. For the penetrating orbits the δ-values could be calculated by different quantum mechanical approximation methods, with reasonable accuracy.

The problem of the fine structure of the alkali and hydrogen spectral lines is very elegantly dealt with by Dirac's relativistic theory (*13*), which is a further developed form of the quantum mechanics. Dirac's wave equation presents the electron spin and the spin quantum number as the principal quantum number just as did Schrödinger's equation. By means of this extended theory of quantum mechanics practically all phenomena of spectroscopy can be handled. But in nearly all cases the mathematical treatment is very difficult and the computational work is enormous. It is, therefore, customary in practical spectroscopy to retain many ideas and the whole picture developed by the old quantum theory, particularly when some general and more qualitative information is desired. Quantum mechanics is used as a control and is supplying quantitative data when necessary. A typical procedure of this type is the vector model treatment of spectra of many-electron systems.

D. Vector Model Treatment of Many-Valence-Electron Atoms

The complexity of spectra and term systems is considerably increased as we proceed to two- or more-valence-electron atoms, due to the increase of chances for interaction, which lead to a great variety of possible energy states.

The quantum mechanical treatment of problems is not simple and is even more difficult and laborious for complicated electron configurations. Practical spectroscopy, however, usually requires merely the establishment and qualitative characterization of the possible energy states. This modest aim can be achieved by the use of a simpler procedure, which has grown out of the old quantum theory and has, accordingly, a descriptive character.

As shown before, the possible energy states or terms of atoms with only one valence electron are determined by the quantum numbers n and l of this electron though somewhat modified and split by the spin-orbit interaction. For atoms with more valence electrons, the most important line series and energy levels result from the excitation of only one valence electron. In spite of this, the energy levels of such atoms are not defined merely by the quantum numbers of one electron due to the interactions with the other valence electrons, which are associated with definite energies.

The electrostatic repulsion energy of the electrons will depend on the relative orientations of the orbits of the individual valence electrons, characterized by their quantum numbers n_i and l_i. As this energy is also quantized, the relative orientations must follow a quantum rule. The orientations of the orbits are expressed by the angular momentum vectors designated by $\mathbf{l}_i$. Consequently, their quantum rule may be most easily formulated by the use of these vectors. The possible orientations are determined by the requirement that the $\mathbf{l}_i$ vectors must give a resultant $\mathbf{L}$, the magnitude of which is also an integer multiple of $(h/2\pi)$

$$\mathbf{L} = \sum \mathbf{l}_i \quad \text{and} \quad |\mathbf{L}| = L\left(\frac{h}{2\pi}\right)$$

Evidently, L may have the values of all integers from $|l_1 - l_2|$ to $|l_1 + l_2|$. The energy levels corresponding to $L = 0, 1, 2, 3 \ldots$ are now designated by the letters $S, P, D, F \ldots$

In the simple case of the alkaline earth atoms with two valence electrons, both are on the same s-orbit in the ground state. If only one of them is excited to higher level s-, p-, f- $\ldots$ orbits, $l_1 = 0, 1, 2, 3, \ldots, l_2 = 0$, and, therefore, $L = 0, 1, 2, 3 \ldots$ That is, for the electron excited to an s-, p-, d-, f-$\ldots$ orbit, terms designated by $S, P, D, F \ldots$ are obtained, just as in the case of one-valence-electron atoms.

In addition to the electrostatic interaction between the valence electrons, the magnetic spin-orbit interactions must be taken into account as well. As a first approximation, this may be done by taking the vector sum of the spin vectors $\mathbf{s}_i$ of all valence electrons

$$\mathbf{S} = \sum \mathbf{s}_i$$

and determining its possible orientations relative to the $\mathbf{L}$ vector. The quantum rule, as usual, demands that the magnitude of vector sum

$$\mathbf{J} = \mathbf{L} + \mathbf{S}$$

should be $|\mathbf{J}| = J(h/2\pi)$, where J is one of the values: $L+S, L+S-1, \ldots$ $L-S$.

When taking the vector sum of the spin vectors, we must remember that they may be parallel or antiparallel only. Again in the case of the

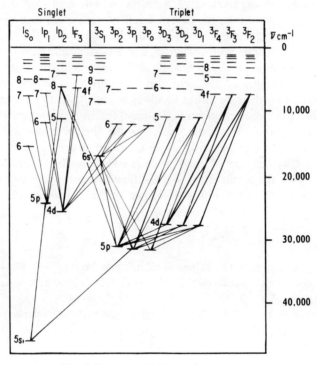

Fig. 8. Term system for strontium atom.

alkaline earth atoms, S may be 0 or 1 and the possible values of J, which is again called the inner quantum number, are

$$
\begin{array}{llll}
J = 0 & \text{or} & 1 & \text{for } L = 0 & (S\text{-terms}) \\
J = 1 & \text{or} & 2, 1, 0 & \text{for } L = 1 & (P\text{-terms}) \\
J = 2 & \text{or} & 3, 2, 1 & \text{for } L = 2 & (D\text{-terms})
\end{array}
$$

For the alkaline earth atoms (and similarly for helium) there are a singlet and a triplet system of terms. Figure 8 presents the two term-systems for the strontium atom. Transitions between singlet and triplet levels—the so-called intercombination lines—are only occasionally observed; the two term-systems are almost separate, the more so the lighter is the atom in question. In the singlet states, the two electron spins are antiparallel ($S = 0$). In the triplet states, on the other hand, the two electron spins are parallel ($S = 1$). Intercombination lines imply an electron transition that is coupled with a change of spin orientation, apparently a rare event. It is furthermore, remarkable, that in the ground state ($5S$) for the strontium atom, only the singlet term $^1S_0$ is observable. Of course, this is a direct consequence of the Pauli exclusion principle.

The selection rules are otherwise the same, as in the case of the alkali atoms:

$$\Delta L = \pm 1, \qquad \Delta J = 0, \pm 1 \qquad (0 \rightarrow 0 \text{ excluded})$$

with the difference that some transitions with $\Delta L = 0$ are allowed and, in addition, the exclusion of intercombinations:

$$\Delta S = 0$$

It is not difficult to extend the method to atoms with more than two valence electrons. In Table 1, the possible values of S are given for 1 to 7

TABLE 1

Number of valence electrons	Possible values of S	Example
1	$\frac{1}{2}$	Potassium
2	$1, 0$	Calcium
3	$\frac{3}{2}, \frac{1}{2}$	Scandium
4	$2, 1, 0$	Titanium
5	$\frac{5}{2}, \frac{3}{2}, \frac{1}{2}$	Vanadium
6	$3, 2, 1, 0$	Chromium
7	$\frac{7}{2}, \frac{5}{2}, \frac{3}{2}, \frac{1}{2}$	Manganese

electrons. Table 2 presents the corresponding J-values and indicates the term multiplicities. Finally, in Table 3, the multiplet characters of the term systems are listed for the elements mentioned as examples in Table 1. The many-electron spectra are very complex. This is true especially in the case of the heavier elements whose terms are so widely split that a very complicated superposition of different line series occurs in the spectra.

As we have seen, the method used here to obtain at least qualitative information about the structure and the characteristic features of spectra of different atoms may be of very great help to the spectroscopist. It is

TABLE 2

State	Values of J	Values of J
$l = 0S$	0 $\quad S = 0$	$\frac{1}{2}$ $\quad S = \frac{1}{2}$
$1P$	1	$\frac{1}{2}$ $\frac{3}{2}$
$2D$	2	$\frac{3}{2}$ $\frac{5}{2}$
$3F$	3	$\frac{5}{2}$ $\frac{7}{2}$
$4G$	4	$\frac{7}{2}$ $\frac{9}{2}$
$0S$	1 $\quad S = 1$	$\frac{3}{2}$ $\quad S = \frac{3}{2}$
$1P$	0 1 2	$\frac{1}{2}$ $\frac{3}{2}$ $\frac{5}{2}$
$2D$	1 2 3	$\frac{1}{2}$ $\frac{3}{2}$ $\frac{5}{2}$ $\frac{7}{2}$
$3F$	2 3 4	$\frac{3}{2}$ $\frac{5}{2}$ $\frac{7}{2}$ $\frac{9}{2}$
$4G$	3 4 5	$\frac{5}{2}$ $\frac{7}{2}$ $\frac{9}{2}$ $\frac{11}{2}$
$0S$	2 $\quad S = 2$	$\frac{5}{2}$ $\quad S = \frac{5}{2}$
$1P$	1 2 3	$\frac{3}{2}$ $\frac{5}{2}$ $\frac{7}{2}$
$2D$	0 1 2 3 4	$\frac{1}{2}$ $\frac{3}{2}$ $\frac{5}{2}$ $\frac{7}{2}$ $\frac{9}{2}$
$3F$	1 2 3 4 5	$\frac{1}{2}$ $\frac{3}{2}$ $\frac{5}{2}$ $\frac{7}{2}$ $\frac{9}{2}$ $\frac{11}{2}$
$4G$	2 3 4 5 6	$\frac{3}{2}$ $\frac{5}{2}$ $\frac{7}{2}$ $\frac{9}{2}$ $\frac{11}{2}$ $\frac{13}{2}$

TABLE 3

K	Ca	Sc	Ti	V	Cr	Mn
	Singlet		Singlet		Singlet	
Doublet		Doublet		Doublet		Doublet
	Triplet		Triplet		Triplet	
		Quartet		Quartet		Quartet
			Quintet		Quintet	
				Sextet		Sextet
					Septet	
						Octet

really a semiclassical picture, called the vector model of the atom, as its results are based on operations (vector additions) performed with the spin and orbital momentum vectors, following definite rules. Perhaps it is somewhat surprising that such a simple and rather formal method is capable of providing acceptable results at all. However, the vector model method as a whole is justified by modern quantum mechanics.

If quantitative results are required, such as interaction energies or term separations, quantum mechanics cannot be dispensed with. Furthermore, the vector model, as used here, presumes the spin-orbit interaction to be small compared with the electrostatic repulsions between the electrons. Therefore, these latter were taken into account at first, and the spin-orbit interactions left as corrections. This procedure is called the *Russell–Saunders coupling:* It implies an approximation that is acceptable only for light atoms. For heavier atoms another ideal case must be considered, the *jj*-coupling. If, as a first approximation, the electrostatic interactions between electrons are neglected, the spin and orbital momentum vectors of each individual electron must be coupled, that is, combined vectorially, to give the total angular momentum

$$\mathbf{j}_i = \mathbf{l}_i + \mathbf{s}_i$$

of each electron. The total angular momentum for all valence electrons is then found as the vector sum

$$\mathbf{J} = \sum \mathbf{j}_i$$

By the use of appropriate quantum rules the possible energy states may be established. It is sufficient here to state that this so-called *jj*-coupling provides the same number of states as does the Russell–Saunders coupling scheme. It is possible to make a unique correlation of the states in one coupling scheme with those in the other. This makes it possible to use the more usual Russell–Saunders notation even when *jj*-coupling predominates. The differences between the two coupling schemes lie in the quantitative results and the relative positions of the energy levels. These details, however, cannot be dealt with here.

E. Intensity Relations

The intensity relations within spectra are of greatest importance for practical spectroscopy. Quantitative spectrochemical analysis is based on the existence of a definite relationship between the concentrations of the atoms and molecules to be determined and the intensity of the specific radiations. Usually we have to measure intensities of spectral lines, that is, the rates of emission of light energy at definite frequencies. According

to Bohr's theory, energy is emitted when transition occurs from one energy
level of an atom to another,

$$E_n \rightarrow E_m$$

As the energy emitted in any transition is the light quantum hv, the
intensity I_v of the spectral line corresponding to the frequency v may be
calculated if the number dN_{nm} of such transitions over some time interval
dt is known. This number is proportional to the population N_n of the
initial state of the atom and to dt

$$dN_{nm} = A_{nm}N_n \, dt \tag{11}$$

where the coefficient A_{nm} is the Einstein transition probability of spontaneous emission.

Of course, transitions in the opposite direction—i.e., absorption of
radiation of frequency v—will also take place. The number of absorption
transitions may be expressed by a similar equation

$$dN_{mn} = B_{mn}\rho(v)N_m \, dt \tag{12}$$

where $\rho(v)$ is the spectral volume density of the radiation, N_m is the population of states m, and B_{mn} is the Einstein transition probability of
absorption.

In producing new excited states, the absorption of radiation gives rise
to induced or stimulated emission. The number of corresponding transitions
may be expressed by

$$dN_{nm}^* = B_{nm}\rho(v)N_n \, dt \tag{13}$$

where B_{nm} is the Einstein transition probability of induced emission.

The three Einstein coefficients are of great importance. They describe
the emission and absorption properties of the analyte. As may be expected,
they are not independent of each other. At equilibrium $dN_{nm} + dN_{nm}^*$ must
be equal to dN_{mn}. Therefore,

$$[A_{nm} + B_{nm}\rho(v)]N_n = B_{mn}\rho(v)N_m \tag{14}$$

An expression for the ratio N_m/N_n can be derived by applying principles
of statistical mechanics to quantized systems:

$$\frac{N_m}{N_n} = \frac{g_m}{g_n} \exp\left[-\frac{E_m - E_n}{kT}\right] = \frac{g_m}{g_n} \exp\left(\frac{hv}{kT}\right) \tag{15}$$

Equation (15) is the well-known Boltzmann relation, where g_m and g_n are
the statistical weights of the states m and n, k is the Boltzmann constant,

and T the absolute temperature. The density function $\rho(v)$ is expressed by Planck's radiation law:

$$\rho(v) = \frac{8\pi h v^3}{c^3} \frac{1}{\exp{(hv/kT)} - 1} \tag{16}$$

Equations (14–16) provide the following relationships for the Einstein coefficients:

$$B_{nm} = \left(\frac{g_m}{g_n}\right) B_{mn}$$

and

$$A_{nm} = \frac{8\pi h v^3}{c^3} B_{nm}$$

The intensity of a spectral line may be easily calculated, if the A_{nm} coefficient is known for the radiation in question:

$$I(v) = A_{nm} N_n h v \tag{17}$$

The A_{nm} coefficients may be determined by means of quantum mechanical calculations which involve the wave functions Ψ_n and Ψ_m of states n and m.

The classical theory of light emission characterized the atoms in respect to their emission properties by a quantity called oscillator strength, which is still in use, although it has lost its original physical meaning. Oscillator strength f_{nm} is now defined by its relation to the corresponding A_{nm} Einstein coefficient:

$$A_{nm} = \frac{8\pi^2 e^2}{\lambda^2 m_e c} f_{nm} \tag{18}$$

where e and m_e are the electronic charge and mass, respectively, λ is the wavelength of the light emitted, and c the velocity of light. The intensity $I(v)$ may be expressed by the use of the oscillator strength as follows:

$$I(v) = \frac{8\pi^2 e^2 h}{m\lambda^2} N_n f_m \tag{19}$$

Equation (19) provides a route for determining the oscillator strength (and the Einstein coefficient) experimentally from intensity measurements.

When deriving the foregoing intensity relations the absorption inside the light source, or *self-absorption*, was neglected. Absorption phenomena may be easily accounted for by the use of the Einstein coefficients B_{mn}

and B_{nm}. Practically, however, self-absorption may be neglected for all spectral lines other than the resonance lines, that is, for frequencies corresponding to transitions from all excited states to the ground state of the atoms. It is not difficult to derive a formula for the self-absorption of resonance lines in light sources of simple geometry and sufficient homogeneity by the use of the relations already established. The intensity received from a unit cross section of a homogenous light source, limited

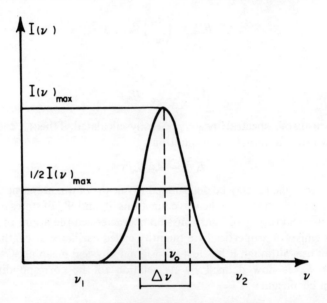

Fig. 9. Intensity distribution of a spectral line.

by two parallel planes and radiating a resonance line, may be calculated by

$$I = \alpha \frac{8\pi hc}{\lambda^3} \frac{N_i}{N_o} \frac{g_o}{g_i} \left[1 - \exp\left(-\frac{\pi e^2}{m_e c} N_o f d \right) \right] \tag{20}$$

where α is a constant factor depending only on the characteristics of the measuring device, λ is the wavelength of the resonance line, N_i and N_o are the populations of the excited and the ground state, g_i and g_o the corresponding statistical weights, f the oscillator strength of the resonance line in absorption, and d the width of the light source.

The total line intensity defines the sensitivity of the spectrochemical analysis. It is influenced by the excitation conditions through the population of the excited state desired. In addition to instrumental factors, resolution will be limited by the finite width of the spectral lines, that is, by the distribution of the total line intensity over a certain wavelength or frequency interval. Figure 9 presents a picture of the usual line shape, that is, the shape of the intensity distribution, in which the density of the spectral intensity $dI/dv = I(v)$ is plotted as a function of the frequency. The total intensity measured is

$$I = \int_{v_1}^{v_2} I(v)\, dv \tag{21}$$

the integral being taken over the region where $I(v)$ is different from zero. To give information about the width of a line, the limiting frequencies v_1 and v_2 are not suitable because they are not well defined, but the half-width can be used.

The Bohr frequency condition implies an infinitely narrow line width for the spectral lines. However, as a consequence of the uncertainty principle, the mean lifetime results in an uncertainty ΔE_n on the energy E_n of the quantum state n as given by the relation

$$\Delta E_n = \frac{h}{2\pi} \frac{1}{\tau_n} \tag{22}$$

τ_n being the radiative lifetime of the given atomic state.

For transitions to the ground state, for which the lifetime τ_o is infinite and $\Delta E_o = 0$, the natural half-width Δv_N is given by

$$\Delta v_N = \frac{1}{2\pi\tau_n} = \frac{A_{no}}{2\pi} \tag{23}$$

where A_{no} is the transition probability from the level n to the ground level. Expressed in wavelengths the half-width is

$$\Delta \lambda_N = \frac{c\,\Delta v_N}{v^2} \tag{24}$$

$\Delta \lambda_N$ increases with decreasing v^2 or with increasing λ^2. The order of magnitude for $\Delta \lambda$ is from 10^{-5} to 10^{-3} Å, increasing with λ^2 in the interval from about 2C0O to 10,000 Å. The natural broadening is thus negligible for combustion flames in comparison with other broadening phenomena to be discussed.

The Doppler effect increases the line broadening to a much greater extent. The radial velocity u (velocity component on the line joining the atom to the observer) of the emitting atoms brings about a frequency shift $v_o \to v$, the magnitude of which is given by

$$\frac{v - v_o}{v_o} = \frac{u}{c} \tag{25}$$

The intensity distribution due to the Doppler effect corresponds to the distribution of the radial velocities of the emitting atoms centred on v_o, and the density of the spectral intensity is given by the relation

$$I(v)_{max} = f(u - u_o) \tag{26}$$

Where $f(u)$ is the velocity distribution function.

At thermal equilibrium $f(u)$ is given by the Maxwell-Boltzmann equation and, accordingly, a symmetrical Gaussian line shape arises with the half-width

$$\Delta v_D = 2v_o \sqrt{\frac{2kT \ln 2}{m_e c^2}} \tag{27}$$

Evaluating the constant term and expressing the half-width in wavelengths, Eq. (27) becomes

$$\Delta \lambda_D = 7.16 \times 10^{-7} \lambda_o \sqrt{\frac{T}{M}} \tag{28}$$

where T is the absolute temperature and M the relative atomic or molecular mass of the emitting particles on the scale $C^{12} = 12.000$. Doppler line-width increases linearly with the wavelength and as the square root of the temperature, and decreases with the increasing mass of the atoms or molecules. For the yellow line of the sodium atom at 2000°K, a line broadening with a half-width of about 0.040 Å arises.

The product of the maximum intensity $I(v)_{max}$ and the Doppler half-width is equal to the total intensity of the spectral line within about 6.5%, if Gaussian distribution may be assumed. All these formulas are valid in absorption as well as in emission, $I(v)$ and I_o being replaced by $k(v)$ and k_o.

Another effect leading to broadening of spectral lines is the decrease of the lifetimes of excited atoms taking place because of collisions with other atoms and molecules before emitting their excess energy. If such deactivating collisions occur on the average Z times per second, the time $\tau_c = 1/Z$ is the collision lifetime. The corresponding broadening, often called

Lorentz broadening, produces for spectral lines belonging to ground state a halfwidth, noted Δv_L, given by

$$\Delta v_L = \frac{Z}{2\pi} \tag{29}$$

Equation (29) may be deduced from the natural broadening. For the general case we obtain

$$\Delta v_L = Z/\pi \tag{30}$$

or the double line width, due to the fact that both the initial and the final states of the atom have the same mean lifetime.

The rate of collisions Z may be calculated from statistical gas kinetics and is proportional to the density of particles, that is, to their total pressure. Lorentz broadening is, therefore, sometimes called *pressure broadening*. A second factor increasing the value of Z is temperature, more exactly the square root of the temperature. Accordingly, Lorentz broadening may be decreased by lowering both the pressure and temperature.

For comparison with the Doppler broadening, a Lorentz broadening of 0.082 Å is to be expected for the yellow line of sodium at atmospheric pressure and a temperature of 2000°K.

The three broadening effects act independently of each other. Therefore, in principle, it is possible to calculate their total effect without any fundamental difficulty. The formula of the corresponding line shape, however, is too complicated for practical use.

If a considerable number of ions and electrons are present in the light source (as in an ordinary arc of high current density), a special line broadening effect will take place. The excited atoms in the immediate vicinity of the charged particles, upon collisions with them, are subjected to strong local electric fields. The emitted spectral lines are split due to their quantized orientation in the field (Stark effect). These local fields, however, are continually changing and strongly inhomogenous, giving rise, therefore, to a line broadening instead of a group of discrete lines. Beside ions, dipole and quadrupole molecules may cause a similar effect.

The Stark broadening may be of the same order of magnitude as the Doppler or Lorentz broadening. For example, the Stark effect broadening is responsible for the diffuseness of the diffuse and fundamental line series in the alkali spectra.

F. Essentials of the Theory of Band Spectra

Band spectra were very soon identified as spectra emitted by molecules instead of atoms. The greater abundance of spectral lines could be interpreted by taking into consideration the increased possibilities of changes in energy.

The energy of a molecule consists of three parts. In addition to changes of the electronic energy, taking place in a similar way as in atoms, changes of the molecular rotational and vibrational energies are also involved. As all three types of the molecular energy are quantized, a great variety of transitions is available to explain the origin of the lines and bands, and the regularities found in the spectra of different molecules.

Spectra of molecules extend from the far infrared into the ultraviolet and may be divided into three regions which correspond to the three types of molecular energy. In the far infrared, we find a series of nearly equidistant lines in the case of diatomic molecules and a few line series of rather simple structure in the case of the polyatomic molecules. This is the rotational spectrum of the molecules; the rotational energy and its changes are the smallest. The rotation-vibration spectra are located in the near infrared. The spectra originate from energy changes in which, besides the rotational energy, the much greater vibrational molecular energy is also involved. Finally, in the very near infrared, visible, and ultraviolet regions, are found the most complex molecular spectra. These are the band spectra which originate from energy changes of all three types: rotational, vibrational, and electronic. The electronic energy, being the greatest, defines their location in the electromagnetic spectrum.

To summarize, the total molecular energy is a sum of three types—rotational, vibrational, and electronic:

$$E = E_r + E_v + E_e$$

where

$$E_r \ll E_v \ll E_e$$

The differences have roughly two orders of magnitude. All these energies are quantized, and transitions between two possible states bring about emission (or absorption) of a spectrum line according to Bohr's frequency condition:

$$hv = E_1 - E_2 = \Delta E = \Delta E_r + \Delta E_v + \Delta E_e$$

To understand the structure and regularities of molecular spectra, the different possible energy levels must be determined. To do this, we shall confine ourselves to the most simple case of diatomic molecules. The relation for the rotational energy of a diatomic molecule

$$E_r = \tfrac{1}{2}I\omega^2 \tag{31}$$

is furnished by classical mechanics. It is valid for quantum mechanics with the addition of the quantized condition of the angular momentum:

$$\omega = \frac{h}{2\pi I} \sqrt{J(J+1)}$$

where J, the rotational quantum number, is any integral number: 0, 1, 2, ...
Introducing this value of ω into Eq. (31), we have for the rotation energy
levels the values

$$E_r = \frac{h^2}{8\pi^2 I} J(J+1) \tag{32}$$

In these expressions I is the moment of inertia.

Transitions between levels are governed by the quantum selection rule

$$\Delta J = \pm 1$$

The rotational spectrum consists of equidistant lines with a wave number
or term difference; $2B = 2(h/8\pi^2 cI)$; B is called the rotational constant.
A slight deviation from experimental results is due to a small increase of I
with increasing angular velocity. The intensity of rotational lines becomes
negligible for symmetric molecules, such as H_2, O_2, and Cl_2, because their
electric dipole moment is zero.

Assuming the diatomic molecule to be a harmonic oscillator, the possible
values of the quantized vibrational energy are given by

$$E_v = \frac{h}{2\pi} \sqrt{\frac{k}{\mu}\left(v+\frac{1}{2}\right)} \tag{33}$$

where k and μ are the force constant and the reduced mass of the two
atoms, respectively, and v, the vibrational quantum number, is any integral
number 0, 1, 2 ... governed by the selection rule

$$\Delta v = \pm 1$$

In reality the molecular vibrations are anharmonic. Taking the anharmon-
icity into account, the expression for vibrational energy becomes

$$E_v = \frac{h}{2\pi} \sqrt{\frac{k}{\mu}\left(v+\frac{1}{2}\right)} - \frac{h^2}{2\pi^2}\frac{k}{\mu}\frac{1}{4D_o}\left(v+\frac{1}{2}\right)^2 \tag{34}$$

where D_o is the dissociation energy of the molecule. From Eq. (34), the
energy levels no longer are equidistant, but converge to a limit which is
determined by the dissociation energy, as v increases. The selection rule is
also modified:

$$\Delta v = \pm 1, \pm 2, \pm 3, \ldots$$

In a sense there is really no selection rule for v. The transition probability and the intensity of the corresponding spectral lines are, however, decreasing as Δv increases.

To excite vibrational transitions, more energy is needed than in the case of rotational levels. It is obvious, therefore, that along with vibrational excitations rotational excitations will always also take place and a vibration–rotation spectrum arises. A pure vibration spectrum does not exist.

A vibrational transition $(v_1 \rightarrow v_2)$ may combine with all rotational transitions: $J_1 \rightarrow J_2 = J_1 \pm 1$. The spectral lines which arise are, of course, very closely spaced due to the slight differences between the rotational levels, and appear as "fine structure" of the lines (really bands) corresponding to vibrational transitions.

For any values of J_1, two transitions are possible, one to $J_1 + 1$, another to $J_1 - 1$. The different changes in energy bring about two lines of different wavelength. Accordingly, the vibration bands may be divided into two branches: The P-branch consists of lines of longer wavelength; the R-branch, those of shorter wavelength.

Finally, the energy associated with the electrons of the molecule will be considered. Let us use a simplified image of the diatomic molecule whose electrons may be divided into two groups. The inner or core electrons remain, practically unaffected, around the nuclei in their closed shells. The valence electrons, on the other hand, are no longer attached to their individual parent nuclei; they belong to the molecule as a whole. As in the case of atoms, the valence electrons are responsible for the optical properties of the molecules. From the point of view of the valence electrons, a diatomic molecule resembles an atom around which they revolve while in the field of the electrically charged central system. On the other hand, the valence electrons experience significant differences. The central system and its field has a cylindrical symmetry around the internuclear axis and not a spherical symmetry as in atoms.

This simplified image suffices to determine qualitatively the possible electronic energy levels inside a molecule. Besides the quantum numbers n_i and l_i of the valence electrons, the energy is to some extent influenced by the relative orientations of the electron orbits. Both the orientations and the quantum rule imposed on them may be conveniently determined and formulated, respectively, by the help of the angular momentum. In this case, however, quantum mechanics require the magnitude not of the resultant angular momentum $\mathbf{L} = \sum \mathbf{l}_i$ but that of its projection Λ on the internuclear axis to be an integral multiple of $h/2\pi$:

$$|\Lambda| = \Lambda\frac{h}{2\pi} \qquad (35)$$

The possible values of Λ are

$$\Lambda = L, L-1, L-2 \ldots -L+1, -L$$

Λ is a quantum number which contributes to the electronic energy. The existence of a physically distinguishable direction, that is, the direction of the internuclear axis, which is at the same time the axis of the electric field inside the molecule, makes the negative values of Λ understandable. These represent the Λ vectors having a direction opposite to the axis. Angular levels corresponding to $\Lambda = 0, 1, 2, \ldots$ are designated by the Greek symbols $\Sigma, \Pi, \Delta, \ldots$ in analogy with the atomic notation $S, P, D, \ldots$

The effect of the electron spins will be considered by coupling the resultant spin $\mathbf{S} = \sum s_i$ with the resultant orbital angular momentum $\mathbf{L}$. This procedure of defining the possible energy levels is the Russell–Saunders coupling scheme, the better approximation in the case of molecules. The projection of the resultant vector on the internuclear axis is given by

$$|\Sigma| = \Sigma\frac{h}{2\pi} \qquad (36)$$

The possible values of Σ are:

$$S, S-1, S-2 \ldots -S+1, -S$$

for a total of $2S+1$. These values of Σ produce a splitting of the electronic terms. Individual terms of the multiplet will be distinguished in notation similar to the atomic multiplet terms, that is, by the value Ω of the final resultant vector

$$\Omega = \Lambda+\Sigma \qquad (37)$$

As an example, the term symbol $^4\Delta_{5/2}$ designates a Δ-term/$(\Lambda = 2)$, that belongs to a multiplet of multiplicity 4 and its Ω quantum number is 5/2. Analysis of band spectra shows that multiplicities are not high and seldom exceed 3.

Electronic spectra of molecules arise, of course, in consequence of transitions between different possible levels of electronic energy. Such transitions are, however, always accompanied by simultaneous transitions between rotational and vibrational levels. To an electronic transition, therefore, there belongs a system of bands, instead of a spectral line or a multiplet line. Each band indicates a different change in the vibrational energy; their individual lines correspond to the still smaller changes of the rotational energy.

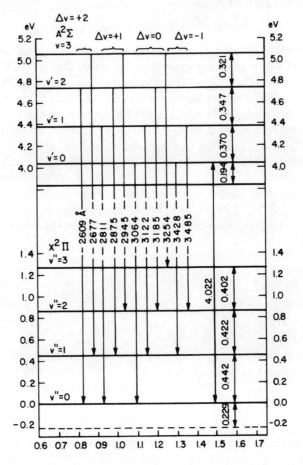

Fig. 10. Vibrational energy levels diagram of $A\ ^2\Sigma$ and $X\ ^2\Pi$ states, and transitions of OH radical.

The rules for selecting the possible transitions between electronic energy states are about the same as the selection rules of the many electron atoms: $\Delta\Lambda = \pm 1$ and also $\Delta\Lambda = 0$, $\Delta\Omega = 0, \pm 1$, $\Delta\Sigma = 0$.

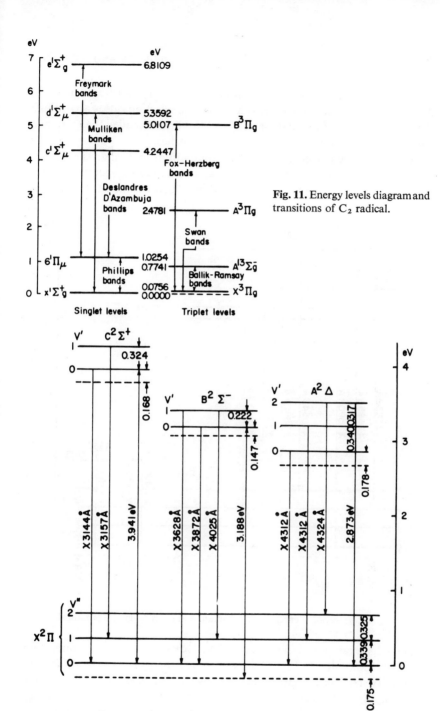

Fig. 11. Energy levels diagram and transitions of C_2 radical.

Fig. 12. Vibrational energy levels diagram and transitions of CH radical.

In the bands of the electronic spectra, rotational transitions may also be found in lines corresponding to $\Delta J = 0$. The selection rule is accordingly $\Delta J = 0, \pm 1$. Therefore, in these bands a third branch, called the Q-branch, also appears in addition to the P- and R-branches.

As may be seen from this short recapitulation, molecular spectra and their theory are quite complicated compared with atomic spectra. Further details could not be dealt with in this abbreviated treatment. Instead, we

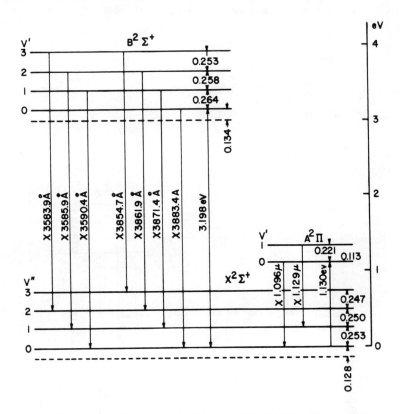

Fig. 13. Vibrational energy levels diagram and transitions of CN radical.

present as examples a few energy levels diagrams of some important diatomic molecules. In Fig. 10 the vibrational energy level diagram of $A\,^2\Sigma$ and $X\,^2\Pi$ states of the OH radical is shown along with transitions and the wavelength of the corresponding lines. Figure 11 is the electronic energy level diagram of the C_2 molecule. The individual electronic states are represented by their vibrational level corresponding to $v = 0$. The possible transitions and the names of the corresponding bands are indicated. In Fig. 12 vibrational energy levels of the CH molecule may be seen. The possible transitions and the corresponding wavelength are indicated. The same is presented in Fig. 13 for the CN molecule. In all diagrams the energy differences are expressed in electron volts. The dotted lines represent the vibrational energy zero levels. The Latin letters before the term symbols denote the differences between terms of the same types, usual notation in practical molecular spectroscopy. The signs $+$ and $-$, and the indices μ and g, indicate symmetry properties.

II. Self-Emission of Various Flames

A. INTRODUCTION

The emission spectrum of a flame depends on its composition, the temperature, and reactions between species in the flame which result in the excitation of some atoms, radicals, and molecules. Before discussing the emission spectra of the various unsalted flames used in flame spectrometry, let us outline the effect of the foregoing parameters. All of the reactions in the flames are functions of the original composition of the burned gases, the heat of reaction liberated, and the pressure and the nature of reaction products. Therefore, we must consider separately the spectra of rich and lean flames and, in some cases, that of the stoichiometric flame; also the spectra of laminar and turbulent flames and the various types of combustible gas systems.

The discussion of the flames and their emission characteristics is made easier if we examine the flames of different composition separately. The order of discussion will be from the simpler to the more complex systems. The classification, according to the fuel gas, is as follows: (1) hydrogen flames, (2) hydrocarbon flames, and (3) other flames.

B. HYDROGEN FLAMES

1. Composition and Basic Reactions of Hydrogen Flames

Hydrogen flames require as an oxidant either oxygen, a mixture of oxygen and nitrogen, or other oxygen-containing gases such as perchloryl fluoride, nitrous oxide, etc. Depending on the composition of the original combustion mixture, the basic reactions of hydrogen and oxygen are accompanied by other characteristic reactions.

If the original gas mixture contains only hydrogen and oxygen, the following general reactions occur (14).

$$
\begin{array}{lll}
H_2 + O_2 & \rightarrow H + HO_2 & \Delta H = +55 \text{ kcal} \\
H + O_2 & \rightarrow OH + O & \Delta H = +15 \text{ kcal} \\
OH + H_2 & \rightarrow H + H_2O & \Delta H = -14 \text{ kcal} \\
O + H_2 & \rightarrow OH + H & \Delta H = 0 \text{ kcal}
\end{array}
$$

If the original gases are not dry, the above reactions are complicated by those produced by water

$$
\begin{array}{ll}
H_2O + O_2 & \rightarrow HO_2 + HO \\
HO_2 + H_2O & \rightarrow H_2O_2 + OH \\
HO_2 + HO_2 & \rightarrow H_2O_2 + O_2 \\
OH + H_2 & \rightarrow H_2O + H \\
H + HO_2 & \rightarrow HO + HO
\end{array}
$$

These chain reactions produce a large number of free radicals in the reaction zone; the most important species are the OH and H radicals. Besides these, the oxygen–hydrogen flame contains the end product of the reaction between H and OH, i.e., water and any unburned original gas mixture.

Water reaches a thermal dissociation equilibrium by the following reactions (15, 16):

$$
\begin{array}{l}
H_2O \rightleftharpoons H + OH \\
2H_2O \rightleftharpoons 2H_2 + O_2
\end{array}
$$

The quantity of H and OH radicals produced in the reaction zone exceeds the equilibrium amounts.

Thermal dissociation occurs also for other components of the flame. For a flame containing only H_2, O_2, and H_2O, only the dissociation of hydrogen, oxygen, and water need be taken into account at equilibrium. If, instead of oxygen, a mixture of oxygen and nitrogen is used, the dissociation of nitrogen also must be considered.

The degree of dissociation of these components is shown in Fig. 14.

In the range of temperature given by the flames in normal use (below 3000°C), the radicals produced in the combustion process take part in a number of reactions. In an oxygen–hydrogen flame, the following very important reaction occurs:

$$
H + H_2O \underset{k_{-1}}{\overset{k_1}{\rightleftharpoons}} HO + H_2 \tag{38}
$$

Reaction (38) does not decrease the number of radicals but sets up an equilibrium between the H and OH radicals. The reaction rate constants are as follows (17):

$$k_1 = 10^{15}e^{-\frac{2500}{\mathscr{R}T}} \text{ ml sec}^{-1}\text{mol}^{-1}$$

and

$$k_{-1} = 2.5 \times 10^{14}e^{-\frac{10,000}{\mathscr{R}T}} \text{ ml sec}^{-1}\text{mol}^{-1}$$

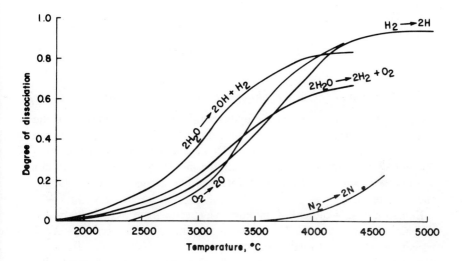

Fig. 14. Dissociation equilibria of some molecules as a function of temperature.

Reaction (38) is very fast. Equilibrium between the H and OH radicals is attained above the combustion zone. Recombination of the radicals can be brought about if the excess energy can be dissipated.

The number of radicals is generally decreased by reactions involving a three-body collision:

$$H+H+X \rightarrow H_2+X \tag{39}$$
$$H+OH+X \rightarrow H_2O+X \tag{40}$$

where X may be an excitable atom, molecule, or solid particle having many degrees of freedom, which enables it to take up any kind of energy. Such a third body may be H_2O, metal atoms, or N_2.

Individual metal atoms do not promote the recombination reactions to the same extent as do molecules (18). Lead atoms only promote the recombination reaction of OH and H:

$$H + OH + Pb \rightarrow H_2O + Pb^*$$

whereas Tl promotes that of H and H (40):

$$H + H + Tl \rightarrow H_2 + Tl^*$$

where an asterisk indicates the excited atomic state. Other metals, such as Na, promote both reactions:

$$H + H + Na \rightarrow H_2 + Na^*$$
$$H + OH + Na \rightarrow H_2O + Na^*$$

2. The Emission of Oxygen–Hydrogen or Air–Hydrogen Flames

Among the components of the hydrogen flame, the examination of the emission of OH radicals is the most important. Many papers in the literature have dealt with this topic. Dieke and Crosswhite (19) discuss this in detail. However, in this chapter the molecular transitions will not be discussed in detail. If further information is needed, refer to (19, 20) and Chapter 5.

Emission of OH radicals dominates the spectra from oxygen–hydrogen and air–hydrogen flames. The emission is principally due to $A\,^2\Sigma - X\,^2\Pi$ transitions. The most intense band system emission is obtained from the (0, 0) transition at 3064 Å. At about 9000 Å a less intense peak occurs due to the rotation–vibration system of water. The spectrum of an oxygen–hydrogen flame measured under low resolution is shown in Fig. 15. These flames have relatively low background emission.

The OH spectrum is an important interference in flame-spectrometric determinations. The emission of OH radicals can be used both for the determination of OH concentrations and for the measurement of the flame temperature by means of the excited levels of the OH radicals (21, 22). In the reaction zone, the OH radicals are not in equilibrium with their environment; rather, the excess of reaction energy is retained in the molecules in their various degrees of freedom.

Figure 15 demonstrates that the unsalted oxygen–hydrogen and air–hydrogen flames are very low in emission between 3300 and 6000 Å. Using higher amplification a low emission appears between 3400 and 6000 Å with a maximum at about 4500 Å. The cause of this emission has been

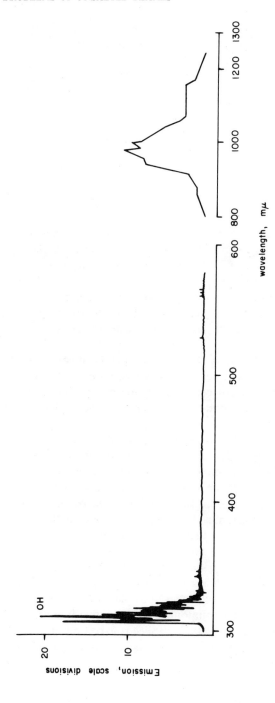

Fig. 15. Spectrum of oxygen–hydrogen flame.

extensively studied (23–26). Padley (26) has proved unambiguously that the emission is produced by the following reaction:

$$H + OH \rightarrow H_2O + h\nu \qquad (41)$$

and not by these reactions (25):

$$H + H + OH \rightarrow H_2 + OH^*$$
$$OH + OH + H \rightarrow H_2O + OH^*$$

since the intensity of the emission can be described by the following equation:

$$I = k[H][OH]$$

where k contains the collision factor, the probability constant of water formation, the lifetime of excited water molecules, and the number of collisions per second of the radicals with water which result in a deactivation of their excited states.

Water sprayed into the flame influences the emission of the unsalted flame in several ways: by cooling the flame, by altering the relation between the H and OH radicals, and by increasing the emission of water at longer wavelengths.

Except in the region of the OH and H_2O emission, these alterations in the emission are not very important because the background emission is very low. Proper correction for flame background is necessary for low concentrations of metals which emit in the regions 2500–4000 Å and 6000–9000 Å.

Addition of hydrocarbon solvents to the flame produces an important change in the flame spectrum. Reaction products contribute to the emission spectrum. The spectrum obtained using n-butanol is shown in Fig. 16 (27). Naturally the spectrum is altered by a change in the various parameters of the flames. In Fig. 17, the emission of the oxygen–hydrogen flame into which benzene is atomized is shown. An increase in the amount of hydrogen in the flame greatly influences the OH emission through the equilibrium between H and OH. In addition, the hydrogen content of the flame affects the emission of the various carbon compounds.

Carbon compounds sprayed into the oxygen–hydrogen flame produce a number of radicals which seem to play an important role in the chemi-excitation of various compounds (28). Another important characteristic of these flames is their very high electron concentration, which shifts the ionization equilibria of metals. The electron concentration of oxygen–

hydrogen flames containing carbon compounds is determined mainly by the following equilibria (*29–32*):

$$C_2 + OH \rightleftharpoons CO + CH$$
$$CH + O \rightleftharpoons CHO^+ + e^-$$
$$CHO^+ + H_2O \rightleftharpoons CO + H_3O^+$$

This effect is extremely important in the measurement of very low concentrations of alkali and alkaline earth metals. The evaluation of emission data when organic solvents are used is also complicated because of their surface-active behavior (*33*).

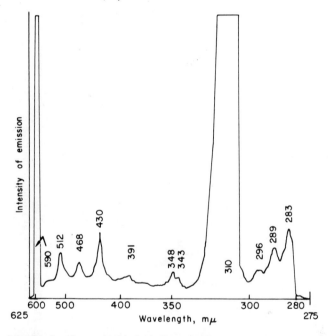

Fig. 16. Emission from *n*-butyl alcohol sprayed into an oxygen–hydrogen flame.

Perchloryl fluoride can be used for combustion of hydrogen instead of oxygen (*34*). In this flame, molecular fluoride and chloride spectra dominate. The bands in the spectrum are sharper and therefore are better for analytical purposes than the oxide bands. The spectrum of this flame when unsalted has, in addition to the emission discussed previously for the oxygen–hydrogen flame, bands due to ClO (*35*) which are spread over the region 3600–4200 Å.

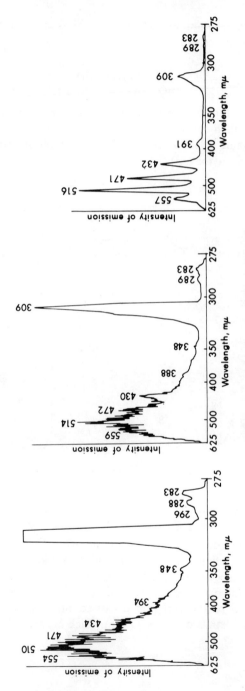

Fig. 17. Emission from benzene. Flame conditions: oxygen, 5 psig; hydrogen, (a) 1 psig, (b) 2.5 psig, (c) 7.5 psig.

Emission from hydrogen flames depends on the region of the flame in which emission measurements are carried out. The concentration of radicals decreases with increasing distance from the combustion zone. In a laminar flame, where the combustion zone is clearly defined, the case is simple. Since, for hydrogen flames, a turbulent burner is generally used because of the great burning velocity of the flame, the apparent combustion zone is enlarged and more diffuse. Consequently, defocusing the combustion zone from the photosensor is difficult. The great amount of radicals produced in the expended reaction zone of the turbulent flame results in the intense emission of the unsalted flames, particularly by the recombination of OH and H radicals. Therefore, when measuring very low concentrations of metals, measurements should be carried out above the turbulent reaction zone.

So far we have discussed only unsalted hydrogen flames. The characteristic emission spectra obtained when salts are sprayed into the flame can be used for their quantitative determination. However, it is not unimportant to consider the effect of salts on the self-emission of flames. Chemiluminescent emission of some metals decreases greatly the concentration of radicals. There is another type of reaction which produces emission over a large region of the spectrum. To understand this, the following reaction should be considered. It is known that lithium is in thermal equilibrium with hydrogen radicals

$$Li + H_2O \rightleftharpoons LiOH + H \tag{42}$$

Lithium hydroxide is very stable at the temperature of the hydrogen flame, but the other alkali hydroxides show lower stabilities (Table 4). Sodium

TABLE 4

Heats of Formation of Gaseous Alkali Metal Hydroxides
from Radicals, Calculated to $0°K$

Hydroxides	Heats of formation (kcal/mole)
LiOH	102 ± 2
NaOH	80
KOH	87
RbOH	90
CsOH	92

hydroxide has the least stability and therefore, at flame temperatures higher than 1500°C, its formation by an equilibrium reaction similar to reaction (42) is negligible. However, a small amount of sodium hydroxide forms by the reaction:

$$Na + OH \rightarrow NaOH + h\nu$$

The maximum of this continuous radiation lies at about 4500 Å. Its intensity depends on the concentration of sodium atoms, but it is only significant at higher sodium concentrations. Other alkali metals at higher concentrations behave similarly; the intensity of emission is lower with a greater heat of formation of the hydroxide. Continuous radiation from these flames is a problem in the determination of very low concentrations of some metals.

C. Hydrocarbon Flames

1. *The Composition and Basic Reactions of Hydrocarbon Flames*

The combustible component of a hydrocarbon flame may be propane, butane, or acetylene, while the supporter of combustion is oxygen, air, or, more recently, nitrogen oxides. In practice, the most widely used flame is the air–acetylene flame. Recently, the nitrous oxide–acetylene flame has become important for atomic absorption.

Reactions in hydrocarbon flames are quite complex (*36–38*). Hydrocarbon flames may contain CH_3, CH_2O, CH_2, CHO, CO, and H_2O_2, besides OH and H radicals.

The composition of the flame is even more complex if the combustible component has more than one carbon atom. The following components have been identified in hydrocarbon–air flames (*29*): O_2, N_2, CO_2, CO, H_2O, C_2H_2, CH_3–CH, CHO, CH, CH_2, CH_3, C_2H, C_2, C_3, C_5, H_2, H, O, OH, HO_2, CHO^+, $C_2O_2H^+$, $C_3H_3^+$, NO^+, CO^+, OH^+, H_2O^+, H_3O^+, $H_5O_2^+$, $H_7O_3^+$. So far, no theoretical description of the flame involving all these products has been given. The oxidation of acetylene may be described as follows (*39–42*):

$$
\begin{aligned}
H + O_2 &\rightarrow OH + O \\
OH + C_2H_2 &\rightarrow H_2O + C_2H \\
O + C_2H_2 &\rightarrow OH + C_2H \\
C_2H + C_2H_2 &\rightarrow C_4H_2 + H \\
C_2H + O_2 &\rightarrow CO_2 + CH^* \\
CH^* + O &\rightarrow CO^* + H \\
C_2H + O &\rightarrow CO + CH^*
\end{aligned}
$$

The most thoroughly investigated reaction is that in which electrons are produced. The species which induces this reaction is, according to experiments (43) using a C^{13} isotopic tracer, the C_2 radical formed as follows (44):

$$2CH \rightarrow C_2^* + H_2$$

This reaction is in contradiction to the model used by Gaydon and Wolfhard (45), who presumed the C_2 was formed by the decomposition

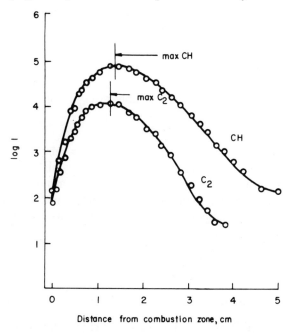

Fig. 18. Variations in the C_2 and CH emission along the vertical axis of the flame in a stoichiometric oxygen–acetylene flame.

of carbon polymers. At the same time, CH is reformed by the following reaction:

$$C_2 + OH \rightleftharpoons CO + CH$$

Variation in the concentration of C_2 and CH with height in the flame is shown in Fig. 18. The series of reactions producing the high electron concentration is restricted to a few millimeters above the reaction zone. On the other hand, C_2 and CH can be found relatively far from the reaction zone.

When nitrogen compounds are introduced into the flame, the composition of the flame is further altered. These compounds can be organic solvents sprayed into the flame or nitrogen oxides used for supporting combustion. In the presence of these, CH and NH are formed in the flame. Among the nitrogen oxides, nitrous oxide has become important recently in the N_2O–C_2H_2 flame used in atomic absorption spectrometry. The resulting reactions can be summarized as follows (46):

$$5N_2O \rightarrow 5N_2 + \tfrac{5}{2}O_2$$
$$C_2H_2 + \tfrac{5}{2}O_2 \rightarrow 2CO_2 + H_2O$$

The temperature of this flame (2955°C) is about the same as that of an oxygen–acetylene flame (3000°C) (47). The efficiency of this type of flame in atomic absorption is consequently due not to a difference in temperature but to its strongly reducing atmosphere, especially in fuel-rich environments. In the reducing zone metal oxides probably react as follows (48):

$$MO + NH \rightarrow M + N + OH$$
$$MO + CN \rightarrow M + CO + N$$

In an acetylene-rich flame, the reducing zone is relatively large. The presence of unburned carbon particles, and a relatively high vapor pressure of carbon, provide a reducing environment for some metal oxides. On the other hand, in acetylene-lean flames the content of CN and NH is decreased to a very low value probably by the following reactions:

$$CN + OH \rightarrow CO + NH$$
$$NH + OH \rightarrow H_2 + NO$$
$$CN + NO \rightarrow CO + N_2$$
$$NH + NO \rightarrow OH + N_2$$

2. The Emission of Hydrocarbon Flames

The self-emission of hydrocarbon flames is caused by the components of the burnt gases. The structure of hydrocarbon flames is more complicated than that of oxygen hydrogen flames. The emission of hydrocarbon flames is much more intense than that of the oxygen–hydrogen flames in the region of the spectrum used in flame photometry. The study of Fassel and Golightly (49) gives a brief account of the emission in the region 3000–6000 Å for a premixed flame (Fig. 19). Emission bands of C_2, CH, and CN appear plus the emission of OH radicals, which has been already discussed for hydrogen flames.

If the turbulent flame is used, the picture changes considerably. It is difficult to follow the reactions taking place in the expanded reaction zone. Bands appearing separately in Fig. 19 flow together as shown in Fig. 20.

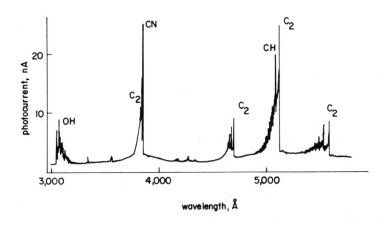

Fig. 19. Spectrum of premixed oxygen–acetylene flame.

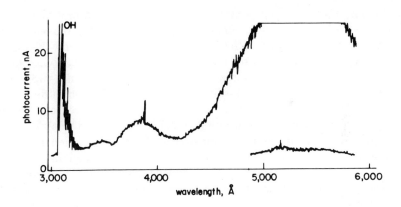

Fig. 20. Spectrum of the turbulent oxygen–acetylene flame.

Let us now consider the emission of the most important species present in hydrocarbon flames.

C_2 radicals emit in more than one wavelength region of the complete spectrum from the ultraviolet to the infrared. Characteristic bands appear in the ultraviolet region with bandheads at 2149.2 and 2312.6 Å, in the regions 2378–3000 and 3580–3860 Å, and the Swan bands in the visible region at 4350–6860 Å. In the infrared, emission appears at 12,091 and 17,657 Å. Primarily, the bands between 3580 and 3860 Å and the Swan bands are of importance in flame spectrometry. The C_2 bands are faint in acetylene-lean flames.

Three band systems can be identified as due to CH radicals. In the visible region, CH gives emission in the regions 4130–4470 Å and 4720–4910 Å; the latter is overlapped by the Swan bands. CH emission is found in the ultraviolet in the regions 3620–3710 Å and 3870–4120 Å and also between 3080 and 3220 Å. The latter band coalesces with the OH bands.

The presence of HCO in acetylene flames was proved spectroscopically by experiments with flames containing deuterium (50).

Among the CN bands, the most intense is the (0, 0) bandhead at 3883 Å. This band is overlapped by the C_2 band, while the system with a bandhead at 4216 Å is affected by the CH band. Bandheads also appear at 3590, 5730, 5860, 6190, 6330, and 6470 Å.

An intense NH emission appears at 3360 Å. However, the line at 3370 Å is quite faint.

In a lean nitrous oxide–acetylene flame, the flame can be divided into two parts. Above the combustion zone, which is white-blue, the blue outer zone appears. In acetylene-rich flames, three zones can be seen—the white-blue combustion zone, the red zone above this, and the blue outer zone. However, if the flame is extremely acetylene-rich, then only two zones appear—the white-blue combustion zone and the yellow outer zone.

CN, NH, and NO radicals can be found both in the red and yellow outer zones; they give intense emission at 2320, 2480, and 2600 Å.

Naturally, the emission accompanying the recombination reactions discussed for hydrogen flames is present in hydrocarbon flames also. Hydrocarbon flames, especially the acetylene flame, are very suitable for flame spectrometry. One advantage is that the C_2, CN, and CH radicals participate in reactions which make possible the liberation of metal atoms from relatively stable metal oxides. On the other hand, in comparison with the hydrogen flames, the background emission of the flame is spread over practically the whole region of the spectrum and the intensity is appreciable. The fact that the reactions taking part in a hydrogen flame can be understood relatively simply because of the simple flame composition, can be looked on as an advantage of hydrogen flames. However, the advantage of acetylene flames, especially when used with N_2O, is that because of their low flame velocity, they can easily be used to make laminar flames.

D. OTHER FLAMES

Among other types of flames, cyanogen and carbon subnitride should be mentioned. The flame of the former with oxygen is of low flame velocity—about 30 cm/sec. The reactions are as follows (51):

$$C_2N_2 \rightarrow 2CN$$
$$CN+O_2 \rightarrow NCO_2$$
$$NCO_2+C_2N_2 \rightarrow NCOOCN+CN$$
$$NCOOCN \rightarrow N_2+2CO$$
$$CN+CN+X \rightarrow C_2N_2+X$$

The temperature of the flame is high (Table 5). The temperature of the C_4N_2 flame can be raised above 5000°C.

TABLE 5

Temperature of Oxygen–Cyanogen Flames

Oxygen, % (v/v)	Cyanogen, % (v/v)	Temperature, °K	
		Obs.	Calc.
25.3	74.7	2610	—
26.8	73.2	3105	—
33.3	66.7	3270	3200
36.5	63.5	3333	—
50.0	50.0	4640	4810
62.0	38.0	4453	—
66.7	33.3	4065	3700

In these flames, CO and CN are emitting species. In the rich flame, C_2 appears also. These species are in addition to the species mentioned in foregoing sections. CO emission is not important in flame spectrometry, because it appears only at the lower end of the ultraviolet spectrum (2000–2600 Å) and in the infrared region.

The situation is altered significantly when water is sprayed into the flame. Water affects the flame velocity and, naturally, the number and concentration of radicals in the flame and, by this, the emission of OH and H_2O species.

REFERENCES

1. G. D. Liveing and J. Dewar, *Proc. Roy. Soc. (London)*, **29**, 398 (1879).
2. W. N. Hartley, *J. Chem. Soc.*, **43**, 390 (1883).
3. J. J. Balmer, *Ann. Physik*, **25**, 80 (1885).
4. J. R. Rydberg, *Phil. Mag.*, [5] **29**, 333 (1890) (summary).
5. W. Ritz, *Z. Physik*, **9**, 521 (1908).
6. E. M. Rutherford, *Phil. Mag.*, **21**, 669 (1911).
7. N. Bohr, *Phil. Mag.*, **26**, 1, 476, 857 (1913).
8. A. Summerfeld, *Ann. Physik*, **51**, 1 (1916).
9. E. Schrödinger, *Phys. Rev.*, **28**, 1049 (1926).
10. W. Heisenberg, *Z. Physik*, **43**, 172 (1927).
11. L. de Broglie, *Phil. Mag.*, **47**, 446 (1924); *Comp. rend.*, **180**, 498 (1925).
12. D. R. Hartree and W. Hartree, *Proc. Roy. Soc. (London)*, **166**, 450 (1938).
13. P. A. M. Dirac, *Proc. Roy. Soc. (London)*, **117**, 610 (1928); **118**, 351 (1928).
14. N. N. Semenov, *Some Problems of Chemical Kinetics and Reactivity*, Vol. II, Pergamon, London, 1959, p. 149.
15. B. Lewis and G. von Elbe, *Combustion, Flames and Explosions of Gases*, Academic, New York, 1951.
16. G. Ribaud and D. Seferian, *Chaleur & Ind.*, **167**, 130 (1934).
17. C. P. Fenimore and G. W. Jones, *J. Phys. Chem.*, **63**, 1834 (1959).
18. E. Pungor, B. Weszprémy and M. Pályi, *Mikrochim. Acta*, 436 (1961).
19. G. H. Dieke and H. M. Crosswhite, *J. Quant. Spectry. Radiative Transfer*, **2**, 97 (1962).
20. R. Mavrodineanu and H. Boiteux, *Flame Spectroscopy*, Wiley, New York, 1965.
21. M. Charton and A. G. Gaydon, *Proc. Roy. Soc. (London)*, **245**, 84 (1958).
22. S. S. Penner, *Symp. Combust., 4th, Cambridge, Mass., 1952*, Williams and Wilkins, Baltimore, 1953, p. 218.
23. A. G. Gaydon, *The Spectroscopy of Flames*, Chapman and Halls, London, 1957.
24. D. Diederichsen and H. G. Wolfhard, *Proc. Roy. Soc. (London)*, A236, 89 (1956).
25. P. J. T. Zeegers and C. T. J. Alkemade, *Symp. Combust., 10th, Univ. Cambridge, Cambridge, Engl., 1964*, The Combustion Institute, Pittsburgh, 1965.
26. P. J. Padley, *Trans. Faraday Soc.*, **56**, 449 (1960).
27. J. W. Robinson and V. Smith, *Anal. Chim. Acta*, **36**, 489 (1966).
28. P. T. Gilbert, *Chemiluminescent Flame Photometry*, Rept. No. 37, Beckman Instruments, Inc., Fullerton, Calif.
29. H. F. Calcote, *Symp. Combust., 8th, Pasadena, Calif., 1960*, Williams and Wilkins, Baltimore, 1962, p. 184.
30. T. Fueno, N. R. Mukherjee, T. Ree and H. Eyring, *Symp. Combust., 8th, Pasadena, Calif., 1960*, Williams and Wilkins, Baltimore, 1962, p. 222.

31. J. A. Green and T. M. Sugden, *Symp. Combust.*, *9th, Cornell Univ., Ithaca, N.Y., 1962*, Academic, New York, 1963, p. 607.

32. N. R. Mukherjee, T. Fueno, H. Eyring and T. Ree, *Symp. Combust.*, *8th, Pasadena, Calif., 1960*, Williams and Wilkins, Baltimore, 1962, p. 1.

33. E. Pungor and M. Mahr, *Talanta*, **10**, 537 (1963).

34. G. E. Schmauch and E. J. Serfass, *Appl. Spectry.*, **12**, 98 (1958).

35. A. G. Gaydon and G. Pannetier, *Nature*, **161**, 242 (1948).

36. N. S. Enikolopyan, *Symp. Combust.*, *7th, London, Oxford, 1958*, Butterworths, London, 1959, p. 157.

37. R. M. Fristrom, *Symp. Combust.*, *9th, Cornell Univ., Ithaca, N.Y., 1962*, Academic, New York, 1963, p. 560.

38. E. Pungor, *Flame Photometry Theory*, D. Van Nostrand, London, 1967.

39. C. W. Hand, *J. Chem. Phys.*, **36**, 2521 (1962).

40. G. B. Kistiakowsky and L. W. Richards, *J. Chem. Phys.*, **36**, 1707 (1962).

41. J. N. Bradley and G. B. Kistiakowsky, *J. Chem. Phys.*, **35**, 254 (1961).

42. N. R. Mukherjee, *Encyclopaedic Dictionary of Physics*, Pergamon, London, 1961.

43. R. E. Ferguson, *J. Chem. Phys.*, **23**, 2085 (1955).

44. R. Bleckrode and W. C. Nienwpoort, *J. Chem. Phys.*, **43**, 3680 (1965).

45. A. G. Gaydon and H. G. Wolfhard, *Proc. Roy. Soc. (London)*, **A201**, 561 (1950).

46. M. D. Amos and J. B. Willis, *Spectrochim. Acta*, **22**, 1325 (1966).

47. W. G. Parker and H. G. Wolfhard, *Symp. Combust.*, *4th, Cambridge, Mass., 1952*, Williams and Wilkins, Baltimore, 1952, p. 420.

48. G. F. Kirkbright, M. K. Peters and T. S. West, *Talanta*, **14**, 789 (1967).

49. V. A. Fassel and D. W. Golightly, *Anal. Chem.*, **39**, 466 (1967).

50. G. N. Spokes and A. G. Gaydon, *Proc. Phys. Soc. (London)*, **74**, 639 (1959).

51. H. James, *Rev. Inst. Franc. Pétrole Ann. Combust. Liquides*, **12**, 1241 (1967).

4 Fundamental Aspects of Decomposition, Atomization, and Excitation of the Sample in the Flame

C. Th. J. Alkemade

FYSISCH LABORATORIUM
RIJKS-UNIVERSITEIT, UTRECHT
THE NETHERLANDS

I. Introduction

A. GENERAL SURVEY

Chemical analysis by flame methods requires the reproducible and effective conversion of the sample into the gaseous state in the flame. When atomic absorption or fluorescence methods are applied, or when atomic emission lines are used in the analysis, at least part of the sample must be atomized, i.e., converted into free atoms in the gaseous state. The requirement of (partial) atomization can be disposed of in the emission method, when molecular compounds of the sample emit useful spectral bands. With the flame emission method, however, additional requirements arise with regard to the efficient and reproducible excitation of these atoms or molecules.

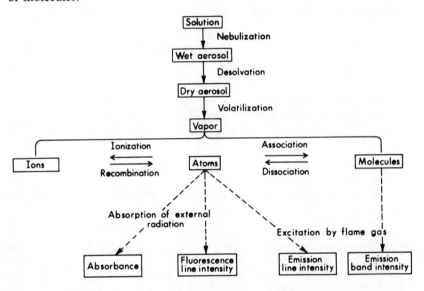

Fig. 1. Transformation of sample during its passage through nebulizer and flame, and the relevant processes.

Figure 1 shows the different stages of sample transformation into an optical signal and the processes that subsequently play a role herein. The analyte is assumed to be present as a salt or in complexed form in a solution. After fragmentation of the liquid sample into a fine haze of spray droplets by means of a nebulizer, the solvent is evaporated—desolvation. With a chamber-type nebulizer this evaporation commences in the air conduit before the aerosol enters the flame. After desolvation dry aerosol particles in the solid or molten state remain. These are volatilized subsequently under influence of the flame temperature and yield atoms or molecules in the gaseous state. Whereas desolvation and volatilization proceed in an irreversible way, rapid and reversible chemical reactions normally set up a certain balance between the atomic and molecular species in the gaseous state. The same holds also for the disintegration of neutral metal atoms into free ions and electrons, and the inverse recombination process. Figure 1 shows how, finally, free metal atoms produce an emission, absorption, or fluorescence line spectrum. Molecular metal compounds are detected normally by their emission band spectrum; ionic spectral lines are of little importance in flame work.

In Section II the decomposition of the analyte contained in the aerosol into free species in the vapor state will be discussed. The nebulization and transport of the aerosol into the flame, with the associated problems of coagulation and spray losses (1–8) will not be considered in this chapter. Desolvation will be considered only insofar as it takes place in the high-temperature environment of the flame. In Section III the processes that determine the atomization of the sample in the vapor state will be treated, This includes the dissociation of metal compounds into metal atoms, and the ionization of metal atoms. In Section IV the processes of excitation and quenching of excited metal atoms will be discussed with some emphasis on suprathermal excitation by fluorescence and chemiluminescence.

The analytical significance of the processes to be described will be dealt with only briefly. We shall consider in particular their possible relation to the spectrochemical sensitivity, the shape of the analytical curve, and the interference effects caused by concomitants in the solution. Methods to avoid or minimize disturbing effects in practical flame emission and absorption methods will be discussed in later chapters.

The discussions to be given in this chapter stress rather the general relationships and fundamental aspects of the sample transformations in the flame. A discussion with a more experimental character, including numerical data and methods of observation, will be found in the related chapter (Chap. 1) of the book: "Analytical Flame Spectroscopy, Selected Topics," edited by R. Mavrodineanu. Both chapters are in certain respects complementary to one another, but they can be read separately and independently.

B. General Discussion on Heat Consumed by the Sample Transformations

All sample transformations and subsequent processes in the gaseous state involve, somehow, the consumption or conversion of energy. One may then inquire to what extent the properties of the flame, in particular the temperature, might be changed by the introduction of a sample.

The energy required per second to dissociate the metal compounds in the gaseous state, or to ionize the metal atoms and excite them to light emission, is practically negligible compared with the chemical energy released per second in the combustion reaction. When a 1 M metal solution is sprayed into an oxygen–hydrogen flame with a total-consumption Beckman burner, a maximum concentration of about 2×10^{15} metal particles per cubic centimeter can be expected on the flame axis (9). This corresponds to a maximum partial pressure of about 10^{-3} atm since the total concentration of molecules in a flame at 1 atm is of the order of 3×10^{18} cm^{-3}. Suppose now that all analyte is initially delivered in the gaseous state as oxide molecules with a dissociation energy of 5 eV. Taking into account the heat content of the flame gases, which amounts roughly to $4kT$, or 1 eV, per flame molecule (where k is the Boltzmann constant and T the absolute temperature in degrees Kelvin) and the above partial pressure of the metal oxide vapor, one calculates that about 0.3 % of the heat content of the flame would be consumed in the complete dissociation of the metal oxide vapor. The energy consumed would be much less in premixed flames and for trace concentrations of the metal salt.

The heat of sublimation for metal compounds is usually several electron volts per compound molecule and thus comparable to the heat of dissociation. Thus, we may conclude that the heat consumed for complete volatilization of the dry aerosol particles is of little importance in the energy balance of the flame. The energy of order kT that is required per atom to heat the metal vapor to the final flame temperature T is one order of magnitude less than the heat consumed in the preceding processes, and fully negligible.

The heat loss conveyed by the radiation of the metal spectrum is also negligible. Even for atomic sodium vapor at a partial pressure of 10^{-3} atm and 3000°K, the energy radiated per millisecond per cubic centimeter by the Na–D doublet amounts to less than 0.1 % of the heat content per cubic centimeter of the flame. During this period the flame gases travel upward over a distance of about 1 cm. In this estimate the flame was assumed to be homogeneously colored by sodium vapor over a cross section of about 1.5 cm in thickness. Under this condition the fraction of all photons that are generated in the flame and are able to escape, in spite of self-absorption, is of the order of 1 % [compare the corresponding emission curve of growth presented in Fig. 16 of (10)].

In contrast to the outcome of the preceding estimates, the energy required for evaporation of the solvent and for the subsequent heating and eventual dissociation of the solvent vapor can be a significant fraction of the heat content of the flame. For water, the two quantities amount to 0.3 and 0.6 %, respectively, when water at a rate of 0.025 ml/min is introduced into a flame burning with 5 liters/min of air and 2.5 liters/min of hydrogen ($T \simeq 2160°K$). For a flame fed by 8.2 liters/min of hydrogen and 3.5 liters/min of oxygen, and into which 1.7 ml/min of water is injected, the two quantities amount to 6 and 15%, respectively ($T = 2700°K$) according to calculations made by Dr. P. J. Th. Zeegers, based on data in (9). The considerable cooling of flames fed by total-consumption nebulizers, with normal rates of liquid intake, is well established experimentally. For example, at a rate of intake of 6 ml of water per minute into an oxygen–hydrogen flame, the temperature decrease is 600°C (11). By contrast, in flames fed by a chamber-type nebulizer, this cooling effect is only about 10°C and thus insignificant.

Solvent evaporation can also alter the chemical flame composition, especially when the solvent contains organic material and is sprayed directly into the flame. The combustion of the solvent, which consumes extra oxygen, may then result in an enhancement or a depression of the flame temperature, depending on whether a fuel-lean or a fuel-rich combustion mixture is used (12).

II. Sample Decomposition in the Flame

A. DESOLVATION

1. *Rate of Desolvation*

The rate of desolvation of a spray droplet with radius r may be defined as the mass loss in unit time interval, $-dm/dt$, owing to evaporation of the solvent. In the flame the solvent boils at temperature T_b. The rate of desolvation is determined mainly by the rate of heat transport from the flame (with $T_{flame} > T_b$) to the droplet (13). Heat is consumed in the evaporation of the solvent as well as in heating the vapor to the final flame temperature. Assuming that heat is transferred mainly by conduction through the ambient gas and that the thermal conductivity λ of the gas is approximately independent of temperature, we have (6, 14)

$$-dm/dt = (4\pi r\lambda/C_p)\ln[1 + C_p(T - T_b)/L] \qquad (1)$$

where L is the specific heat of vaporization of solvent, C_p is the average specific heat of the vapor at constant pressure and T is the flame temperature. Since $-dm/dt$ varies proportionally to r, we find that the rate $-dA/dt$ at which the surface area of the droplet decreases per unit of time is constant. The total time t required for complete evaporation of a droplet with initial area A_o is then

$$t = (\rho A_o C_p / 8\pi\lambda)/\ln[1 + C_p(T - T_b)/L] \tag{2}$$

where ρ is the density of the liquid. Water droplets with an initial diameter of 10 μ will be evaporated within 0.3 msec in an air–acetylene flame. For a flame with a vertical rise-velocity of 10 m/sec, this period corresponds to a height interval of 3 mm. The average initial droplet diameter may be considerably less in flames fed by a chamber-type nebulizer (15). In flames fed by a total-consumption nebulizer, however, much larger droplets may occur (16), some of which are not completely evaporated during their passage through the flame. The linear relationship (2) between t and A_o has recently been confirmed experimentally for isolated droplets that were injected by a special droplet generator into the flame and analyzed by the MgO impression method (13). The experimental values of the rate of desolvation appeared to exceed the rather uncertain theoretical values by a factor of 2–4.

In turbulent flames additional transport of heat to the boiling droplet by convection could be important. When important, the right-hand side of Eq. (1) should be multiplied by a factor $1 + 0.276 \, \mathrm{Re}^{1/2} \, \mathrm{Pr}^{1/3}$, where Re and Pr are the dimensionless Reynolds and Prandtl numbers (14). These numbers are defined by

$$\mathrm{Re} = 2\upsilon r\rho_g/\mu_g \qquad \text{and} \qquad \mathrm{Pr} = \mu_g C_p/\lambda$$

where υ is the droplet velocity relative to the gas stream at large distances from the droplet, ρ_g is the density of the gas, and μ_g is the gas viscosity coefficient. For ideal gases and water vapor, $\mathrm{Pr} \simeq 1$.

When combustible organic solvents are used, the rate of desolvation is enhanced by the heat of combustion of the vapor released. An extra term $[+(\Delta H/L)\phi]$ should then be added to the term $C_p(T - T_b)/L$ in Eq. (1) (14), ΔH is the heat of combustion per unit mass of reacting mixture, and ϕ is the mixture strength of the combustible species in the solvent vapor and the oxidizer.

With some organic solvents the average time required for complete evaporation of the droplets is also reduced considerably owing to the smaller initial diameter of the droplets formed by the nebulizer. This is a consequence of the lower surface tension which leads to a finer dispersion of the spray. The lower boiling temperature of organic solvents, however, has not an important effect as such on the rate of desolvation in the flame. The value of $(T - T_b)$ in Eq. (1) increases but slightly, even when T_b is lowered by, say, 50°C. The boiling temperature and related saturation pressure of the solvent at room temperature are, of course, important factors for the rate of desolvation in the spray chamber (6).

In fluorescence experiments with total-consumption nebulizers, scattering of the lamp radiation was, indeed, found to be absent, if alcoholic solvents were used instead of water (17).

2. Consequences of Incomplete Desolvation in Analytical Flame Spectrometry

Incomplete desolvation of the spray droplets in the flame obviously causes a loss in spectrochemical sensitivity. Such losses are not feared for chamber-type nebulizers, since here practically all droplets leaving the burner will be completely desolvated near the base of the flame. Problems may arise, however, with total-consumption nebulizers, especially so when the rate of liquid intake is high and the point of observation is at a short distance from the burner tip. Since these nebulizers are usually combined with unpremixed, turbulent flames with high flow speeds, a noticeable portion of the droplets may be hurled out of the flame before they have had time for complete evaporation. The adjective "total-consumption" should thus be understood to indicate only that all aspirated liquid is consumed, but *not* that all analyte contained in the liquid is released as vapor in the flame. Nevertheless, for a given Na solution the concentration of free Na atoms found in these turbulent flames may still be larger by an order of magnitude than the concentration found in premixed flames with chamber-type nebulizers (18).

Higher flame temperatures [see the occurrence of T in Eq. (1)], observation further downstream in the flame gases, and organic solvents may be employed profitably in reducing the effect of incomplete evaporation on the sensitivity.

Interference effects can result when concomitants in the solution alter the time needed for complete desolvation of the droplets obtained with total-consumption nebulizers. Such effects may be expected, for instance, when the solution contains organic material in bulk concentrations. This kind of interference is denoted as nonspecific, since the magnitude of its effect is independent of the kind of element analyzed (5).

Interference effects may also arise in an indirect way, as when the concomitant alters the amount of solvent evaporated in the flame and by that the temperature, composition, and/or form of the flame (Section I.B). The intensity of the analysis line in emission or absorption may depend on one or more of the latter quantities and thus indirectly on the concentration of the concomitant in the solution.

The percentual loss of free atoms or molecules of the analyte in the flame, owing to incomplete desolvation, is independent of the analyte concentration in the solution. Consequently, if the analytical curve is linear in the case of complete desolvation, it will remain so, when the desolvation becomes incomplete.

B. VOLATILIZATION

1. *The Processes of Formation and Volatilization of Dry Aerosol Particles*

The actual processes of formation and subsequent volatilization of the minute particles that remain after desolvation of the sprayed solution are largely unknown and often complicated in nature. These processes, which develop rapidly and at high temperature, cannot be described by equilibrium laws and ordinary chemistry; they form a part of pyrochemistry. The composition and state of the dry aerosol particles may depend on many factors, such as the form and concentration in which the analyte was present in the sprayed solution, the kind of solvent, the presence of concomitants in the solution, the flame temperature, and the existence of oxidizing or reducing conditions in the flame. In complex solutions, competitive chemical reactions in the aqueous phase during desolvation may also be important (*19*). Often, the desolvated particles may pass through different states in rapid succession, while in composite samples fractional distillation may occur.

In default of a systematic and comprehensive theory of these processes, we shall only mention here, by way of illustration, some mechanisms that have been suggested in the literature for typical metal compounds.

When a single NaCl solution is sprayed, a NaCl particle will be formed, which has a melting point of about 1100°K and a boiling point of about 1750°K. Since the flame temperature usually exceeds these values and sodium has no tendency to form stable oxides at high temperature, we may expect that this NaCl particle is rapidly converted into the vapor phase. This may occur either as NaCl molecules or directly as atomic vapor. When the original mass of the particle is large, because of a very high solution concentration, the time of passage through the flame might not be sufficient for complete volatilization. A time delay of the order of 1 msec between complete desolvation and the appearance of Na radiation has been experimentally found for an isolated droplet of an aqueous

NaCl solution with an initial diameter of 50 μ and a Na concentration of 10 mg/liter (13).

It should be stressed that a melting or boiling point below the flame temperature is not a necessary condition for complete volatilization. The final partial pressure of the analyte in the flame, when it is completely volatilized, is usually very low (Section I.B). As long as the actual vapor pressure is below the saturation pressure of the particle in the molten or solid state in the flame, volatilization will ultimately tend to completion. Saturation effects rarely seem to play a role in limiting the extent of volatilization in flame methods. Rhenium has been reported as a case where possible saturation should be considered (20). Carbon particles in the flame may act as condensation centers for this element and prevent oversaturation of the rhenium vapor.

Of course, melting and boiling points that are comparable to, or even higher than the flame temperature are usually indicative of a low rate of volatilization. A final state of complete volatilization might then not be attained because the available time of residence in the flame is insufficient. A typical example of this is magnesium whose refractory monoxide has a melting point of about 3075°K and a boiling point of 3850°K. The behavior of the magnesium absorption in an air–propane flame and for different anions in the solution might be explained as follows (21, 22).

Magnesium sulfate in the condensed phase decomposes at 1160°K into MgO and sulfur oxides. Solid MgO has a sublimation temperature of 3040°K, which is slightly less than its melting point. Thus, in hot flames solid MgO might sublime completely before it melts (23). In cool flames, however, sublimation of MgO would be a slow process. A surface reaction of H radicals with MgO, from which OH radicals and Mg atoms would be produced in the gas phase, has been proposed (21). The rate of such a surface reaction is limited and, indeed, the amount of magnesium vapor released increases with height of observation above the burner. A similar decomposition scheme might be valid for magnesium phosphate and oxalate.

A typically different situation exists for magnesium chloride. The hexahydrate salt loses water at 430°K to form $MgCl_2 \cdot H_2O$ in the condensed phase. In the flame the latter reacts in one of these ways:

$$MgCl_2 \cdot H_2O(s) \rightarrow MgCl_2(s) + H_2O(g) \qquad (3)$$

$$MgCl_2 \cdot H_2O(s) \rightarrow MgO(s) + 2HCl(g) \qquad (4)$$

Now $MgCl_2$ boils at 1685°K. Reaction (3) may be an efficient way to release Mg particles in the gas phase in cool flames. However, the possibility of reaction (4) shows that the presence of $MgCl_2$ in solution need not necessarily lead to the formation of a chloride-containing particle in the final stage of volatilization. The same holds true for the chlorides of chromium, manganese, and iron in aqueous solutions which are transformed into oxides with higher boiling points in the condensed phase (24).

Magnesium nitrate decomposes to MgO at 594°K in the solid state. However, if the nitrate is heated rapidly, it may melt before it is decomposed to the oxide. Volatilization will then occur directly from the molten state. Similarly, aluminum nitrate decomposes at 423°K into the oxide. The formation of a nonvolatile aluminum oxide at the high temperature of the flame seems to explain the low concentration of free aluminum atoms and aluminum compounds in usual flames. Addition of HF to the solution leads to the formation of AlF_3 particles which have a melting point of 1310°K and a sublimation temperature of 1475°K, and thus are more volatile.

Addition of ammonium chloride enhances the concentration of rare earths in the vapor phase (3). The explanation again revolves about the formation of unhydrolyzed chlorides which are more volatile than the corresponding oxides (25).

The low concentration of free aluminum atoms in cool flames, when compared to those of molybdenum atoms for equal solution concentrations, suggests that the volatility of the corresponding oxides, and not that of the metallic states, is relevant. For example (26), metallic aluminum is more volatile than molybdenum, whereas the reverse is true for their oxides. In both cases volatilization follows the formation of oxide particles.

When aluminum or magnesium are present in solution as an organic complex (with EDTA or 8–hydroxyquinoline), the volatilization appears to be considerably enhanced (21, 27–30). Possibly the organic ligands decompose at a relatively low temperature and release the analyte directly in the vapor state before a nonvolatile oxide can be formed.

Calcium chloride and nitrate appear to be released rather quickly as vapors under normal flame conditions (31); their melting points are 1045° and 834°K, respectively. The formation of a CaO particle (mp 2850°K), as a decomposition product of calcium oxalate, may result in a noticeable reduction of the calcium signal. On the other hand, the well-known depression of the calcium signal by phosphate is explained by the formation of a relatively nonvolatile calcium pyrophosphate species (1, 2, 5, 6). In contrast, the depressing effect of phosphate on the magnesium absorption is explained by the decomposition of magnesium phosphate into a nonvolatile MgO particle. In any case, the depression of calcium by phosphate must be based on an effect in the condensed phase and not in the gas phase of the flame. This follows from the absence of any observed depression when a calcium chloride solution and a phosphate solution are introduced into the flame by separate sprayers. Supporting this conclusion is the observation that the relative extent of the depression increases with increasing solution concentration, that is, with increasing particle diameter. (See also Section II.B.3 and Fig. 2.)

When two metal salts are present in the same solution, a mixture may be formed in the desolvated aerosol particles. Formation of mixed calcium and aluminum oxides, or calcium aluminates, can depress strongly the calcium signal because these compounds have low volatility. The melting point of $CaAl_2O_4$ is about 1850°K. Conversely, the formation of a more volatile mixture of magnesium and calcium might explain the appreciable enhancement of the magnesium absorption in an air–propane flame upon addition of calcium (21). The curve representing the magnesium enhancement as a function of added calcium concentration shows prominent peaks at certain calcium concentrations which are commensurate to the magnesium concentration. On the other hand, the calcium signal is depressed by added magnesium (22), suggesting that the volatility of this mixed calcium–magnesium compound is lower than that of the particle formed from the calcium solution alone.

Reference (18) summarizes experimental methods needed to decide whether or not volatilization in flames is complete.

2. The Rate of Volatilization

The loss of particle mass per unit of time under given flame conditions cannot be easily calculated from theory as was the rate of desolvation. Sufficient information is lacking on the state and properties of the particles at elevated temperatures. From formulas for the rate of volatilization of a particle in the liquid phase in the flame, one can derive the expression (2)

$$-dm/dt = 4\pi r M D_g p_s / \mathscr{R}T \tag{5}$$

where r and m are the radius and mass of the particle, M is the molecular weight of the evaporating substance, D_g is the diffusion coefficient of the vapor in the ambient flame gases, p_s is the saturation vapor pressure of the vapor at the surface of the particle and $\mathscr{R}$ is the gas constant. Equation (5) is, in fact, Langmuir's equation for the evaporation rate of a droplet at rest in a stagnant gas, when the vapor pressure at a large distance from the droplet is small compared to p_s. This equation is based on the assumption that the evaporation rate is determined by the rate of vapor transport through diffusion processes only. A similar equation describes the rate of desolvation of a spray droplet in the spray chamber at room temperature (5, 6). The time t required for complete volatilization of a droplet with initial surface area A_o follows from Eq. (5) and is given by

$$t = \rho_{\text{liq}} \mathscr{R} T A_o / 8\pi M D_g p_s \qquad (6)$$

where ρ_{liq} is the density of the liquid. Application of Eq. (5) requires that the particle be in the liquid state below its boiling point, and that the evaporating species be known. It is interesting to compare Eq. (5) with Eq. (1) which holds for a boiling droplet. It should be realized that in turbulent flames the rate of volatilization might be markedly enhanced by the contribution of convection to the transport of vapor from the evaporating liquid.

When volatilization occurs by sublimation from the solid state, the assumption of a spherical particle might be doubted, especially in composite particles. Simultaneous evaporation of different chemical species could complicate theoretical calculations. In addition, chemical reactions with flame gas components at the particle surface could interfere with the rate of volatilization. Because of these uncertainties, only a qualitative summary will be given of the factors and parameters that are believed significant in determining the extent of volatilization.

(*a*) The values of the melting and boiling points, and sometimes the sublimation point, are generally a good indication of the rate at which a given particle will volatilize at a particular flame temperature. If the boiling point is below the flame temperature, complete volatilization may be obtained quickly.

(*b*) Volatilization of substances with high melting or boiling points may be enhanced considerably by selecting a higher flame temperature. The hot nitrous oxide–acetylene and oxygen–acetylene flames are advantageous when handling elements that form refractory compounds or whose volatilization is inhibited by concomitants in the sprayed solution (*32, 33*).

(*c*) The reducing conditions that exist in fuel-rich, or even incandescent, flames often promote the volatilization of elements that would form stable oxides in normal flames in the condensed phase. For example, particles of chromium oxide occur to a much greater extent in stoichiometric hydrogen flames than in fuel-rich ones (*34*).

(*d*) Higher solution concentrations result in a larger average particle size and may thus retard complete volatilization in the flame.

(*e*) For a given solution concentration, the average initial size of the dry aerosol particles will be larger the coarser the spray introduced into the flame (35). This is true because a given quantity of solute will then be distributed over a smaller number of particles.

(f) The fraction of a given aerosol that is volatilized increases with increasing residence time of the particles in the flame. Consequently, the choice of a greater height of observation above the burner tip, or a lowering of the vertical rise-velocity of the flame gases, can result in a more complete volatilization.

3. Consequences of Incomplete Volatilization in Analytical Flame Spectrometry

Some analytical consequences of incomplete volatilization will now be briefly mentioned (36; also 1–8). In general, these effects will be more pronounced with total-consumption nebulizers than with chamber-type nebulizers because of the influence of the initial size-distribution of the spray droplets introduced into the flame (Section II.B.2).

Loss in spectrochemical sensitivity is one obvious consequence of incomplete volatilization. The very low fraction of aluminum present as atomic vapor in a premixed air–acetylene flame, according to absorption measurements (37), may be explained in this manner. The low atomic concentration of aluminum cannot be explained by a low degree of dissociation of AlO molecules in the gaseous state; the oxides of manganese, iron, and aluminum have comparable oxide dissociation energies, but the two former elements yield much larger atomic fractions in the flame.

If the fraction of volatilized aerosol particles depends on the solution concentration, a convex bending of the analytical curve may arise in the high concentration range (35). When this fraction decreases with increasing concentration, no proportionality exists between the amount of analyte sprayed and the amount of analyte released as vapor in the flame. The resulting effect on the shape of the analytical curve is the same for atomic lines as for molecular bands because the concentrations of free atoms and molecules have a constant ratio in a given flame.

The occurrence of nonvolatilized, incandescent particles, such as aluminum oxide and vanadium oxide, may raise the intensity of the continuous background spectrum of the flame. The origin of this radiation is usually thermal, although evidence (38) has been found for the occurrence of nonthermal candoluminescence of vanadium oxide particles in hydrogen flames which was caused by recombination of free excess H and OH radicals at the surface of the particles. In flame fluorescence analysis, nonvolatilized particles may cause a disturbing background signal due to scattering of the exciting lamp radiation.

Interferences with solute volatilization are perhaps the phenomena most frequently studied in recent literature devoted to emission and absorption flame spectrometry. Often obscure still are the underlying mechanisms. The inhibition or enhancement of the volatilization of an analyte by concomitants present in the sprayed solution is markedly more complicated than the volatilization of a simple salt particle alone. These interference effects may be classified into two broad categories (2, 6, 36).

a. *Category I.* The first category encompasses all effects that are based on the formation of a chemical compound of the analyte and concomitant

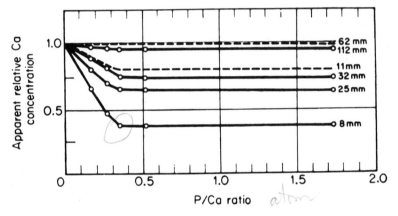

Fig. 2. Apparent Ca concentration (see text) is plotted as a function of the atomic ratio P : Ca. The height of observation above the inner cones of the laminar air–C_2H_2 flame is indicated. A chamber-type nebulizer was used. Solid curves refer to 8.3 meq/liter Ca; broken curves refer to 0.55 meq/liter Ca. Reprinted from Ref. (*39*), p. 95, by courtesy of Springer Verlag.

(or their decomposition products) in the condensed phase. In this compound the numbers of analyte and concomitant atoms are in a certain proportion to each other. This proportion may have different values under different conditions in the flame. When the compound particle has a higher melting or boiling point than the particle formed from the analyte alone, a depression of the analysis signal can result. In the reverse case where the particle formed from the analyte alone is not easily volatilized, an enhancement may be expected.

The depression of a calcium signal by added phosphate or aluminum chloride is a classic example of such truly chemical interference effect. (See also Section II.B.1.) Figure 2 shows the apparent calcium concentration, measured in emission, as a function of the ratio of phosphorus and calcium atoms in the solution. Observations were made at different heights in a laminar, premixed, air–acetylene flame with a separate spray-chamber. The apparent calcium concentration is the value that would be found if no corrections were made for the depressing effect of phosphate; the ratio of apparent to actual calcium concentrations is plotted as the ordinate. Initially there is a linear decrease of apparent calcium concentration with increasing concentration of phosphorus. Beyond a certain P/Ca ratio (about, 0.3–1), the apparent calcium concentration remains constant and a plateau region develops. The P/Ca ratio at the knee of the curve is independent of the height of observation and of the calcium concentration in the solution sprayed. A similar experiment with an air–propane flame yielded the same P/Ca ratio at the knee of the curve; however, the relative depression was considerably greater (39). The ratio at the "knee" corresponds to the P/Ca ratio in the compound formed. The increase of the plateau ordinate with increasing height of observation reflects the progression of volatilization with increasing residence time of the particles in the flame [(40); Section II.B.2]. The depression of calcium is markedly reduced, for a given P/Ca ratio and height in the flame, when the calcium concentration in the solution sprayed is lowered.

Addition of increasing amounts of sodium acetate to a thallium solution yields a depression curve for the thallium absorption which is similar in appearance to the curves in Fig. 2 (41), provided a small peak of enhancement for relatively small concentrations of the interferent is disregarded. It has been suggested that certain organic thallium salts, such as thallium acetate, are decomposed under the action of water into rather nonvolatile thallium oxide compounds. However, thallium nitrate particles are believed to be released partly as thallium nitrate vapor and partly decomposed into solid Tl_2O_3. This gives rise to higher vapor concentrations of thallium in the flame.

A good example of a positive interference effect is the enhancement of an aluminum signal that is observed when HF or 8-hydroxyquinoline is added to an aluminum solution (Section II.B.1).

b. *Category II.* The second category encompasses all volatilization interference effects that are based either on the occlusion of the analyte in a less volatile matrix of the concomitant or on its dispersion in a more volatile matrix. In the former case a depression of the analysis signal can result. In the latter case an enhancement can occur if the particles formed from the analyte alone are less quickly volatilized than the matrix in which they are dispersed. Whereas interferences in the first category have already set in for commensurate concentrations of analyte and concomitant, matrix effects usually require relatively higher concentrations of the concomitant. A particular chemical compound between analyte and concomitant need not be formed. Rather it is the low or high volatility of the matrix itself that explains the depression or enhancement of the analysis signal.

The depression of calcium by addition of an excess of aluminum nitrate, which forms a very involatile matrix, fits well into this picture (42). In contrast to the depressing effect of phosphate on calcium, the calcium depression by aluminum nitrate is virtually not removed at greater heights in the flame. The depression of calcium by aluminum chloride differs significantly from that caused by aluminum nitrate. In fact, the curve representing the calcium depression as a function of added aluminum chloride resembles closely that shown for phosphate in Fig. 2, and can be explained also by the formation of a rather involatile calcium aluminate.

The recently reported depressing effects on the absorption of strontium in premixed air–acetylene and air–propane flames, caused by excess concentrations of alkali and alkaline earth salts in the solution, is also most probably a matrix effect (43).

A positive matrix effect may underlie the enhancement of Ca signal in the presence of an excess of aliphatic salts in a turbulent oxygen–hydrogen flame (44). Quick volatilization of the matrix in which the analyte was finely dispersed may here have resulted in a finer comminution of the analyte particles. This, in turn, would promote their volatilization in the rapidly moving gas of this flame (Section II.B.2).

III. Atomization of the Sample

A. DISSOCIATION OF METAL COMPOUNDS

1. *Survey of Metal Compounds Occurring in Flames*

First a brief account is given of the various kinds of metal compounds that can be expected under different flame conditions; for a more extensive survey see (7, 18).

In the flame, metal atoms can be bound to other partners; these may be a constituent of the flame gases, such as O atoms, or partners introduced as a component of the solution sprayed, such as chlorine in the form of

HCl. In equilibrium at a given temperature, the fraction of metal atoms tied up as molecules depends on the bond strength as well as on the concentration of the "partner" in the flame. A rather stable bond can be expected under flame conditions if the bond strength exceeds a few electron volts.

Metal compounds in the flame are usually simple diatomic molecules, such as CaO, or triatomic molecules, such as LiOH. More complex compounds, such as Na_2SO_4 or organometallic species, are not stable at flame temperatures. Since metal atoms are usually present as trace additives in the flame, the formation of dimers, such as Na_2 and Sr_2O_2, can be neglected. This follows from the law of mass action which predicts that the concentration of dimers would be proportional to the square of atomic concentrations, and the latter are very low. For similar reasons, intermetallic compounds are not expected to be important in flames.

Elements such as Na, Cu, Tl, Ag, and Zn are practically completely atomized in the flame; that is, they do not form molecular compounds with flame partners in noticeable proportions. Only under rather exceptional conditions—cool, oxygen-rich flames—are NaO_2 molecules formed. Absolute measurements of the intensities of the foregoing elements in respect to their emission or absorption lines are sometimes used to calculate the fraction of the sprayed sample that is actually converted into the gaseous state in the flame (18).

Metal monoxides are the most common compounds found in flames burning with air, oxygen, or nitrous oxide. Whereas the alkali metals form practically no oxides, a major fraction of the alkaline earth elements is present as monoxides unless very fuel-rich flames are used. Certain other metals, such as La, U, and Ti, form refractory oxides which are extremely stable. As a consequence, the free atomic concentrations of these elements are virtually negligible in flames of stoichiometric composition and moderate temperature. However, in fuel-rich, hot, oxygen–acetylene or nitrous oxide–acetylene flames, these oxides may be sufficiently dissociated to enable these elements to be analyzed by atomic absorption spectrometry.

Hydroxide species can be expected for some alkali and alkaline earth elements in hydrogen and hydrocarbon flames. The tendency to form monohydroxides increases in the order: Na < K < Rb < Cs < Li. Whereas sodium forms practically no NaOH, the concentration of LiOH molecules often exceeds the atomic lithium concentration by a factor of 10. None of the alkali hydroxides emits spectral bands in the visible or ultraviolet portion of the spectrum. This contrasts with the appearance of visible bands of the alkaline earth monohydroxides which can be used for flame emission spectrometry. The tendency to form monohydroxides increases in the order: Sr < Ca < Ba. In fuel-rich hydrogen flames the concentrations of the monohydroxides may dominate over those of the corresponding monoxides. In fuel-rich hydrogen flames even dihydroxides, such as $Ba(OH)_2$, may dominate. Other elements, such as In, Ga, and Cu also form hydroxides, but the concentrations of InOH and CuOH are usually insignificant although visible bands of CuOH are often seen in flames containing hydrogen. Formation of BeOH has been suggested as an explanation for the failure in determining beryllium by atomic absorption in conventional flames (45).

If halogens are present in bulk concentrations in the solution sprayed, the free atomic concentration of the alkali and alkaline earth metals appears to be lowered due to halide formation. The formation of mono-halides of alkaline earth metals can be seen from the appearance of their bands in the flame spectrum. When the halogen supply to the flame is increased, the intensities of these bands increase initially also, but they attain a maximum value followed by a gradual decrease in the range of very high halogen concentrations (46). This decrease has been explained by assuming that dihalides are formed at the cost of the monohalides. Metal halides may be a dominant species in special halogen–hydrogen flames.

2. Consequences of the Law of Mass Action in Equilibrium

A quantitative discussion of the degree of dissociation can be given on the basis of the law of mass action in thermodynamic equilibrium. Let us consider the dissociation and reverse association reaction for a metal compound MX where M is a metal atom:

$$MX \rightleftharpoons M + X \tag{7}$$

The degree of dissociation, α_d, is defined by

$$\alpha_d = [M]/([M] + [MX]) \tag{8}$$

where the concentrations are expressed in cm^{-3} of free metal atoms and metal compounds in the gaseous state. If an equilibrium is set up between the partners of reaction (7) at a flame temperature T, the law of mass action requires that

$$K_p^d = [M][X]/[MX] \tag{9}$$

The dissociation constant, K_p^d, is expressed in cm^{-3} and depends on the flame temperature as well as on the kind of species involved. It does not depend on the concentration values nor on the composition of the flame gases. In full thermodynamic equilibrium, Eq. (9) holds independently of the specific reaction paths through which MX may actually be formed and dissociated in a given flame.

Combining Eqs. (8) and (9), the degree of dissociation is obtained

$$\alpha_d = 1/(1 + [X]/K_p^d) \tag{10}$$

From Eq. (10) we learn that the dissociation is promoted by an increase in the dissociation constant and a decrease in $[X]$. If $[X] \ll K_p^d$, the dissociation is nearly complete and $\alpha_d \simeq 1$; that is, reaction (7) is shifted strongly to the right. If $[X] \gg K_p^d$, $[M]$ is much less than $[MX]$ and will vary approximately as $[M] \propto K_p^d/[X]$ for a constant total metal concentration: $[M] + [MX]$. When $[M] = [X]$, we obtain the degree of dissociation as: $\alpha_d = \{1 + [M]/K_p^d\}^{-1}$. Rearranging: $\alpha_d^2/(1-\alpha_d) = K_p^d/([M]+[MX])$.

The dissociation constant can be calculated from the atomic and molecular constants of the species involved by means of statistical mechanics. In the special case where MX is a heteronuclear diatomic molecule, such as CaO or NaCl, we have (47, 48):

$$\log K_p^d = 20.432 + \tfrac{3}{2} \log (M_M M_X/M_{MX}) + \log [(Q_e)_M (Q_e)_X/(Q_e)_{MX}]$$
$$+ \log B + \log (1 - 10^{-0.625\bar{v}/T}) + \tfrac{1}{2} \log T - 5040 D_0/T \tag{11}$$

where Q_e denotes the electronic partition function of the individual species, B is the rotational constant and $\bar{v}$ is the fundamental vibrational frequency of the molecule (both in cm^{-1}), M is the atomic or molecular mass in atomic weight units, and D_0 is the dissociation energy (in eV). In Eq. (11), the temperature is expressed in degrees Kelvin on the absolute scale, and K_p^d in cm^{-3}. Equation (11) is usually valid to a good approximation in flames (49). If the atom does not possess low-lying excitation levels, the partition function may be replaced by the statistical weight of the atom in its ground state. A recent tabulation contains tables of atomic partition functions as a function of temperature (50); values of the atomic and molecular constants occurring in Eq. (11) may be found in (7, 51). Relations for the equilibrium constants of more complex molecules, such as LiOH, may be found in (7, 18, 48).

The dependence of the equilibrium constant on the flame temperature is governed mainly by the last term containing D_0 in Eq. (11). For a typical value of D_0 (4–5 eV) at a medium flame temperature of 2500°K, the absolute value of the last term is of the order of 10. Lowering D_0 by 0.5 eV appears to raise K_p^d about 10-fold, all other parameters remaining constant. The same increase in K_p^d is achieved through a temperature increase of approximately 250°C. The other temperature-dependent terms in Eq. (11) are usually of little significance under usual flame conditions for molecules whose values of D_0 exceed a few electron volts. The dependence of the dissociation constant on the temperature appears to be stronger the larger the value of the dissociation constant, that is, the more endothermic the dissociation reaction is.

When X is a flame constituent, for example, atomic oxygen, its concentration is usually much larger than the concentration of MX. The latter cannot exceed the total concentration of element M introduced into the flame. Even when a $1M$ solution of metal salt is sprayed directly into the flame, the total element concentration will be less than 0.1 % of the total concentration of flame molecules (Section I.B). The value of $[X]$ will be virtually unaffected by the consumption of free X atoms due to the formation of MX. This may still be true when one considers metal oxide formation in fuel-rich flames where $[O]$ might be less than the total metal concentration. This holds because $[O]$ is related through chemical equilibria to the bulk concentrations of other flame constituents; the latter equilibria bring about a stabilization of $[O]$. Consequently, in calculating the degree of dissociation from Eq. (10), one may use the equilibrium value of $[X]$ calculated in the absence of the metal species. This conclusion implies that the degree of dissociation is independent of the absolute metal concentration in the flame. In other words, the percentual loss of free metal atoms due to molecule formation remains the same for low as for high metal concentrations in the solution sprayed. A similar conclusion can usually be reached when the partner X is delivered to the flame as a constituent of the solution sprayed. For example, any appreciable formation of NaCl in the vapor phase is expected only if chlorine compounds are present in bulk concentration in the solution sprayed. By contrast, the concentration of metal salt is normally insignificant (Section III.A.4), so that the removal of X by formation of MX hardly affects $[X]$ in the flame.

For an illustration, consider the calculated equilibrium values of α_d for the oxides of Fe, Ca, Al, and Ba in a fuel-rich, oxygen–hydrogen flame at 2640°K. Calculations were made by Dr. P. J. T. Zeegers using data from (52). These are 0.95, 0.60, 0.08, and 0.03, respectively. The calculated concentration of atomic oxygen is 1.3×10^{15} cm^{-3}. Now in a stoichiometric oxygen–hydrogen flame of comparable temperature, $[O]$ is larger by a factor of 10 and the values of α_d for the four elements are 0.7, 0.2, 0.008, and 0.003, respectively. In the calculations, the D_0 values employed were 4.3, 4.0, 5.5, and 5.0 eV for FeO, CaO, AlO, and BaO. For BaO, CaO, and FeO, Q_e was assumed to be 6.

For a constant mixture strength of oxidant and fuel gases, an increase in temperature raises not only K_p^d but also [O] because of a shift in the dissociation equilibrium of O_2. The latter effect partly counteracts the favorable effect of increased K_p^d on the metal oxide dissociation.

The depressing effect of chlorine or fluorine on the atomic metal concentration in hydrogen and hydrocarbon flames is greatly diminished through the binding of these halogens in the form of HCl or HF in the flame. In fuel-rich oxygen–nitrogen–hydrogen flames at 2200°K, the equilibrium ratios [HCl]/[Cl] and [HF]/[F] are of the order of 10^2 and 10^4, respectively (53). This explains why generally halide formation is important in flame spectrometry only if halogen compounds are present in the sprayed solution at approximately molar concentrations. The greater stability of HCl, as compared to HBr, explains why the suppression effect of bromine on sodium exceeds that of chlorine for a similar halogen concentration (53). The reverse would be expected if only the stabilities of NaCl ($D_0 = 4.2$ eV) and NaBr ($D_0 = 3.7$ eV) were compared.

Another buffering effect arises in regard to the depression of free atomic lithium concentrations by added chlorine when the major fraction of lithium is tied up as LiOH molecules in the flame. According to the law of mass action, the ratio [Li]/[LiOH] should be independent of the chlorine supply since the ratio depends only on the flame composition and temperature. Consequently, when some free lithium atoms are removed through the formation of LiCl, the loss will be largely compensated for by subsequent dissociation of some LiOH molecules. If LiOH is the dominant species, its concentration will not be particularly affected by this additional dissociation, nor will the concentration of atomic lithium be affected because of the constant ratio between both concentrations in the flame.

3. Deviations from Dissociation Equilibrium

In actual flames, deviations from dissociation equilibrium can occur which may invalidate the outcome of equilibrium calculations. Two kinds of deviations are to be distinguished.

It may happen that not all flame constituents attain their equilibrium concentrations immediately above the primary reaction zone. In particular, H, OH, and O radicals are often found to have concentrations in excess of their equilibrium values near the reaction zone of air–hydrogen and air–acetylene flames. The actual degree of dissociation of a metal compound may then deviate from the value calculated by application of Eq. (9). Substitution in Eq. (9) of the actual (excess) concentration of X, instead of its equilibrium value, need not necessarily yield the correct degree of dissociation. In general, one has to know specifically the dominant reaction path through which MX is formed or dissociated, in order to predict α_d under nonequilibrium conditions.

The case of LiOH may serve as illustration. One might expect from Eq. (9) that the presence of excess OH radicals would decrease its degree of dissociation. This would be the case, indeed, if reaction (7) were the dominant reaction step through which LiOH is actually formed from Li and OH, and vice versa. LiOH is, however, actually formed and dissociated through the following binary exchange reaction:

$$\text{LiOH} + \text{H} \rightleftarrows \text{Li} + \text{H}_2\text{O} \tag{12}$$

As a consequence of the fast rate at which this reaction takes place in both directions, a partial equilibrium is set up between reactants and products. We have to expect then that [LiOH]/[Li] varies proportionally to $[\text{H}_2\text{O}]/[\text{H}]$. The presence of excess H (and OH) radicals will thus lead to a more complete dissociation of LiOH, and not conversely. Since [H] gradually approaches its equilibrium value at greater heights in the flame, whereas $[\text{H}_2\text{O}]$ does not change much with height, the ratio [LiOH]/[Li] must increase with increasing height in the flame. This entails, in turn, a fall in the concentration of atomic Li with height.

On the other hand, a deviation in dissociation equilibrium can also arise, if the dominant reaction through which the metal compound is formed proceeds at a comparatively slow rate. Equilibration between the atomic and molecular metal species is then not attained within the limited time of residence of the metal vapor in the flame. Under this condition a relaxation in the establishment of the dissociation equilibrium of MX results. This occurs also when all other flame constituents were in perfect chemical equilibrium. In order to appreciate this relaxation effect, one should realize that in the reaction zone flame radicals such as H, O, OH, or C may be present in large excess as products of the combustion reactions. Most molecular metal compounds in the gaseous state will be strongly dissociated under the action of some of these radicals or by pyrolysis (54). In the reaction zone of fuel-rich $\text{N}_2\text{O}-\text{C}_2\text{H}_2$ flames, NH and CN radicals may also play an important role in the excessive dissociation of metal oxides (55). Consequently, the metal vapor that emerges from the reaction zone will be found in a state of excessive dissociation that may not correspond to chemical equilibrium at the final flame temperature. It now depends on the rate constant of the corresponding association reaction whether or not equilibrium is attained at a given distance above the reaction zone. For instance, a slow recombination reaction of Na with O_2 explains the delay in establishment of the dissociation equilibrium of NaO_2 in cool ($T < 2000°K$) oxygen-rich, hydrogen flames (56).

By reason of kinetic considerations and of the relatively low metal concentration in the flame, direct reactions between atomic or molecular species of different metals are not expected to be important (57). The gas-phase reaction

$$Ca + MgO \rightleftarrows CaO + Mg \qquad (13)$$

will therefore hardly contribute to the establishment of the CaO or MgO dissociation equilibrium. The rate of such reactions will in general be much lower than that of reactions with flame gas components, such as

$$Ca + CO_2 \rightleftarrows CaO + CO \qquad (14)$$

or

$$Ca + H_2O \rightleftarrows CaO + H_2 \qquad (15)$$

Reactions of the latter kind are believed to explain the rapid equilibration of [MO]/[M], independent of the possible occurrence of excess O radicals in the flame (58).

4. Consequences of Incomplete Dissociation in Analytical Flame Spectrometry

The sensitivity of atomic absorption and atomic fluorescence analysis will, obviously, be reduced when part of the metal atoms is tied up as molecules. In emission flame spectrometry the emission bands, if any, of the molecules formed may be used for analysis when the atomic line intensities become too weak. The emission bands of InCl, CuCl, or CaF can, moreover, be used for the analysis of halogens whose atoms do not even emit a line spectrum in the flame (59).

The shape of the analytical curve will not be affected by molecule formation. This holds because the fraction of analyte that is tied up as a molecule is independent of its solution concentration (Section III.A.2). In principle, formation of NaCl could produce a curvature of the atomic Na curve toward the concentration axis when Na is present as chloride in the solution. The Cl concentration in the flame then varies proportionally to the NaCl concentration in the solution such that [NaCl]/[Na] increases with increasing concentration of analyte in the solution. But in practical analysis the latter concentration is usually too small to give any noticeable compound formation. (See Section III.A.2.) The formation of Na_2 also could cause a similar convex curvature of the atomic Na curve. As mentioned in Section III.A.1, however, the formation of dimers of metallic species is usually negligible in flames.

Since intermetallic compounds in the gaseous phase are not expected in flames, direct interference effects between two metal species through molecule formation is not likely to occur. Direct interference effects can occur, however, between the analyte and a halogen anion, when the latter is present in molar concentration in the solution. This applies especially to flames with direct spray injection.

It should be realized that halide formation is not the only disturbing effect of added HCl. This acid may also have an influence on the atomic metal concentration through an alteration of the nebulization, through a shift in ionization equilibrium (Section III.B.4), or through its effect on the volatilization of elements that tend to form refractory oxides in the condensed phase (32, 33).

Concomitants in the sample that alter the flame temperature or flame composition may interfere indirectly with an analysis element when the latter is partly bound as (hydro–)oxide in the flame. These alterations may then bring about a shift in dissociation equilibrium. This applies especially to flames with direct spray-injection where an alteration of the rate of liquid intake may sensibly affect the flame temperature. Organic material in the sample solution may participate in the combustion and sensibly alter the composition of the flame.

Band emissions of molecules formed from concomitant elements may produce spectral interference in emission flame spectrometry when they overlap the analysis line. If present in high concentrations, some molecular bands may even appear in absorption and cause a sort of spectral interference effect in atomic absorption analysis. The latter effect could be especially serious when flames are used in conjunction with long absorption tubes that prolongate the absorption path (60).

Incomplete dissociation of the analyte can also introduce a sensible temperature dependence in atomic absorption analysis. We saw in Section III.A.2 that the atomic concentration of an element that is largely bound as a molecule in the flame varied proportionally to $K_p^d/[X]$. An increase in temperature will not only raise K_p^d but will also affect $[X]$. For metal oxides with D_0 equal to or higher than about 3 eV, the increase in K_p^d with temperature outweighs the expected increase in $[O]$ (18). It is assumed that the O_2 concentration is approximately held constant. The atomic metal concentration and the atomic absorption signal then experience an exponential dependence on T, which is stronger, the lower the temperature and the higher D_0 (61).

B. Ionization of Metal Species

1. Survey of Metal Ions Occurring in Flames

A brief qualitative discussion on the possible occurrence of metal ions in flames is presented first.

At the high temperature in the flame a free metal atom may be split into a positive ion and a free electron. Alkali metals, which require a comparatively low energy for ionization (about 4–5 eV), often occur in noticeable proportions as ions in flames with $T \gtrsim 2500°K$. In the hot nitrous oxide–acetylene flames (with T exceeding 3000°K), elements with ionization energies of 6 eV, or higher, such as ytterbium, may be markedly ionized also. Double ionization of atoms which possess two or more valence electrons, such as the alkaline earth metals, has not been reported in flames.

Some metal compounds may be found in ionized form. A well-known example is $SrOH^+$. Hydrated ions involving metals are another possible species in flames containing water vapor (62). Negative ions, such as Cl^-, may be found in flames into which halogens are introduced. The extent of their occurrence in a given flame depends on the electron affinity—the energy required to remove the attached electron. The electron affinity of atomic chlorine, for example, is 3.8 eV.

The ionization energy of the molecules and radicals contained in the metalfree flame gas is comparatively high (8 eV, or more). In thermal equilibrium, ions are therefore not expected to occur in noticeable concentrations in flames which are not seeded by metal vapor. However, in the reaction zone of hydrocarbon flames, positive and negative ions are formed in excess concentrations as a product of the combustion reactions. Some of these so-called natural flame ions of positive sign can persist for a while above the reaction zone, owing to the slowness of their recombination with electrons. The principal persisting flame ion is H_3O^+ whose concentration decays slowly downstream from the reaction zone. Contrary to earlier suppositions, negative flame ions such as OH^-, are not important outside the reaction zone. In H_2 and CO flames, natural flame ions are practically absent.

Carbon particles or solid metal compounds with a low work function may also contribute to the production of free electrons in the flame. Carbon particles may be significant in incandescent hydrocarbon flames burning with a large excess of fuel.

Generally, the local concentration of positive ions in the flame equals that of the negative ions and free electrons together, because of charge balance. When strong electric fields are applied with the aid of electrodes, however, this balance may be broken. [See, for instance, the recent experiments described by Meschkowa and Poluektov (63)*.]

Various experimental techniques have been used to study ionization in flames. Flame spectrometric methods have often been used to yield quantitative information about the degree of ionization of the atomic metal vapor. From the observed shortage of neutral metal species in the flame, conclusions are drawn about the fractional extent of ion formation. With some metals direct observation of the ionic lines is also possible (Fig. 3).

Radio-frequency and microwave measurements, as well as electrical probe measurements, have been used to determine directly the free electron concentration. Radio-frequency measurements have an advantage over microwave measurements in that they also can detect the presence of the heavier ions (64). The ion mass spectrometer has unique properties in the separate identification of positive and negative ionic species in flames.

For a more extensive survey and for a more detailed study of the problems to be discussed in the following sections, we refer to the literature (6, 7, 18, 62, 65, 66).

2. Consequences of the Saha Equation in Equilibrium

A quantitative treatment of ionization follows now under the assumption that thermodynamic equilibrium exists. The ionization and reverse re-combination processes are represented by

$$M \rightleftarrows M^+ + e^- \tag{16}$$

where M and M^+ denote the neutral and singly ionized metal species, respectively, and e^- is a free electron. We now define the degree of ionization α_i of the metal species considered, as follows

$$\alpha_i = [M^+]/([M^+] + [M]) \tag{17}$$

---

* The removal of free electrons from the cathode region may cause an extra production of positive Cs ions owing to a shift in the Saha equilibrium. [See also Eq. (18).] This explains, according to the cited authors, the observed reduction in absorbance of the atomic Cs line. P. J. Kalff at our Laboratory has found in similar experiments that in the flame region near the cathode the emissions of the neutral Sr atoms and molecules, *as well as that of the Sr ions*, were lowered upon application of a field. In the latter case an air–carbon monoxide flame was used, while the electrodes were placed outside the flame.

where brackets denote concentration in cm^{-3}. A value $\alpha_i \simeq 1$ corresponds to nearly complete ionization, whereas $\alpha_i \simeq 0$ corresponds to negligible ionization.

In equilibrium the ionization and recombination rates are balanced. The concentrations of the species involved in process (16) are then related to one another by the Saha equation which is a kind of mass action law for the dissociation of a neutral particle into two ionized particles. This equation reads (47, 48, 67)

$$[M^+][e^-]/[M] = K_p^i \qquad (18)$$

The ionization constant K_p^i, which corresponds to the dissociation constant occurring in Eq. (9), is specific for the species considered and depends only on T. Its value (in cm^{-3}) can be calculated from statistical mechanics according to

$$\log K_p^i = 15.684 + \log (Q_i/Q_a) + \tfrac{3}{2} \log T - 5040 E_i/T \qquad (19)$$

where Q_i and Q_a are the partition functions of the ion and the neutral atom, respectively, and E_i is the ionization energy in electron volts; T is expressed in degrees Kelvin on the absolute scale. For alkali metals, Q_i and Q_a equal the ground-state statistical weights, and are 1 and 2, respectively. The general discussion on the dependence of K_p^i on T and E_i parallels the discussion on K_p^d in Section III.A.2, if there we replace D_0 by E_i. Values of E_i for elements that are of interest in flame photometry are found in Ref. (7).

The degree of ionization may vary appreciably with the concentration of the element. Assuming that M is the only ionizing species in the flame, we have because of charge balance: $[M^+] = [e^-]$. The Saha equation then yields

$$\alpha_i^2/(1-\alpha_i) = K_p^i/([M]+[M^+]) \equiv K_p^i/[M]_t \qquad (20)$$

where $[M]_t$ is the total concentration of element in the gaseous phase in the absence of compound formation. An increase in $[M]_t$, which is proportional to the solution concentration, lowers the value of α_i. In the limiting cases of very high and very low $[M]_t$ values, α_i approaches 0 and 1, respectively. For $[M]_t = K_p^i$ we find $\alpha_i = 0.61$, so that a considerable fraction of the element is then ionized. Typical values of K_p^i are 1.3×10^{10}, 3.8×10^{10}, and 5.4×10^{11} cm^{-3} for Na ($E_i = 5.14$ eV), Ba ($E_i = 5.21$ eV), and K ($E_i = 4.34$ eV), respectively, at $T = 2500°K$. To appreciate these values, expressed in concentration units, we mention that with a premixed flame and a chamber-type nebulizer the expected order of magnitude of $[M]_t$ is roughly 10^{14} cm^{-3} for a molar solution concentration (18).

If $[M^+] = [e^-]$, we also conclude from the Saha equation that $[M^+]$ varies proportionally to $[M]^{1/2}$. When $\alpha_i \ll 1$, $[M]$ is practically equal to $[M]_t$ which, in turn, is proportional to the solution concentration. Under these conditions the ionic line intensity has a square-root dependence on the solution concentration, if we disregard self-absorption.

The above condition, $[M^+] = [e^-]$, is not always fulfilled. For example, when two ionizable elements M_1 and M_2 are present together, charge balance requires $[M_1^+] + [M_2^+] = [e^-]$. The increase in $[e^-]$ brought about by the addition of a second ionizable element reduces the degree of ionization of the original element according to the Saha equation. The ionization equilibrium of the latter element, as presented by process (16), is then shifted to the left. If we know the total concentration of each element in the flame, we can find their α_i values by applying the Saha equation to each element separately and applying charge balance.

The opposite effect results when the flame is supplied with a halogen that is partly converted into negative ions (X^-). We then have: $[M^+] = [e^-] + [X^-]$. The number of free electrons is now lowered, since a certain fraction of them is bound to halogen, and an increase in metal ionization must be expected on the basis of the Saha equation. We can treat this problem quantitatively by applying the Saha equation to the balance between X^- and X, while substituting the electron affinity for E_i.

In the case of alkaline earth elements, ionization of metal atoms and metal monohydroxides may occur simultaneously. We then have the equation for charge balance: $[M^+] + [MOH^+] = [e^-]$. The concentration of molecular ions usually outweighs that of the ionized atoms.

The equality of $[M^+]$ and $[e^-]$ is further disrupted when natural flame ions are present. The free electrons that are associated with natural flame ions raise the value of $[e^-]$ and thus shift the metal ionization equilibrium. When the concentration of natural ions largely outweighs the total metal concentration, $[e^-]$ and α_i may become virtually independent of the amount of metal introduced into the flame. A typical range of natural ion concentrations in an air–acetylene flame immediately above the reaction zone is 10^{10} to 10^{11} cm^{-3}. The same buffering effect results when a large excess of an easily ionizable element, such as cesium, is added to the solution. In this sense cesium acts as a de-ionizer.

A buffering effect of a different kind arises when the major part of the element is tied up as a molecular compound such as LiOH. The loss in free Li atoms, due to partial ionization, may then be largely compensated for by a further dissociation of LiOH molecules into lithium atoms. This buffering action is quite analogous to that discussed in Section III.A.2 in connection with the loss of free Li atoms due to halide formation.

In the evaluation of the degree of ionization from measurements of the atomic and ionic line intensities of alkaline earth elements as a function of added potassium concentration, the formation of molecules and molecular ions should be considered. In particular, the sum of the atomic and ionic concentrations must not, in general, be considered as independent of the amount of potassium added as de-ionizer [compare (68)].

3. Deviations from Ionization Equilibrium and Specific Ionization Mechanisms

In two respects deviations from ionization equilibrium may occur in practical flames and may restrict the general validity of the conclusions drawn in the foregoing section.

It may occur that for the element considered the Saha equation strictly holds, but that concurrently other ionizable species are present, for which the Saha equation does not hold. The value of $[e^-]$ to be inserted in Eq. (18) for the considered element then deviates from that expected were the flame in thermodynamic equilibrium. The actual value of α_i will then deviate from its equilibrium value and will depend on the state of disequilibrium of the other ionized species. This situation occurs immediately above the reaction zone of hydrocarbon flames where natural flame ions exist in excess over their equilibrium concentration, which is usually negligible. (See Section III.B.1.) In this case Eq. (18) should be considered rather as a partial equilibrium relation that holds for the metal ionization alone. This case may be compared with the analogous case of partial dissociation equilibrium discussed in Section III.A.3. The continuous fall in concentration of the natural flame ions with increasing vertical distance from the reaction zone then induces a rise in metal ionization. As a consequence, the atomic metal concentration decays with increasing height (all other factors being supposedly independent of height). The quantitative treatment of this case can be complicated when the metal ions, or the electrons produced by them, would interfere with the gradual disappearance of the natural ions above the reaction zone (62). Their concentration at a given height in the flame would then not be independent of the amount of metal introduced in the flame.

Another case of deviation from ionization equilibrium occurs when the metal under consideration itself has a comparatively low ionization and recombination rate. When the metal is present at the flame base as neutral atoms only, it then takes some time before sufficient ions are formed to bring the degree of ionization near to its final equilibrium value. Until this value is reached, the ionization and recombination rates are not balanced and the Saha equation does not hold. This case applies, for example, to sodium in an air–H_2 or air–CO flame where typical relaxation times of the order of 10^{-2} sec at $T \simeq 2500°K$ have been found (69, 70). This relaxation time may be compared to the time of 1 msec needed for the flame gases to rise over a distance of the order of 1 cm. As a consequence of the slow ionization rate the atomic Na concentration will gradually decrease with increasing height in the flame, if we assume T and $[Na]_t$ to be independent of height. This decrease continues until α_i approaches the value predicted by the Saha equation. Conversely, a slow recombination rate explains why elements such as lead and chromium with high E_i values have been found to persist for some time as ions above the reaction zone. In this zone they are excessively ionized, whereas their degree of ionization in equilibrium at flame temperature should be negligible.

Observation of relaxation effects for various metal atoms under different flame conditions has recently shed new light on the question regarding which specific ionization and recombination mechanisms predominate in flames. Apart from photo-ionization which is insignificant in flames, we generally distinguish three categories of ionization processes: (a) ionization by inelastic collisions, (b) ionization by charge transfer, and (c) chemi-ionization.

a. *Collisional Ionization.* Collisional ionization occurs when, for example, the internal (vibrational) energy of an excited flame molecule is used to ionize a metal atom upon collision. From the large difference in rate constants for metal ionization that have been found for molecules (such as N_2) and atoms (such as Ar) as collision partners, we conclude that the kinetic energy of translational motion is not readily converted into ionization energy (10, 70). This conclusion does not hold, however, for ionization by electron impact, which is quite an efficient process. The difference in efficiency between atoms and free electrons as collision partners is related to their difference in mass. The low ionization efficiency of noble gas atoms parallels their low efficiency in raising metal atoms to higher electronic states upon collision (Section IV.A.2).

When we consider collisions of excited flame molecules with metal atoms in their ground state only, the rate constant of ionization calculated from gas–kinetic cross sections turns out to be less by some orders of magnitude than the experimental value. This discrepancy can be removed if collisions between excited flame molecules and excited metal atoms are also considered (69, 70). The presently accepted scheme for collisional ionization and recombination of alkali elements in air–H_2 and air–CO flames, outside the reaction zone and by N_2 molecules, is as follows:

$$M^{(0)} + N_2^* \rightleftarrows M^+ + e^- + N_2$$
$$\vdots \tag{21}$$
$$M^{(n)} + N_2^* \rightleftarrows M^+ + e^- + N_2$$

Here $M^{(0)}$, $M^{(1)}$, ..., $M^{(n)}$ represent metal atoms in the ground and first and upper excited states; and N_2^* represents a N_2 molecule with sufficiently large rotational and vibrational energy to ionize the atom with which it collides. These reversible processes will not be balanced in both directions as long as the Saha equilibrium has not yet been attained. Under these conditions even a deviation from the Boltzmann distribution law could be expected for the occupancy of the higher metal states that lie close to the ionization limit.

Ionization of alkali atoms by collisions with free electrons is insignificant in flames. This may be concluded (71) from the observation that the rate of ionization for a given metal in an air–CO flame is independent of the absolute metal concentration (10). The free electrons in this flame are produced only by ionization of the metal. Their absolute concentration must therefore depend sensitively on the absolute metal concentration. This again would make the rate of ionization by electron impact depend on metal concentration. Inside the reaction zone of hydrocarbon flames, however, "hot" electrons might contribute to the metal ionization (62).

b. *Ionization by charge transfer.* Ionization of metal atoms by charge exchange plays an important role in the reaction zone of hydrocarbon flames where natural flame ions such as $C_3H_3^+$ and H_3O^+ exist in comparatively high concentrations. These species (Y^+) act as donor ions in the transfer process

$$Y^+ + M \rightarrow Y + M^+ \tag{22}$$

It is believed that in this zone lead is ionized excessively by such reactions.

Above the reaction zone of hydrogen flames containing $SrOH^+$, the charge transfer process

$$SrOH^+ + Na \rightarrow SrOH + Na^+ \tag{23}$$

could be an efficient mechanism for the ionization of Na atoms (72). The presence of $SrOH^+$ thus accelerates the rate of ionization of sodium and reduces the relaxation time for the ionization equilibrium of sodium. As will be seen later, $[SrOH^+]$ itself rapidly attains its equilibrium value owing to an efficient chemi-ionization process.

c. *Chemi-ionization.* Chemi-ionization processes are generally characterized by partial conversion of chemical reaction energy into ionization energy, and vice versa. It may occur that the partner to be ionized does not itself undergo a chemical reaction, for example (70), in

$$CO+O+K \rightarrow CO_2+K^+ +e^- \tag{24}$$

Here atomic potassium acts as a third body in a recombination reaction between two other partners; part of the chemical energy released is used to ionize potassium. On the other hand, the ionized species may be a direct reaction product, as for example in the reactions:

$$Sr+OH \rightarrow SrOH^+ +e^- \tag{25}$$

$$SrOH^+ +H \rightarrow Sr^+ +H_2O \tag{26}$$

Reactions (25) and (26) contribute to the rapid establishment of ionization equilibrium for the alkaline earth elements in hydrogen flames, if the flame radicals are in equilibrium. Due to the chemical energy released, the overall activation energy required to produce Sr^+ from atomic Sr is considerably less than when Sr^+ would be produced directly in a collisional process. This favorably affects the rate of ionization of strontium.

In fact, reaction (26) is a combination of a charge transfer and a chemi-ionization process. Reactions of this type may also occur in the reaction zone and lead to the formation of metal ions (73):

$$H_3O^+ +MO \rightarrow H_2O+OH+M^+ \tag{27}$$

In the reaction zone, excited CO in the $^3\Delta$ state may be formed. Its subsequent reaction with a metal oxide may lead simultaneously to dissociation of the oxide and ionization of the metal atom. The following reaction

$$CO(^3\Delta)+CdO \rightarrow Cd^+ +e^- +CO_2 \tag{28}$$

has been suggested to explain the excessive dissociation and ionization of some metal species which would normally occur mainly as neutral molecules in the flame (20, 74). The sum of the ionization energy of Cd (9.0 eV) and the dissociation energy of CdO ($\leq$ 3.4 eV) is, indeed, less than the sum of the excitation energy of CO ($^3\Delta$) (7.6 eV) and the energy released when $CO+O$ combine to form CO_2 (5.5 eV).

The formation of intermediate $(Na \cdot H_2O)^+$ ions from a reaction between Na and H_2O is no longer considered as an important contribution to the ionization of alkali atoms in hydrogen flames (34, 69).

In concluding this discussion, we should add that the ionization mechanisms which are operative in air–acetylene flames, for example, are not yet fully understood. In these flames the Saha equilibrium for sodium seems to be attained more rapidly than in CO or hydrogen flames of comparable temperatures (75, 76). The interpretation of experimental results in an acetylene flame is complicated by the simultaneous occurrence of natural flame ions. Their effect on the degree of sodium ionization as a function of sodium concentration and height in the flame (under assumption of partial Saha equilibrium) would be almost indistinguishable from a possible relaxation effect caused by a slow ionization rate of the Na atoms. [See Fig. 26 in (10).] This holds true if we assume that the concentration of natural flame ions would be independent of the metal additive and would fall off exponentially with height in the flame.

4. *Consequences of Partial Ionization in Analytical Flame Spectrometry*

Here we shall content ourselves with summarizing some consequences of partial ionization of the analysis element in analytical flame spectrometry. Methods to eliminate certain disturbing effects will be discussed in other chapters.

A loss in spectrochemical sensitivity must obviously result from partial ionization when the atomic line or molecular band intensities are measured. The fractional loss is the same for the atoms as for the molecules since a constant ratio between their concentrations is usually maintained through the law of mass action (Section III.A.2). In the hot oxygen–acetylene flame the ionization of the alkaline earth elements may be so strong that their ionic emission lines can be used for analysis. In a nitrous oxide–acetylene flame the absorbance of the ionic 4554 Å Ba line was even reported to be eight times larger than that of the atomic 5536 Å Ba line (68).

The fractional loss of neutral species is expected to be the more serious, the lower the absolute metal concentration in the flame. However, the possible presence of natural flame ions or of metal ions due to impurities may buffer this loss owing to their repressing effect on the degree of ionization. Without such buffering effect, microanalysis of sodium in the parts-per-billion range would be inconceivable were the ionization of sodium to correspond to the Saha equilibrium. A possible relaxation effect, as discussed in Section III.B.3, may also limit the extent of this atomic loss.

Partial ionization also leads to the well-known concave curvature of the analytical curve for the atomic lines as well as for the molecular bands.

This curvature results from the fact that the fractional loss of atoms or molecules generally increases with decreasing metal concentration. Ionic line intensities show a square-root dependence on the concentration in the range of higher concentrations where $\alpha_i \ll 1$. When $\alpha_i \simeq 1$ for lower solution concentrations, the ionic curves should be nearly linear. The strong curvature of the atomic lines in the low concentration range would make hazardous the extrapolation of the analytical curve to smaller concentration values and calculations of detection limits. Fortunately, the aforementioned buffering action of natural flame ions or ions from

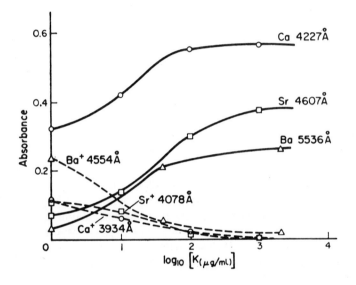

Fig. 3. Effect of increasing amounts of K on the absorbance of atomic and ionic spectral lines of Ca (5 mg/liter), Sr (5.5 mg/liter), and Ba (30 mg/liter) in a $N_2O–C_2H_2$ flame. Reprinted from Ref. (*77*), p. 1340, by courtesy of Pergamon Press.

impurities often straightens the analytical curve in the range near the detection limit. This may explain the observation (*20*) that the analytical emission curve for sodium is straight even below 0.1 ng/ml. However, a slow relaxation of the ionization equilibrium of sodium (Section III.B.3) might also explain it.

Mutual interference effects caused by a reduction in the degree of ionization occur when two ionizable elements are present together in the sample. This kind of interference is presently the best understood one and is easily recognized in practice. All atomic lines and molecular bands of the analysis element are enhanced to the same relative extent when a second ionizable element is added, if we disregard self-absorption of the resonance emission lines. A characteristic feature of this kind of interference is the saturation observed when the concentration of the interfering element is increased to relatively high values. This saturation is attained when α_i is virtually suppressed to zero for the analysis element. This element is then present mainly as neutral species and cannot be further disturbed by a shift in the ionization equilibrium. The relative extent of ionization interference, for fixed concentration ratio of analyte and concomitant, generally increases with decreasing concentration of the analyte.

Figure 3 shows the effect of increasing concentrations of potassium on the absorbance of some atomic and ionic lines of alkaline earth metals. The strong ionization effects observed are explained by the high temperature of the nitrous oxide–acetylene flame employed. As expected, a saturation sets in for the enhancement of the atomic lines just at that concentration of potassium where the ionic line absorbance practically drops to zero. Similar observations have been made on the neutral and ionic emission lines of Eu in a nitrous oxide–acetylene flame, when KCl was added (78).

The stimulating influence of chlorine on the degree of metal ionization, owing to the removal of free electrons by Cl^- formation, explains the aggravation of the above disturbing ionization effects when halogen compounds are present in the solution in large concentrations. The concentration of Cl^- ions in the flame gases depends on the concentration of free H radicals through the partial equilibrium

$$Cl^- + H \rightleftarrows HCl + e^- \qquad (29)$$

In hydrogen and hydrocarbon flames most of the chlorine is bound as HCl molecules, so that [HCl] is fairly constant for a given halogen supply. It then follows from the partial equilibration of reaction (29) that the ratio $[Cl^-]/[e^-]$ must vary proportionally to $[H]^{-1}$ at a given flame temperature and halogen supply. Any deviation in chemical equilibrium of the flame radicals thus affects the extent to which chlorine interferes with the metal ionization.

For the sake of completeness we should add that chlorine may also act as a catalyst in a series of reactions that effectively lead to the ionization of Na atoms in hydrogen flames. A discussion of this effect is given in the literature (79).

IV. Excitation of the Sample

A. GENERAL THEORETICAL CONSIDERATIONS

1. *Introduction*

The processes and problems of excitation and quenching of metal species in the vapor phase are generally of less interest in analytical flame spectrometry than the decomposition and atomization processes discussed earlier. In atomic absorption analysis they play no role at all. Since the relative population of the excited states is usually very small, the population of the ground state is virtually unaffected. Only in the rare case when the

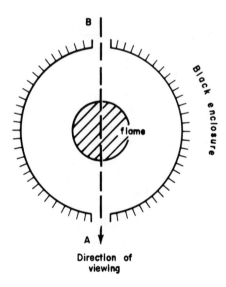

Fig. 4. Flame is placed in black enclosure of same temperature in order to obtain full thermodynamic equilibrium as far as the radiation density is concerned. Flame spectrometry is then possible only if flame is viewed along the line that connects two opposite (small) holes A and B in the enclosure.

lower level of the absorption line (e.g., the 2355 Å Sn line) lies above the ground state, does excitation come into play.

In principle, the detailed excitation and quenching mechanisms are not relevant in emission flame spectrometry, if full thermodynamic equilibrium exists. The occupation of the excited state, from which the atom or molecule radiates, is then determined by the universal Boltzmann distribution law, regardless of the specific ways by which M^* is populated. The number of photons emitted per cm^3 of metal vapor is found simply by multiplying the equilibrium value $[M^*]_e$ by the transition probability per second, A. However, full thermodynamic equilibrium implies that the spectral radiation density, $\rho(\lambda)$, in the flame obeys the Planck radiation law. This could be realized by placing the whole flame in a black enclosure with walls at flame temperature T. Flame spectrometry would then be possible only if we would make two small holes in this enclosure, at opposite ends on the line of viewing that intersects the flame (Fig. 4). The hole B at the back end is necessary, because otherwise the observed radiation intensity would invariably be equal to that of a black body and independent of the amount of metal vapor introduced in the flame. Practical flame spectrometers are not equipped with such an enclosure so that radiative disequilibrium may occur, in principle at least. To evaluate its effect on the metal line intensity, we must consider the detailed (de-)excitation mechanisms (Section IV.A.2).

In emission flame spectrometry the suprathermal chemiluminescent emission of some metal lines under special flame conditions is sometimes exploited to attain better detection limits. Here again, absence of chemical equilibrium requires a closer consideration of the detailed (de-)excitation mechanisms.

In fluorescence flame spectrometry an explicit consideration of the processes by which excited metal atoms are quenched is needed in calculating the fluorescent line intensity.

The principle of microscopic reversibility adds to each possible excitation process the corresponding reverse process as a possible mode of de-excitation, and vice versa. As a consequence, both kinds of processes can be treated on a common basis. Moreover, the principle of detailed balance requires that in full thermodynamic equilibrium the rate of each specific excitation process just equals that of the corresponding de-excitation process. The latter principle thus enables us to relate quantitatively to each other the rate constants of both processes. This relation is often valid in cases of partial disequilibrium also.

In the following sections we shall discuss some basic types and important aspects of (de-)excitation processes, mainly in relation to fluorescent and chemiluminescent flame spectrometry. Certain simplifications will be introduced to make this discussion surveyable. In particular, the temperature in the flame is assumed to be homogeneous, and self-absorption is disregarded. The experimental work and the analytical possibilities of fluorescent and chemiluminescent flame spectrometry will not be considered.

For a more complete description of excitation processes we refer to the literature (6, 7, 18, 80–82).

2. General Classification of (De-)Excitation Processes

A survey of typical processes that may be relevant in flames is given in Table 1. For simplicity let us consider a metal atom with a ground state (M) and one excited electronic state (M*) with excitation energy E. Both states are supposed to be nondegenerate, that is, their statistical weight factors equal unity.

TABLE 1

Different Types of (De-)Excitation Processes[a]

Type	Process and rate constants	Rate equation
Radiative	$M + h\nu \underset{A}{\overset{B}{\rightleftharpoons}} M^*$	$\left(\dfrac{d[M^*]}{dt}\right)_r = -A[M^*] + B\bar{p}_{\Delta\lambda}[M]$
Collisional	$M + Z \underset{k_{-1}}{\overset{k_1}{\rightleftharpoons}} M^* + Z$	$\left(\dfrac{d[M^*]}{dt}\right)_c = -k_{-1}[Z][M^*]$ $\qquad\qquad + k_1[Z][M]$
Chemiluminescent	$M + X + Y \underset{z_1}{\overset{z_{-1}}{\rightleftharpoons}} M^* + XY$	$\left(\dfrac{d[M^*]}{dt}\right)_{ch} = -z_1[XY][M^*]$ $\qquad\qquad + z_{-1}[X][Y][M]$

[a] A metal atom with two discrete levels (ground state M and excited state M*) is considered. $\bar{p}_{\Delta\lambda}$ is the spectral volume density of the radiation field averaged over the absorption line–width $\Delta\lambda$ of the metal atom. X, Y, and Z are flame radicals or molecules.

a. *Radiative Excitation.* Radiative excitation by absorption of a photon with energy $h\nu = E$, is the reverse of the process of photon emission by an excited atom. De-excitation by induced emission can be fully disregarded in comparison to spontaneous emission in flames. The ratio of both emission rates in case of full thermodynamic equilibrium is given by $\exp(-E/kT)$. This ratio is very small at optical frequencies and at flame temperatures.

The rate of de-excitation by radiation per unit volume is given by the product of transition probability, A, for spontaneous emission (in sec^{-1})

and the concentration $[M^*]$ of excited atoms. A typical order of magnitude of A is 10^7 sec^{-1}. The excitation rate by photon absorption per unit volume can be written: $B\bar{\rho}_{\Delta\lambda}[M]$. Let us assume, for simplicity, a rectangular spectral profile for the absorption line with width $\Delta\lambda$. Then $\bar{\rho}_{\Delta\lambda}$ represents the spectral volume density of the radiation field, averaged over the interval $\Delta\lambda$. If $\rho(\lambda)$ is the spectral volume density of the field as a function of λ, we have

$$\bar{\rho}_{\Delta\lambda} = \frac{1}{\Delta\lambda} \int_{\Delta\lambda} \rho(\lambda)\mathrm{d}\lambda$$

where the integration extends over the interval $\Delta\lambda$. In the general case, excitation depends on the spectral distributions of the absorption coefficient and of the radiation field present. A relation between A and B can be found by applying detailed balance in thermodynamic equilibrium. Detailed balance requires that $(d[M^*]/dt)_r = 0$ (see the corresponding rate equation in Table 1), and equilibrium implies that $[M^*]/[M] = \exp(-E/kT)$, as well as $\bar{\rho}_{\Delta\lambda} = \rho_e$. Here ρ_e is given by the Planck radiation law for a black body at flame temperature T. Thus $B\rho_e = A \exp(-E/kT)$.

b. *Collisional Excitation.* Collisional excitation occurs when a metal atom is excited by transfer of translational and/or internal energy from another particle (Z) with which it collides (Table 1). Conversion of translational energy into electronic excitation energy is an inefficient process if the mass of Z is large compared to the electron mass. Excitation by collisions with noble gas atoms, which only possess translational energy, is therefore an improbable process. (The contribution of noble gas atoms in excited electronic states can be neglected in flames.) When Z is a free electron, the efficiency of collisional excitation is much greater. However, the relatively small concentration of free electrons in the flame makes their contribution to the excitation of metal species outside the reaction zone usually insignificant (*18*). Collisional excitation by atoms of another metal that occur in an excited state at near resonance with the level considered, may also be an efficient process. However, the relatively small concentration in which metal species usually occur in flames makes this process of little significance in flame spectrometry (*83*).

Metal excitation by collisions with molecules that occur in bulk concentrations in the flame is normally the predominant process in flames. Molecules possess many densely spaced rotational and vibrational energy levels. Conversion of vibrational energy into electronic excitation energy of the metal atom is believed to proceed readily. A possible discrepancy in energy between the electronic excitation level and the molecular vibrational level can be easily made up by the additional conversion of some rotational or translational energy.

All considerations given so far to the relative importance of certain types of collisional excitation processes in flames also hold for the corresponding de-excitation processes. Thus, quenching of excited metal species by collision with noble gas atoms is much less efficient than collision with

TABLE 2

Values of Quenching Cross Sections S Deduced from Fluorescence Measurements in Flames[a]

Quenching species	$S \times 10^{16}$ (cm²) for Na(^3P)		$S \times 10^{16}$ (cm²) for K(^4P)		$S \times 10^{16}$ (cm²) for Rb(^5P)	
	H[a]	J[c]	H[b]	J[c]	H[b]	J[c]
N_2	21	22	19	17.5	25	19
CO_2	50	53	66	67	—	—
H_2	8	9	3.4	3.3	3.6	1.9
O_2	34	38	49	49	83	79
CO	41	37.5	44	39	—	—
H_2O	2.2	1.6	2.7	2.8	$\lesssim 4.0$	4.0

[a] The quenching cross section S is related to the quenching rate constant k_{-1} by $S\bar{v} = k_{-1}$, where $\bar{v}$ is the mean velocity of the quencher relative to the alkali atom.

[b] Values obtained by Hooymayers et al. (84, 86); the values for Na were corrected for a calibration error, and those for K were recalculated by assuming $S \approx 0$ for Ar as quencher (personal communication by Hooymayers). The values listed refer to a flame temperature of about 1900°K, except those for H_2O, which refer to 2100°K.

[c] Values obtained by Jenkins (85) at a flame temperature of about 1400°K.

molecules. The quenching rate constant k_{-1} can be found from the inverse excitation rate constant k_1 and vice versa, by applying the principle of detailed balance to the equilibrium case. We have then (Table 1) $(d[M^*]/dt)_c = 0$ and $[M^*]/[M] = \exp(-E/kT)$, so that $k_1 = k_{-1} \exp(-E/kT)$.

The quenching rate per excited atom of sodium in the ^2P state, in flames at 1 atm and 2000°K where N_2 is the dominant molecule, is $k_{-1}[N_2] =$

1.3×10^9 sec^{-1} (84, 85). It is interesting to note that this quenching rate exceeds the rate of spontaneous emission, A, for the same metal state by a factor of 20. Values of k_{-1} have been determined from measurements of the yield factor η of resonance fluorescence [Eq. (34)] in flames of varying composition (84–86) (See Table 2). Water was found to have a very low efficiency, as shown in Table 2.

Since little or no activation energy is expected to be involved in the quenching process, k_{-1} will not depend strongly on temperature. However, it follows from the relation between k_1 and k_{-1}, which includes an exponential temperature factor, that k_1 must increase strongly with increasing temperature. It may be recalled that k_1 was defined as the excitation rate per unit concentration of Z (and M), where Z referred to a molecule in any state of excitation, including the ground state. Consequently, k_1 implies a factor that describes the fraction of Z molecules that have sufficient internal energy to excite the metal atom. This fraction depends exponentially on temperature.

c. *Chemiluminescence.* Chemiluminescence occurs when a metal atom or molecule is excited through the assistance of a chemical reaction. Part of the chemical energy released is consumed in the excitation process. In Table 1 a particular kind of chemiluminescent reaction, and its reverse, are shown. The reverse reaction, which leads to a de-excitation of an excited metal atom, without emission of a photon, represents a case of chemical (*in casu* dissociative) quenching.

Chemiluminescent excitation can *a priori* be expected in flames, as the energies released in chemical reactions occurring therein lie mostly in the range of 1–10 eV. Thus, they are comparable to the energies required for metal excitation. However, the possibility of a chemiluminescent reaction is not only determined by considerations of the energy balance, but also by the Wigner–Witmer rule for total spin conservation. Not always strictly obeyed, this rule states that the resultant spin of the reactants must be the same as that of the reaction products (7, 81). The concept of chemiluminescent excitation may be extended to include ions or free electrons as reaction partners also. Examples will be given in Section IV.C.

The rate constants z_1 and z_{-1} occurring in the rate equation for chemiluminescent excitation and dissociative quenching (Table 1) can again be related to each other by applying detailed balance at equilibrium. The relationship is: $z_1 = z_{-1} K_p^d \exp(E/kT)$ since chemical equilibrium requires that $[X][Y]/[XY] = K_p^d$. The relationship between the rate constants is also expected to hold in case the concentrations of reactants and products are not equal to their equilibrium values as long as at least their internal and translational energies are equipartitioned at the flame temperature (18).

Because of the principle of detailed balance, each chemiluminescent excitation process is always accompanied by the reverse chemical quenching process which proceeds at an equal rate in chemical equilibrium. Sometimes it is overlooked that the occurrence of a chemiluminescent excitation process in the flame does not lead *per se* to suprathermal emission of the metal line. It does so only if $[X][Y]/[XY]$ *exceeds* the value K_p^d required for chemical equilibrium. Therefore, it is misleading to consider the concepts "thermal" and "chemiluminescent" excitation as opposed to each other.

B. INFRATHERMAL EXCITATION DUE TO RADIATIVE DISEQUILIBRIUM

In emission flame spectrometry, the spectral density $\rho(\lambda)$ of the radiation field at the wavelength λ of the metal line is normally lower than the value $\rho_e(\lambda)$ required by the Planck law for full thermodynamic equilibrium. For low metal concentrations and in the absence of incandescent particles, $\rho(\lambda) \simeq 0$. The resulting nonequilibrium value of $[M^*]$ can now be found by considering the total rate equation, $(d[M^*]/dt)_{total} = 0$, in the stationary state:

$$(d[M^*]/dt)_{total} = (d[M^*]/dt)_r + (d[M^*]/dt)_c + (d[M^*]dt)_{ch}$$
$$= -(A+k_{-1}[Z]+z_1[XY])[M^*]+(B\bar\rho_{\Delta\lambda}+k_1[Z]$$
$$+z_{-1}[X][Y])[M]$$
$$= 0 \qquad (30)$$

It is assumed that only one (de-)excitation process of each kind is operative. Substituting $\bar\rho_{\Delta\lambda} = 0$, and assuming that in other respects the flame is in thermal and chemical equilibrium,

$$[M^*]/[M] = (k_1[Z]+z_{-1}[X][Y])/(A+k_{-1}[Z]+z_1[XY]) \qquad (31)$$

In full thermodynamic equilibrium with $\bar\rho_{\Delta\lambda} = \rho_e$, we would have instead

$$[M^*]_e/[M] = (B\rho_e+k_1[Z]+z_{-1}[X][Y])/(A+k_{-1}[Z]+z_1[XY]) \qquad (32)$$

Using

$$B\rho_e/A = k_1/k_{-1} = z_{-1}[X][Y]/z_1[XY] = [M^*]_e/[M] \qquad (33)$$

as required by detailed balance, and defining

$$\eta = A/(A+k_{-1}[Z]+z_1[XY]) \qquad (34)$$

we get

$$[M^*]/[M^*]_e = 1 - \eta \qquad (35)$$

In normal flames where molecular constituents dominate, η is of the order of several percent for the first resonance lines of the alkali atoms (84, 85). Thus, the infrathermal excitation caused by radiative disequilibrium is of little consequence here. For higher metal concentrations, the value of $\bar{\rho}_{\Delta\lambda}$ increases owing to the increased radiation intensity of the metal vapor, and the deviation from thermal excitation will then be even less (84).

It has been argued that a strong suprathermal ultraviolet emission from the flame background could enhance the ultraviolet emission lines of iron which appear as peaks superimposed on the continuous background spectrum (87). If the iron lines are excited only by absorption of photons from the background radiation at the same wavelengths at which they can radiate, then the presence of Fe vapor in the flame would effectively form a sink for these photons. This would hold because the probability that an excited Fe atom (after absorption of one photon) re-emits a photon is less than unity. This probability is determined by η in Eq. (34). If the thermal emission of iron can be neglected, the iron lines would then appear in absorption against the suprathermal emission spectrum of the flame backgound (83).

C. SUPRATHERMAL EMISSION OF FLUORESCENT RADIATION

The volume radiation density, $\int_{\Delta\lambda}\rho(\lambda)\,d\lambda$, in the spectral interval $\Delta\lambda$, can be made to exceed the Planck radiation density $\rho_e\,\Delta\lambda$ by a large factor when the flame is irradiated by an external light source such as a hollow cathode lamp. This is especially true in the ultraviolet portion of the spectrum where ρ_e becomes very small. Disregarding self-absorption, the intensity of the fluorescent radiation emitted per cm^3 of flame gases with metal vapor is determined by $A[M^*]$. In general, $[M^*]$ will exceed the thermal equilibrium value $[M^*]_e$. The gain in line intensity obtained by the fluorescence method over the thermal line intensity is given by $[M^*]/[M^*]_e$. This ratio can be derived in a manner similar to that outlined in Section IV.B; it is given by

$$[M^*]/[M^*]_e = 1 + \eta[(\bar{\rho}_{\Delta\lambda}/\rho_e)-1] \qquad (36)$$

where

$$\bar{\rho}_{\Delta\lambda} = \frac{1}{\Delta\lambda} \int_{\Delta\lambda} \rho(\lambda)d\lambda$$

and $\rho(\lambda)$ is determined by the intensity of the radiation beam from the lamp. If $\bar{\rho}_{\Delta\lambda} = \rho_e$, the gain factor is unity, as expected. For $\bar{\rho}_{\Delta\lambda}/\rho_e > 1$, the gain factor increases for increasing value of η. It follows from Eq. (34) that η has a maximum value equal to unity. A value of $\eta \simeq 1$ implies that the collisional and chemical de-excitation rates per excited metal atom, $k_{-1}[Z]$ and $z_1[XY]$, are small compared with the optical transition probability per second, A. Values of η as high as 74% have been obtained for the Na–D doublet in an Ar–O_2–H_2 flame (85).

The role played by η in the foregoing expressions is easily understood when it is realized that η, in fact, equals the yield factor of resonance fluorescence. This is the fractional probability that an excited metal atom looses its energy by emission of a photon. Actually, the numerator of Eq. (34) denotes the probability of photon emission per second, whereas the denominator denotes the total probability per second of de-excitation by photon emission, collisional, and chemical quenching. Naturally, one expects the intensity of the fluorescent radiation to increase linearly with the yield factor. This explains the improvement obtained in flame fluorescence upon diluting the oxygen–hydrogen flame with argon (17).

D. SUPRATHERMAL CHEMILUMINESCENCE

Suprathermal excitation also results if the flame partners taking part in the chemiluminescent reaction deviate from chemical equilibrium in such a way that the chemiluminescent excitation rate, $z_{-1}[X][Y][M]$, exceeds the chemical quenching rate, $z_1[XY][M^*]$. This situation may occur when excess H and OH radicals exist above the reaction zone of hydrogen and acetylene flames. Recombination of these radicals to H_2O releases energy which is sufficient to excite metal lines whose energy of excitation is about 5 eV.

Assuming that in other respects the flame is in a state of thermodynamic equilibrium and neglecting the part played by radiative de-excitation, the population $[M^*]$ of the excited state, from Eq. (30), is given by

$$[M^*]/[M^*]_e = \{1 + p[X][Y]/([X]_e[Y]_e)\}/(1 + p[XY]/[XY]_e) \quad (37)$$

where the quantities in brackets denote the actual concentrations; a subscript e appended denotes equilibrium concentrations. By definition,

$$p \equiv z_{-1}[X]_e[Y]_e/k_1[Z]$$

and also because of detailed balances

$$p = z_1[XY]_e/k_{-1}[Z]$$

The value of p is a measure of the relative importance of chemical (de-)-

excitation as compared with collisional (de-)excitation at full equilibrium. The partner Z taking part in the collisional de-excitation process is usually a bulk flame molecule such as N_2. Its concentration may be presumed to be unaffected by the disequilibrium of the XY dissociation.

The neglect of radiative excitation in the derivation of Eq. (37) requires some additional explanation in the case of strong suprathermal chemiluminescent emission. Under this condition it is possible for the radiation density to exceed that of a black body at flame temperature, especially for ultraviolet spectral lines. However, if the metal concentration is so low that the probability of reabsorption of emitted photons is small, the contribution of radiative excitation caused by this reabsorption should be negligible nevertheless, as compared with that of chemiluminescent excitation.

As long as the energy released by recombination of X and Y in the chemiluminescent reaction is larger than the excitation energy, E, the chemiluminescent excitation rate, $z_{-1}[X][Y]$, is not expected to depend strongly on E. The collisional excitation rate, $k_1[Z]$, however, falls off exponentially with increasing E. Their ratio, p, is thus expected to increase markedly with increasing E. Since $E = hv$, this explains why chemiluminescence effects caused by excess $[X]$ and $[Y]$ become more conspicuous for ultraviolet metal lines than for lines with lower E.

A lowering of the flame temperature may have little influence on the product of excess $[X]$ and $[Y]$ just above the reaction zone. Very sensitive to temperature, however, is the coefficient $p/[X]_e[Y]_e = z_{-1}(k_1[Z])^{-1}$ which occurs in the numerator of Eq. (37). This is because of the exponential temperature factor contained in k_1, while z_{-1} is only weakly dependent on the temperature. Suprathermal chemiluminescent excitation consequently becomes more pronounced generally in the cooler flames when compared with thermal excitation. At 2000°K, it has been estimated (88) that chemiluminescent excitation rates, in the case of radical recombination reactions, will exceed the collisional excitation rates for lines with $E \simeq 3.5$ eV, while the reverse will be true for lines with $E \simeq 2$ eV.

It should be realized that suprathermal chemiluminescent emission is to be expected only if the deviation from chemical equilibrium is greater for the product $[X][Y]$ than for $[XY]$. Note that $[XY]$ occurs in the denominator of Eq. (37). An equal increase in $[XY]$ would offset the gain obtained by an increase of the product $[X][Y]$. The undissociated partner XY is often a stable flame molecule, such as H_2O, whose concentration usually deviates much less from chemical equilibrium than that of the dissociation products X and Y (for example, H and OH radicals).

It is interesting to note that for the chemiluminescent excitation of the potassium doublet at 4044/7 A by the recombination reaction:

$$K + H + OH \rightarrow H_2O + K^* \tag{38}$$

p has been found to equal 0.12 in an argon–oxygen–hydrogen flame at 1950°K (89,90). In flames with N_2 as diluent gas, much lower values of p are to be expected as collisional de-excitation by N_2 molecules is much more efficient than by Ar atoms (Section IV.A.2). For values of p that are small compared with unity, the effect of suprathermal chemi-excitation on the ratio $[M^*]/[M^*]_e$ increases linearly with increasing value of p [Eq. (37)]. This should be expected as p^{-1} describes the extent to which chemical de-excitation is swamped by collisional de-excitation.

Equation (37) makes sense only for chemiluminescent reactions that occur under conditions in the flame where a meaningful temperature can be defined. Usually this can be done for the region above the reaction zone where the flame radicals H, OH, and O, in excess concentrations, can induce suprathermal excitation of metal lines by reactions such as (10, 80, 91):

$$H + OH + M \rightarrow H_2O + M^* \tag{39}$$

$$H + H + M \quad \rightarrow H_2 + M^* \tag{40}$$

$$CO + O + M \rightarrow CO_2 + M^* \tag{41}$$

These reactions are operative for metal lines whose excitation energies are 5 eV or less as, for example, the first resonance lines of thallium. The limit is set by the available recombination energy.

A different kind of suprathermal chemiluminescence has been observed within (and immediately above) the reaction zone of hydrocarbon flames, or of hydrogen flames into which is fed methanol or acetylene. Lines of iron atoms with excitation energies up to 8 eV are affected, for instance. The quantitative and even qualitative explanation for these effects remains unsettled. Proposed reactions are:

$$CH + O + M \rightarrow CHO + M^* \qquad (80, 92) \tag{42}$$

$$CH + O(H) + M \rightarrow CO + H(H) + M^* \quad (92) \tag{43}$$

$$CH + O \rightarrow CO^* + H$$

followed by

$$CO^* + M(O) \rightarrow CO(O) + M^* \qquad (20, 93) \tag{44}$$

$$C + MO \rightarrow CO + M^* \qquad (20, 73) \tag{45}$$

The general conditions in the reaction zone do not allow a meaningful comparison of the actual value of $[M^*]$ with the equilibrium value $[M^*]_e$.

Instead we should consider the fractional metal excitation: $[M^*]/[M]$. Assuming that the inert gas molecules Z are not yet "warmed up" in the reaction zone, that is, $k_1 \simeq 0$, and excitation by photon absorption can be neglected, from Eq. (30) can be derived the expression

$$[M^*]/[M] = z_{-1}[X][Y]/(A + k_{-1}[Z] + z_1[XY]) \qquad (46)$$

In Eq. (46) the coefficients z_1, z_{-1}, and possibly k_{-1}, might differ from their equilibrium values at the final flame temperature because equipartition of internal and translational energy is not expected in the reaction zone. Equation (46) tells us that the suprathermal chemiluminescence emission depends not only on the excess concentrations of the reacting species X and Y, but also on the concentration of XY. However, the latter concentration becomes irrelevant when the collisional and/or radiative de-excitation terms dominate in the denominator of the right-hand side of Eq. (46).

In the preceding discussion, the processes of excitation and de-excitation were presented schematically and were based on simplifying assumptions. In particular, a simple recombination reaction was selected in the quantitative treatment of the chemiluminescence process. The chemiluminescent excitation of molecules such as CuH, which are directly formed in an excited electronic state as a reaction product (94, 95), was not mentioned. The occurrence of more complicated chemiluminescent reactions as, for example, reactions (43–45), the presence of different collision partners, and the possibility of radiative excitation and de-excitation through different excitation levels, would require an extension of the discussed scheme. In addition, proper recognition of the spectral profiles of the metal line and of the radiation field inside the flame, as well as the effect of self-absorption and radiation trapping, would complicate considerably the theoretical analysis. However, the more essential features concerning the problem of sample excitation will stand out more clearly in the simplified analysis given in this section. A more detailed discussion of excitation processes in flames is given in (96).

REFERENCES

1. J. A. Dean, *Flame Photometry*, McGraw–Hill, New York, 1960.
2. B. W. L'vov, *Atomic Absorption Spectral Analysis* (in Russian), Soviet Academy of Sciences, Moscow, 1966.
3. N. S. Poluektov, *Techniques in Flame Photometric Analysis*, Consultants Bureau, New York, 1961.
4. E. Pungor, *Flame Photometry Theory*, Van Nostrand, London, 1967.

5. R. Herrmann and C. Th. J. Alkemade, *Chemical Analysis by Flame Photometry*, Interscience, New York, 1963.
6. R. Herrmann and C. Th. J. Alkemade, *Emission and Absorption Flame Photometry*, 3rd ed. (in preparation).
7. R. Mavrodineanu and H. Boiteux, *Flame Spectroscopy*, Wiley, New York, 1965.
8. F. Burriel-Martí and J. Ramírez-Muñoz, *Flame Photometry*, 3rd ed., Elsevier, Amsterdam, 1960.
9. L. Simon, *Optik*, **19**, 621 (1962).
10. T. Hollander, *Self-absorption, Ionization and Dissociation of Metal Vapor in Flames*, Ph.D. Thesis, Utrecht, 1964.
11. J. A. Dean, *Kresge-Hooker, Record of Chem. Progress*, **22**, 179 (1961).
12. R. Avni and C. Th. J. Alkemade, *Mikrochim. Acta*, 1960, 460.
13. G. M. Hieftje and H. V. Malmstadt, *Anal. Chem.*, **40**, 1860 (1968).
14. F. A. Williams, *Symp. Combust., 8th, Pasadena, Calif., 1960*, Williams and Wilkins, Baltimore, 1962, p. 50.
15. C. Th. J. Alkemade, *A Contribution to the Development and Understanding of Flame Photometry*, Ph.D. Thesis, Utrecht, 1954.
16. J. A. Dean and W. J. Carnes, *Anal. Chem.*, **34**, 192 (1962).
17. C. Veillon, J. M. Mansfield, M. L. Parsons, and J. D. Winefordner, *Anal. Chem.*, **38**, 204 (1966).
18. C. Th. J. Alkemade, *Metal Vapors in Flames*, Pergamon (in preparation).
19. J. I. Dinnin, *Anal. Chem.*, **32**, 1475 (1960).
20. P. T. Gilbert, Jr., in *Proceedings Xth Colloquium Spectroscopium Internationale* (B. F. Scribner and M. Margoshes, eds.), Spartan, Washington, 1963, pp. 171–215.
21. D. J. Halls and A. Townshend, *Anal. Chim. Acta*, **36**, 278 (1966).
22. A. Townshend, *At. Abs. Symp., Praha, 1967* (summary).
23. L. Brewer and R. F. Porter, *J. Chem. Phys.*, **22**, 1867 (1954).
24. S. Eckhard and A. Püschel, *Z. Anal. Chem.*, **172**, 334 (1960).
25. P. T. Gilbert, Jr., in *Analysis Instrumentation—1964*, Plenum, New York, 1964, p. 193.
26. D. J. David, *Spectrochim. Acta*, **20**, 1185 (1964).
27. J. Debras-Guédon and I. A. Voinovitch, *Chem. Anal. (Warsaw)*, **5**, 193 (1960).
28. F. J. Wallace, *Analyst*, **88**, 259 (1963).
29. I. A. Voinovitch, J. Debras-Guédon, and J. Louvrier, *L'analyse des silicates*, Hermann, Paris, 1962.
30. I. A. Voinovitch, G. Legrand, G. Hameau, and J. Louvrier, *Rev. G.A.M.S.*, No. 3, 213 (1966).
31. M. Margoshes and B. L. Vallee, *Anal. Chem.*, **28**, 1066 (1956).
32. D. C. Manning, *At. Abs. Newsletter*, **5**, 127 (1966).
33. W. Slavin, A. Venghiattis and D. C. Manning, *At. Abs. Newsletter*, **5**, 84 (1966).
34. D. E. Jensen and P. J. Padley, *Symp. Combust., 11th, Berkeley, Calif., 1966*, The Combustion Institute, Pittsburgh, 1967, p. 351.
35. J. B. Willis, *Spectrochim. Acta*, **23A**, 811 (1967).
36. C. Th. J. Alkemade, *Anal. Chem.*, **38**, 1252 (1966).
37. L. de Galan and J. D. Winefordner, *J. Quant. Spectry. Radiative Transfer*, **7**, 251 (1967).
38. A. S. Kallend, *Combust. Flame*, **11**, 81 (1967).
39. C. Th. J. Alkemade and M. H. Voorhuis, *Z. anal. Chem.*, **163**, 91 (1958).

40. P. G. de Montgareuil, *Contribution à l'etude des interactions chimiques dans les flammes*, Ph.D. Thesis, Paris, 1954.
41. W. A. Veenendaal and H. L. Polak, *At. Abs. Symp.*, *Praha, 1967* (summary).
42. C. Th. J. Alkemade and M. E. Jeuken, *Z. anal. Chem.*, **158**, 401 (1957).
43. R. Intonti and A. Stacchini, *At. Abs. Symp.*, *Praha, 1967* (summary).
44. A. C. West, *Anal. Chem.*, **36**, 310 (1964).
45. V. A. Fassel, *Symp. Flame Spectr. Methods Anal.*, *1966*, Amer. Chem. Soc., Phoenix (unpublished).
46. V. F. Zhitkevich, A. I. Lyuty, N. A. Nesterko, V. S. Rossikhin, and I. L. Tsikora, *Opt. Spectr. (USSR) (English Transl.)* **14**, 17 (1963).
47. R. H. Fowler, *Statistical Mechanics*, 2nd ed., Cambridge University Press, Cambridge, 1936.
48. J. Rose, *Dynamic Physical Chemistry*, Pitman & Sons, London, 1961.
49. A. G. Gaydon, *Dissociation Energies and Spectra of Diatomic Molecules*, 2nd ed., Chapman and Hall, London, 1953.
50. L. de Galan, R. Smith, and J. D. Winefordner, *Spectrochim. Acta*, **23B**, 521 (1968); P. W. J. M. Boumans, *Spectrochim. Acta*, **23B**, 559 (1968).
51. G. Herzberg, *Molecular Spectra and Molecular Structure. I. Spectra of Diatomic Molecules*, 2nd ed., D. Van Nostrand, 1950.
52. M. L. Parsons, W. J. McCarthy, and J. D. Winefordner, *Appl. Spectry.*, **20**, 223 (1966).
53. E. M. Bulewicz, L. F. Phillips, and T. M. Sugden, *Trans. Faraday Soc.*, **57**, 921 (1961).
54. C. S. Rann and A. N. Hambly, *Anal. Chem.*, **37**, 879 (1965).
55. G. F. Kirkbright, M. K. Peters, and T. S. West, *At. Abs. Symp.*, *Praha, 1967* (summary); G. F. Kirkbright, A. Semb, and T. S. West, *Spectry. Letters*, **1**, 7 (1968).
56. M. J. McEwan and L. F. Phillips, *Combust. Flame*, **11**, 63 (1967).
57. C. Rocchiccioli and A. Townshend, *Anal. Chim. Acta*, **41**, 93 (1968).
58. C. Th. J. Alkemade, T. Hollander, and P. J. Kalff, *Combust. Flame*, **9**, 101 (1965).
59. K. M. Burrows and J. F. Horwood, *Spectrochim. Acta*, **19**, 17 (1963).
60. I. Rubeška and B. Moldan, *Appl. Optics*, **7**, 1341 (1968).
61. L. de Galan and J. D. Winefordner, *Anal. Chem.*, **38**, 1412 (1966).
62. T. M. Sugden, *Agard Conference Proceedings (No. 8)*, NATO, Paris, 1965, Vol. 1, p. 43.
63. S. B. Meschkowa and N. S. Poluektov, *Zh. Prikl. Spektrosk.*, **2**, 21 (1965).
64. A. J. Borgers, *Symp. Combust.*, *10th, Univ. Cambridge, Cambridge, Engl., 1964*, The Combustion Institute, Pittsburgh, 1965, p. 627.
65. K. E. Shuler (ed.), *Ionization in High-Temperature Gases*, Academic, New York, 1963.
66. P. W. J. M. Boumans, *Theory of Spectrochemical Excitation*, Hilger & Watts, London, 1966.
67. A. Unsöld, *Physik der Sternatmosphären*, 2nd ed., Springer Verlag, Berlin, 1955.
68. D. C. Manning and L. Capacho-Delgado, *Anal. Chim. Acta*, **36**, 312 (1966).
69. D. E. Jensen and P. J. Padley, *Trans. Faraday Soc.*, **62**, 2140 (1966).
70. T. Hollander, P. J. Kalff, and C. Th. J. Alkemade, *J. Chem. Phys.*, **39**, 2558 (1963).
71. C. Th. Alkemade, see Discussion following Ref. (72).

72. K. Schofield and T. M. Sugden, *Symp. Combust.*, *10th, Univ. Cambridge, Cambridge, Engl.*, *1964*, The Combustion Institute, Pittsburgh, 1965, p. 589.
73. P. T. Gilbert, Jr., in *Proceedings Xth Colloquium Spectroscopicum Internationale*, Spartan, Washington, 1963, p. 171.
74. P. T. Gilbert, Jr., personal communication.
75. F. W. Hofmann and H. Kohn, *J. Opt. Soc. Am.*, **51**, 512 (1961).
76. P. J. Padley and T. M. Sugden, *Symp. Combust.*, *8th, Pasadena, Calif.*, *1960*, Williams & Wilkins, Baltimore, 1962, p. 164.
77. M. D. Amos and J. B. Willis, *Spectrochim. Acta*, **22**, 1325 (1966).
78. M. D. Amos, *The Element*, Aztec Instruments, No. 17.
79. P. J. Padley, F. M. Page, and T. M. Sugden, *Trans. Faraday Soc.*, **57**, 1552 (1961).
80. T. M. Sugden, *Annual Reviews of Physical Chemistry* (H. Eyring, ed.), 1962, p. 369.
81. K. J. Laidler, *The Chemical Kinetics of Excited States*, Clarendon, Oxford, 1955.
82. J. B. Hasted, *Physics of Atomic Collisions*, Butterworths, London, 1964.
83. C. Th. J. Alkemade, *Appl. Opt.*, **7**, 1261 (1968).
84. H. P. Hooymayers and C. Th. J. Alkemade, *J. Quant. Spectry. Radiative Transfer*, **6**, 501, 847 (1966).
85. D. R. Jenkins, *Proc. Roy. Soc. (London)*, **A293**, 493 (1966); **A303**, 453 (1968); **A306**, 413 (1968).
86. H. P. Hooymayers and G. Nienhuis, *J. Quant. Spectry. Radiative Transfer*, **8**, 955 (1968).
87. J. W. Robinson, *Anal. Chim. Acta*, **24**, 254 (1961).
88. T. M. Sugden, see Discussion following Ref. (*90*).
89. P. J. Th. Zeegers, *Recombination of Radicals and Related Effects in Flames*, Ph.D. Thesis, Utrecht, 1966.
90. P. J. Th. Zeegers and C. Th. J. Alkemade, *Symp. Combust.*, *10th, Univ. Cambridge, Cambridge, Engl.*, *1964*, The Combustion Institute, Pittsburgh, 1965, p. 33.
91. P. J. Padley and T. M. Sugden, *Proc. Roy. Soc. (London)*, **A248**, 248 (1958).
92. J. H. Gibson, W. Grossman, and W. D. Cooke, *Anal. Chem.*, **35**, 266 (1963).
93. J. A. Dean and J. C. Simms, *Anal. Chem.*, **35**, 699 (1963).
94. B. E. Buell, *Anal. Chem.*, **35**, 372 (1963).
95. R. W. Reid and T. M. Sugden, *Discussions Faraday Soc.*, **33**, 213 (1962).
96. C. Th. J. Alkemade and P. J. Th. Zeegers, in *Spectrochemical Methods of Analysis* (J. D. Winefordner, ed.), Wiley (Interscience), New York, Chap. 1, in preparation.

5 Radicals and Molecules in Flame Gases

D. R. Jenkins and T. M. Sugden

SHELL RESEARCH LTD.
THORNTON RESEARCH CENTRE
CHESTER, U.K.

I. The Structure of the Flame

A discussion of the chemical composition of flames involves the application of the principles of chemical thermodynamics and reaction kinetics. Thermodynamic principles determine the final equilibrium state which the flame gases approach and reaction kinetic principles the rate at which this state is approached. By far the easier aspect to describe is the final equilibrium state which is approached in the later stages of combustion. As we shall see later, complete equilibrium is never achieved. In practice the chemical composition in some parts of flames is often very close to the equilibrium state and may be calculated satisfactorily from thermodynamic principles and data.

In the early stages of combustion, however, the composition of flame gases is determined by kinetic processes. The chemical route between the fuel and oxidant supplied to the flame and the final combustion products is usually a complex one made up of a large number of simultaneous and consecutive reactions. Associated with the occurrence of these reactions in flames are steep gradients of temperature and concentration, a situation difficult to explain. Only for flames of the simplest fuels and oxidants can more than a qualitative description be given of the reaction zones. These parts of flames are often marked by above-equilibrium amounts of excited species and similarly of radiative emission.

The different zones of combustion are most apparent in laminar flow flames of premixed fuels and oxidants. Such flames assume their simplest aspects on flat flame burners. The flame is then nearly one dimensional and the distance above the burner of any point in the flame corresponds to a unique value of time of flow from the burner. The composition of the flame is, ideally, uniform in any plane perpendicular to the flame axis. Figure 1 shows the various zones of combustion in a flame of a mixture of three parts of hydrogen to one part of air burned on a flat flame burner at atmospheric pressure with no heat losses and no air entrainment, and the variation of some of its properties through the zones. Although the extent of the reaction zone cannot be defined precisely, it is of the order of 10^{-2} cm thick in hydrogen flames. The temperature increase across the reaction zone is about 2000°K; therefore, the temperature gradient is of the order of 10^5 °C cm^{-1}. This very large temperature gradient causes large amounts of heat to be conducted back into the prereaction zone gases. Rapid changes in concentrations also occur across the reaction zone, as shown diagrammatically in Fig. 1(b) and (c). The profiles shown are only intended to show the general nature of the concentration changes and should not be regarded as exact. The steep concentration gradients of free radicals, such as hydroxyl radicals and hydrogen atoms, cause rapid diffusion of these active species, particularly hydrogen atoms, back into the prereaction zone. As the gases approach the reaction zone, the combustion reactions are initiated thermally and by reactions with free radicals which have diffused backward. Once initiated, the over-all reaction rate increases rapidly by chain. branching reactions and the flame front propagates toward the unburnt gases at a velocity which, for a stable flame, is balanced by the flow rate of the gases leaving the burner. For the mixture being considered, the burning velocity is about 250 cm sec^{-1}, whereas the gases leave the reaction zone at about 1600 cm sec^{-1}. The increase in velocity is due to the net effect of expansion because of increase in temperature which is not offset by a smaller contraction due to chemical reaction at almost constant pressure. The average time taken to pass through the reaction zone is about 10^{-5} sec.

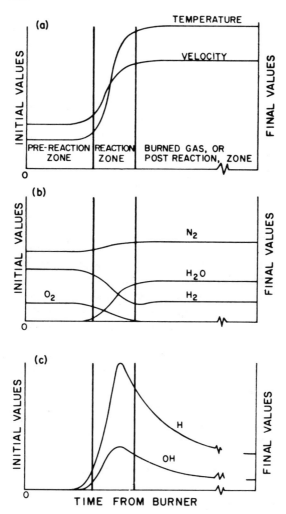

Fig. 1. Diagrammatic structure of steady-state, unidimensional, premixed H_2–O_2–N_2 flame of unburned volume proportions 3/1/4. (*a*) Temperature and velocity, (*b*) bulk species concentrations, (*c*) H and OH concentrations.

The changes in the concentrations of the bulk species, H_2, N_2, O_2, and H_2O, are almost complete as the gases enter the burned gas zone, where the temperature is nearly constant. However, the concentrations of free radicals at this stage are frequently much greater than the final equilibrium values because of the slowness of the recombination reactions by which these species are removed as compared with the rapidity of their production. The "excess" free radicals recombine in the postreaction zone.

For fuel-rich flames there is a fourth zone on the outer surface of the flame where the excess oxidizable constituents such as H_2 and CO burn in the surrounding air. This secondary combustion zone is most apparent for hydrocarbon flames where it has the appearance of a blue sheath or mantle over the flame. The secondary combustion flame is a diffusion flame in which the fuel and oxidant approach the flame front from opposite sides and the combustion products diffuse outward in both directions. This zone extends further toward the center with increasing distance upward along the column of burned gases. The flame is terminated by a cap of secondary combustion zone gases.

In premixed (laminar flow) flames on other burners the different zones take various shapes. In flames produced by Bunsen and Mèker burners the reaction zone has the familiar rounded conical form (single or multiple, respectively) which is the stable form when the flow velocity of the supply gas exceeds the burning velocity. The flame profiles for a Bunsen flame are similar to those shown in Fig. 1 for each streamline of flow in the flame. At any height above the burner, the composition of the flame is an average value corresponding to the average of all the streamlines up to that point in the flame. Because of the more complicated relationship between time and distance, these flames are less convenient than the flat-flame burner for studies of combustion chemistry. It is not difficult, however, to apply the results obtained with a flat flame to Bunsen and Mèker flames, at least in a semiquantitative way.

By increasing the velocity of the gases supplied to the flame, a transition occurs from laminar to turbulent flow. This is accompanied by an increase in the noisiness of the flame and an apparent blurring of the reaction zone. The time-averaged primary combustion zone becomes thicker (partly because of wrinkling of the flame front) and the average temperature and concentration gradients are less because of the intermixing of pre- and post-reaction zone gases with the reaction zone gases. The profiles of the time-averaged concentration versus distance down the flame become more uniform with less pronounced rates of change. The theoretical limit, which is a uniform concentration profile throughout the flame—is approached in high-intensity combustors, such as stirred reactors. In well-developed turbulent flames the whole, or a large part, of the oxygen required for combustion is supplied by entrained air and only the fuel need be supplied through the burner. In this case the combustion takes place along the whole length of the flame. The rate of combustion depends on the aerodynamics of the mixing processes as well as on chemical kinetics.

The discussion of combustion chemistry given in this chapter is largely confined to that in premixed flames on flat-flame burners. These are the flames which have been used most extensively for research into chemical kinetics because the complicating effect of the various purely physical processes is minimal and can largely be neglected or taken into account.

The over-all scheme in the following discussion is to consider, first, the chemistry of unseeded hydrogen and hydrocarbon flames in the reaction zone and in the postreaction zone leading to the equilibrium state, and second, some aspects of the chemistry of metals added in small concentrations to these flames.

II. Natural Flame Gases

A. CHEMICAL REACTIONS IN THE REACTION ZONE

1. *Hydrogen Flames*

Extensive work on the hydrogen–oxygen reaction at relatively low temperatures (around 800°K) has provided a rather clear picture of the important reactions in hydrogen flames (*1–4*). Flame reactions have been recently reviewed in detail by Fennimore (*5*), Fristrom and Westenberg (*6*), and Dixon-Lewis (*7*).

The principal differences between the lower temperature reaction and that occurring in flames are due to the absence of wall reactions in flames, and to the higher temperatures, which alter the relative importance of certain competing reactions as well as increasing the over-all rate.

Combustion of premixed H_2 and O_2 begins as the gases enter the reaction zone by the chain branching sequence:

$$H + O_2 \rightleftharpoons OH + O \qquad \Delta H = \quad 16.9 \tag{1}$$

$$O + H_2 \rightleftharpoons OH + H \qquad \Delta H = \quad 2.0 \tag{2}$$

$$OH + H_2 \rightleftharpoons H_2O + H \qquad \Delta H = -15.1 \tag{3}$$

[Values for ΔH, the heat of reaction at 298°K in kcal mole^{-1}, have been calculated from data in JANAF Thermochemical Tables (8)]. These reactions are written as reversible processes although in the reaction zone the forward step, in which primary reactants are consumed, will predominate. The reactions $H_2 + O_2 \rightarrow 2OH$ or $\rightarrow H_2O + O$ are too slow compared with reaction (1) to be of importance in flames as initiating reactions (9).

Reactions (1–3) cause a rapid increase in the concentrations of free radicals and a rapid removal of the primary reactants. They do not, however, release much heat nor do they lead to the observed near stoichiometry of the over-all reaction, $2H_2 + O_2 \rightarrow 2H_2O$. Instead they lead, by addition, to $3H_2 + O_2 \rightarrow 2H_2O + 2H$. The observed result requires one or more of the following recombination steps.

$$H + H + M \rightarrow H_2 + M \qquad \Delta H = -104.2 \tag{4}$$
$$H + OH + M \rightarrow H_2O + M \qquad \Delta H = -119.4 \tag{5}$$
$$O + O + M \rightarrow O_2 + M \qquad \Delta H = -119.1 \tag{6}$$
$$O + H + M \rightarrow OH + M \qquad \Delta H = -102.2 \tag{7}$$

Not all of these reactions may be important in any given flame. In these reactions M represents any chemical species which can remove some of the dissociation energy from the newly formed molecule and thus allows it to form a stable entity. Reaction (4), for example, combined with reactions (1–3), forms a reaction mechanism for fuel-rich hydrogen flames which gives nearly the observed stoichiometry.

These reactions are written as forward processes only, although they eventually will reach equilibrium with detailed balancing via the reverse process. The reason for the different formulation of reactions (1–3) and (4–7) will become apparent below.

As H_2 and O_2 are consumed and the concentrations of the products of reactions (1–3) increase, the rates of these reactions, which are fast in both the forward and reverse direction, approach equality. The reaction

$$H_2O + O \rightleftharpoons 2OH \qquad \Delta H = 17.1 \tag{8}$$

also contributes to this rate of approach to equality. When the forward and reverse rates are balanced, the concentrations of the various chemical species are then related to each other by equilibrium constants even though the actual concentrations may differ greatly from the equilibrium values. This condition is closely fulfilled as the gases leave the combustion zone and at all downstream points. The point is discussed in more detail in the next section.

Many of the striking features of hydrogen flames arise from the fact that the bimolecular chain branching reactions (1–3) are fast compared with those of the recombination reactions (4–7). These latter reactions are slow in the forward direction because they are termolecular, and in the reverse

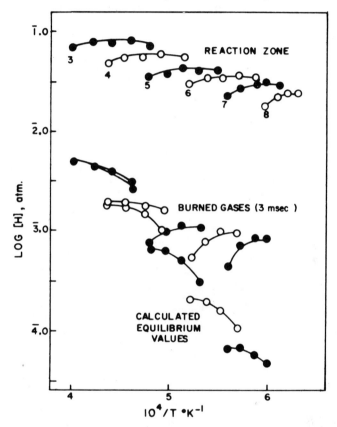

Fig. 2. Hydrogen atom concentration in flames. Flames are grouped into "families" and for each family the N_2/O_2 unburned volume proportion is given on the figure. The H_2/O_2 proportions within each family are 2.5, 3.0, 3.5, 4.0, and, in some families, 4.5, reading in direction of decreasing T. (Reprinted from (10) by courtesy of the Syndics of the Cambridge University.)

direction because of the large activation energies. As a result, the concentrations of free radicals produced in the reaction zone commonly exceed the equilibrium values. Indeed, if recombination reactions did not intervene, examination of the kinetics of reactions (1–3) [even if reaction (8) is added] leads to $[H]+[OH]+2[O]+2[O_2]$ = constant. This is illustrated in Fig. 2, which shows values of $[H]$ in the reaction zones of some $H_2-O_2-N_2$ flames. These values were obtained by Padley (*10*) by extrapolation of measured values in the burned gas region. Also shown are the values at a point 3 msec downstream from the reaction zone and the calculated equilibrium values, $[H]_{eq}$. In flames at lower temperatures and at subatmospheric pressures, values of the ratio $[H]/[H]_{eq}$ in excess of 10^6 have been reported (*11*).

Although the reaction sequences [(1–3) and (8)] together with one or more recombination reactions, can explain many of the features of the combustion of hydrogen, there are features which cannot be explained on the basis of this mechanism alone. The observed rate of oxygen consumption (*12, 13*), the rate of heat release in flames at atmospheric pressure (*13, 14*), and recombination rates in shock-heated, lean, H_2-O_2 mixtures (*15*) are greater than can be accounted for by this reaction scheme alone. It has been proposed that the reaction

$$H+O_2+X \rightarrow HO_2+X \qquad \Delta H = -47.1 \qquad (9)$$

which accounts for the second explosion limit in the static, lower temperature experiments, also plays an important role in flames. The rate constant for reaction (9) is not very dependent on temperature (*16*) and, at temperatures below about 1200°K, this reaction is expected to be faster than reaction (1), which has an activation energy of about 16.5 kcal/mole (*6*). Reaction (9) would account for the fact that O_2 appears to have its maximum rate of disappearance at temperatures below 1200°K even in fuel-rich flames of much higher final temperatures (*7*).

An outstanding problem in hydrogen combustion is the subsequent fate of HO_2 in flames. Numerous rapid bimolecular reactions of HO_2 with other species are possible. These have been discussed (*7, 11–14, 16*). HO_2 is not expected to have a high intermediate (or final) concentration since it is mainly produced by slow termolecular reactions and removed by fast bimolecular reactions. In this respect, it is opposite to the species H, OH, and O.

Likely reactions such as

$$\begin{aligned}
HO_2+H &\rightarrow H_2+O_2 & \Delta H &= -57.1 \\
HO_2+OH &\rightarrow H_2O+O_2 & \Delta H &= -72.2 \\
HO_2+O &\rightarrow OH+O_2 & \Delta H &= -55.2
\end{aligned}$$

provide alternative recombination paths, and

$$HO_2+H \rightarrow 2OH \text{ or } H_2O+O$$

when combined with reactions (2) and (3) gives

$$2H_2 + O_2(+2H) \rightarrow 2H_2O(+2H) \qquad \Delta H = -116$$

which provides an additional route for hydrogen combustion.

At high temperatures and subatmospheric pressure O_2 will be mostly consumed by reaction (1). At lower temperatures and higher pressures, reaction (9) is probably more important. In flames at atmospheric pressure it seems probable that both mechanisms are important in the reaction zone and in the secondary combustion zone of fuel-rich flames.

2. Hydrocarbon Flames

In view of the much greater number of species present in hydrocarbon flames, as compared with hydrogen flames, the reaction mechanism of hydrocarbon combustion is clearly more complex. This is particularly true for fuel-rich flames, in which species may be produced whose molecular weight exceeds that of the original fuel. Nevertheless, much progress has been made, particularly for flames of simple hydrocarbons, and the general features of the combustion mechanism for these flames are reasonably clear. Detailed discussions of hydrocarbon combustion together with extensive lists of pertinent references may be found in (5) and (6).

The later stages of combustion in hydrocarbon flames are the same as those of $CO-H_2-O_2$ flames, the CO and H_2 being supplied by breakdown and oxidation of the fuel in earlier stages. Carbon dioxide appears not to be formed directly but via carbon monoxide; it is generally accepted that the relevant process here is

$$CO + OH \rightleftharpoons CO_2 + H \tag{10}$$

The over-all reaction

$$CO + O(+M) \rightarrow CO_2(+M)(+h\nu) \tag{11}$$

which gives rise to the blue emission characteristic of the outer secondary combustion mantle in fuel-rich flames, is too slow to account for a significant amount of CO_2. Reaction (11) is slow even among termolecular reactions; this is due to the presence of a potential energy barrier in the primary step and not, as was previously supposed, to spin reversal (17).

In flames at atmospheric pressure and temperatures above 1500°K, it appears (18, 26) that reaction (10) is balanced immediately beyond the reaction zone, and this reaction, together with reaction (3), leads to the establishment of the water–gas equilibrium

$$CO + H_2O \rightleftharpoons CO_2 + H_2 \tag{12}$$

in the burned gas zone.

The principal uncertainties in hydrocarbon combustion concern the reactions between fuel and oxygen which lead to the formation of CO and H_2. The direct reaction between fuel and O_2 molecules is very slow; the main reactions are with free radicals. For methane and ethane there is general agreement that the initial reaction is

$$F+H \text{ (or OH)} \rightarrow \dot{R}+H_2 \text{ (or } H_2O) \tag{13}$$

where F is the fuel molecule and $\dot{R}$ the corresponding hydrogen-abstracted radical. Reaction with OH predominates in fuel-lean flames and with H in fuel-rich flames when $[H] \gg [OH]$. For ethylene and acetylene flames, Fristrom and Westenberg (19) believe reaction (13) is the main initiating step although reaction with O has also been proposed (20, 21).

In flames of methane and C_2 hydrocarbons which are not too rich, the subsequent fate of $\dot{R}$ is oxidation by a series of (as yet) incompletely understood steps to CO, with formaldehyde as an intermediate species, at least in methane (22), ethane (19), and ethylene (19) flames. On the grounds that the O_2 disappearance rate can be largely accounted for by reaction (1), reaction with oxygen atoms has been suggested (23) as the first step in the oxidation of $\dot{R}$. However, Fristrom and Westenberg (19) find that the concentration of H in the region of maximum rate of disappearance of O_2 is far too low to account for this rate and, hence, favor reaction between $\dot{R}$ and O_2 as the first step. Subsequent steps are even less certain. If $\dot{R}$ is a large hydrocarbon radical, much of it will break down to give lower molecular weight unsaturated hydrocarbons and radicals, which will eventually react as above, at least in flames that are not fuel-rich.

The breakdown of the fuel and subsequent oxidation of the fragments to CO are the primary reactions in hydrocarbon flames which account for the rapid rate of disappearance of fuel and oxygen in the early stages. Associated with them, of course, are the previously described reactions of hydrogen combustion. Overlapping and extending beyond this region is a zone in which reactions such as (1–3) are approaching equilibration and CO_2 is being formed by reaction (10). In the final stage, extending into the burned gas zone, excess concentrations of free radicals (H, OH, and O) begin to recombine by reactions (4–7) toward final equilibrium.

In fuel-rich flames, particularly near the soot-forming limit, the situation is more complex. The composition of the gases is now such as to promote the recombination of the fuel fragments, and hydrocarbons of higher molecular weight are formed. These, as well as the original fuel, react with H, OH, and, subsequently, with O_2 or O, as described above. In analyses of fuel-rich, low-pressure, acetylene flames (24), hydrocarbons up to $C_{12}H_8$

and including numerous polyacetylenes up to $C_{10}H_2$ have been found. The concentrations of these polyacetylenes were found to increase rapidly with increasing proportion of C_2H_2 in the input gases. In soot-forming flames high concentrations of these substances occur in the reaction zone and also in the burned gas region. Reaction of these polyacetylenes with hydrocarbon radicals, and subsequent addition of polyacetylenes, is the mechanism proposed by which the soot particles are formed.

B. THE BURNED GAS REGION

Many of the reactions occurring in the reaction zone are bimolecular reactions which are fast in both forward and reverse directions. When these rates become equal, the concentrations of participating species are related to each other by equilibrium relationships even though the concentrations may differ greatly from the equilibrium value. Such reactions are then said to be balanced.

In fuel-rich hydrogen flames, reaction (3) is balanced very rapidly, as the following argument will show. Consider a hot mixture of H, H_2O, and H_2. If the concentrations of H_2 and H_2O are assumed constant and, initially, the concentration of OH is zero, the integrated rate equation for the appearance of OH is given by

$$(x_b - x)/x_b = \exp(-t/\tau)$$

where x_b and x are the concentrations of OH when the reaction is balanced and at time t, respectively; τ, the relaxation time, is given by $\tau = (k_3[H_2] + k_{-3}[H_2O])^{-1}$. Using values for k_3 and k_{-3} (6) and assuming partial pressures for H_2 and H_2O of 0.1, τ has a value of approximately 1 μsec at flame temperatures. The reaction will, therefore, become very nearly balanced in times of a few microseconds in flames containing appreciable amounts of H_2 and H_2O. Where both the reactants on either side of the reaction are minor species, the time taken to achieve balancing will be longer. Nevertheless, measurements such as those by Schott (25), Kaskan (26), and McEwan and Phillips (27) indicate that reactions (10), (2), and (3) and hence (8) will be essentially balanced in the burned gas very shortly after the reaction zone, in flames at 1 atm. In fuel-lean flames reaction (1) is probably balanced shortly after the gases leave the reaction zone.

Under these conditions, relationships such as the following apply:

$$[H]/[OH] = K_3[H_2]/[H_2O] \tag{14}$$
$$[O]/[OH]^2 = K_3/(K_2[H_2O]) \tag{15}$$
$$[H]/[OH]^3 = K_3/(K_2 K_1 [H_2O][O_2]) \tag{16}$$

These relationships enable the concentrations of one species to be inferred from measured values of another, e.g., [OH] from [H] in hydrogen-rich flames and from [O] in hydrogen-lean flames.

Conservation of elements requires that certain functions of the species concentration are time invariant in the absence of recombination reactions. For example, in flames containing only the following six species, Kaskan and Schott (28) have shown this function to be

$$a[H] + b[O] + c[OH] + d[H_2] + e[O_2] + f[H_2O] \tag{17}$$

where the coefficients are related by

$$a - c = d - f = b - e; \qquad 2c = f + b \tag{18}$$

It is expedient to eliminate those species which are present in large concentrations. Of the remaining four coefficients, the values of any one may be chosen arbitrarily. For example, in hydrogen-rich flames, putting $d = f = 0$ and setting $a = 1$, the function $([H] + [OH] + 2[O] + 2[O_2])$ is obtained. The concentration of any one of these species cannot change independently of the others, and the recombination reactions must decrease this sum of the concentration as a whole and not just that of the species involved in the recombination reaction. In the presence of recombination reactions Kaskan and Schott showed that the time derivative of function (17) is equal to $-\alpha R$ where $\alpha = 2a - d$ and R is the total rate of recombination.

In fuel-rich hydrogen flames the principal recombination reactions are (4 and 5) and, as the concentrations of O and O_2 are negligibly small, the rate of approach to equilibrium is given by

$$d([H] + [OH])/dt = 2(\sum_M k_4^M[H]^2[M] + \sum_M k_5^M[H][OH][M])$$

where the summation is for all different third bodies M in the flame and allows for different values of k_4, k_5 corresponding to different efficiencies of these third bodies.

Making use of relationship (14) we obtain

$$d[H]/dt = 2k_o[H]^2 \tag{19}$$

where k_o, the apparent recombination rate constant, is given by

$$k_o(1 + K_3[H_2O]/[H_2]) = \sum_M k_4^M[M] + (K_3[H_2O]\sum_M k_5^M[M])/[H_2]$$

Equation (19) shows that the rate of removal of H is second order in [H] so that plots of 1/[H] versus distance in unidimensional flames should give straight lines. Figure 3 shows three such plots. The curvature at long times is owing to the neglect of the reverse of the recombination reactions as final, full equilibrium is approached. The slopes of these plots give k_o for that particular flame, and from measurements of k_o as a function of flame composition, values for the rates of reactions (4) and (5) with various third bodies can be obtained. Values for k_4 and k_5 with different third bodies obtained by this and other methods have recently been summarized by Schofield (29).

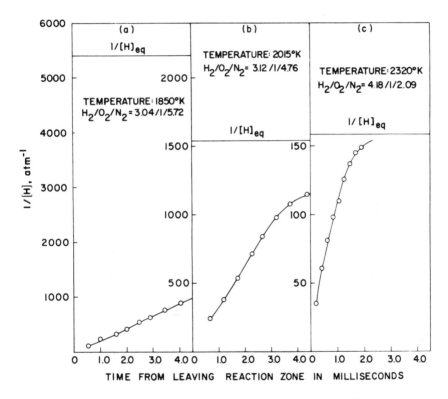

Fig. 3. Recombination of hydrogen atoms in some hydrogen flames.

In fuel-lean flames the important recombination reactions are not established as clearly as for fuel-rich flames. Clearly reaction (9) is important (14). In lean flames, not too far from the stoichiometric ratio, reaction (5) is probably important also since k_5 is about 20 times greater than k_9. Except in very lean flames, reaction (6) is unimportant since k_6 is about two orders of magnitude smaller than k_5.

Similar chemical disequilibria are found in hydrocarbon flames, particularly in flames which are not very fuel-rich. In fuel-lean flames of methane, acetylene, and propane, values of $[O]/[O]_{eq}$ up to 1500 have been measured (30), similar to values found in lean hydrogen flames of the same burning velocity. In fuel-rich flames, lower values of excess concentrations are found, and flames in which hydrocarbon molecules or fragments persist into the burned gas zone show very little, if any, excess concentrations. This is probably due to the occurrence of bimolecular recombination reactions involving hydrocarbon radicals in these flames. The products of these recombination reactions will be relatively large molecules. These have a high probability of not dissociating because they distribute the heat of recombination over several vibrational modes.

The recombination of excess free radicals is the slowest relaxation effect in flames. As is discussed below, nonequilibrium effects are present in other forms in the reaction zone of flames, but these disappear more rapidly than chemical nonequilibria, which are dependent on slow recombination reactions for their relaxation.

The most important factor in determining how closely the equilibrium state is approached is the final flame temperature. The excess concentrations of free radicals in flames are not very dependent on the final flame temperature but the equilibrium values are. Consequently, the higher the final flame temperature, the smaller is the departure from equilibrium. In flames of final temperatures above 2400°K the equilibrium values of [H] and [OH] are very close to the reaction zone values, and chemical equilibrium is reached very quickly. In low-temperature flames, however, [H] and [OH] are so low that comparatively long times would be needed to reach equilibrium; the flame is extinguished before this can occur.

C. Energy Distribution Relaxation Rates

In a system at complete equilibrium the molecules or atoms of each of the constituent species are distributed over the available energy levels according to the Maxwell–Boltzmann expression

$$N_i = N_o g_i \exp[-E_i/kT]/Q \tag{20}$$

where N_i and N_o are the number of particles in the ith level and the total number, respectively, g_i is the statistical weight and E_i the energy of the ith level, and Q the partition function.

$$Q = \sum_i g_i \exp[-E_i/kT] \tag{21}$$

For a good approximation the total energy, E_i, can be separated into contributions from each of the degrees of freedom—translation, rotation, vibration, and electronic—and the distribution of particles over the energy levels in each degree of freedom can be described by a Maxwell–Boltzmann function. At equilibrium, of course, the same value for T applies for each distribution function.

In a chemical reaction the products of reaction are not produced with a Maxwell–Boltzmann distribution of energies. The interaction between reacting species may be such as to favor the formation of products in which the energy with which they are endowed—the activation energy of the reverse reaction—is contained in a limited number of energy levels. Whether or not the observed steady-state distribution is normal, that is, in accordance with Eq. (20) with a common value for T for each degree of freedom, depends on the relative rate of the reaction to the rate at which the product energy is distributed over all accessible energy levels. Examples of opposite extremes would be the slow decomposition of N_2O_5 and the primary step in photochemical reactions.

Generally the rate of redistribution, or relaxation, is faster within a particular kind of motion than between any two different kinds. Because of this it is not uncommon to be able to define the distribution among rotational, vibrational, and electronic energy levels by Eq. (20) with different values for the temperature for each mode of energy.

The rate of relaxation is fast when the quanta of energy which have to be transferred are small compared with kT—the order of magnitude of thermal energy which can be readily supplied or absorbed in collisions. For a system of interacting particles which is initially far from equilibrium, the number of collisions needed to bring about translational equilibrium is less than 10; for rotation, about 10–10^2; and for vibration, in the range 10^3–10^6.

For mixtures of gases the relaxation times are shorter; polyatomic molecules, particularly, have large effects in reducing the vibrational relaxation time of diatomic molecules. This is attributed to efficient exchange of vibrational energy between the components of the mixture, which then approaches equilibrium at the rate of the fastest vibrational-translational step. Small amounts of carbon dioxide, for example, are particularly efficient in reducing the relaxation time of N_2, as found by Taylor et al. (31). This may be seen from Fig. 4, which is taken from their paper. Similar effects have been found for mixtures such as N_2–O_2 (32), N_2–NO (31), CO–NO (31), and H_2O–CO_2 (33). For common flame gas mixtures, therefore, relaxation times for vibration will be considerably shorter than the pure gas values. In addition to this "mixture" effect, chemical interactions, such as the effect of O atoms in reducing the relaxation time of O_2, found by Kiefer and Lutz (36), may well be important

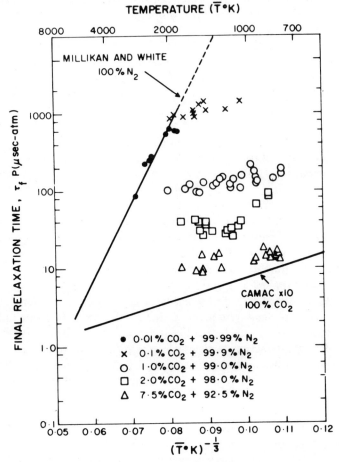

Fig. 4. $\tau_f P$ for various CO_2–N_2 mixtures (τ_f is final relaxation time in μsec; P, pressure in atm) plotted against temperature as $T^{-1/3}$. The lines represent $\tau_f P$ obtained from experimental measurements on pure N_2 by Millikan and White (34) and pure CO_2 by Camac (35). (Reprinted from (31) by courtesy of The Combustion Institute.)

in flames and serve to reduce the vibrational lag still further. For flames at 1 atm pressure a value of about 10^{-4} sec, corresponding to about 3×10^5 collisions, appears to be a reasonable upper limit for vibrational relaxation times.

In flames at atmospheric pressure the primary reactions in the reaction zone are effectively completed in about 10^{-2} cm, which, for gas velocities of about 10^{-3} cm sec^{-1} and a collision number of 3×10^9 sec^{-1}, corresponds to a time of 10^{-5} sec and about 10^4–10^5 collisions. In the reaction zone, therefore, translational equilibrium will be complete. Anomalous distributions of vibrational and rotational energies may occur but these, where they are produced by reactions which only occur in the reaction zone, are unlikely to persist into the burned gas zone. In this latter region any abnormal distribution is more likely to be the result of reactions involving the above-equilibrium amounts of free radicals in this region than slow relaxation of a reaction zone effect.

The only experimental investigation of translational temperatures appears to be by Gaydon and Wolfhard (37), who deduced values from the Doppler width of emission lines of CH and OH. In flames at atmospheric pressure the measured translational temperature agreed with the calculated adiabatic value, though in low-pressure flames—1.9–14 mm Hg—measured translational temperatures were significantly higher than the calculated values, suggesting incomplete translational relaxation at low pressures.

In flames, the most widely studied aspects are those relating to the species OH, CH, and C_2 for which the rotational and vibrational energy distribution can be inferred from measurements of the fine structure of electronic transitions. In the case of OH there have been two main objectives—to examine the rotational and vibrational energy distributions and to determine the total intensity of emission, in comparison with the calculated thermal intensities; that is, to examine for chemiluminescence. For CH and C_2 the thermal intensities are insignificant and the emission is entirely chemiluminescent.

In hot hydrogen flames the rotational and vibrational distributions of OH, as inferred from the fine structure of the $^2\Sigma$-$^2\Pi$ transition near 3000 Å, appear normal, that is, in accordance with Eq. (20) and the calculated flame temperature. This indicates that the relaxation rates are very fast or, more probably, that thermal excitation swamps the chemi-excitation at high temperatures. This latter explanation would account for the vibrational anomalies reported by Gaydon in hydrogen-entrained air flames, which are likely to have much lower temperatures, and is in line with the effect of diluents on hydrocarbon flames, reported by Kane and Broida (38), and described below.

In low-pressure hydrogen flames Hinck et al. (39) find strong over-excitation of the (0,0) band of OH in the early stages of the reaction zone and also above-equilibrium values for the (2,1)/(1,0) and (1,0)/(0,0) vibrational band intensity ratios. At least two mechanisms of excitation are clearly involved since the vibrational band ratios reach maximum values after the (0,0) peak. Above-equilibrium values persist throughout the length of the flame. The excitation mechanism responsible for the anomalous (0,0) intensity is not known; possibilities are the reaction $H + O_2 + H_2 \rightarrow H_2O + OH^*$ proposed by Belles and Lauver (40) or, as the authors suggest, a reaction involving HO_2 since the peak occurs in the cooler part of the reaction zone. The second mechanism is the excitation of OH by bi- or termolecular association of excess concentrations of free radicals. The reaction

$$H + OH + OH \rightarrow H_2O + OH^* \tag{22}$$

suggested by Kaskan (41) seems to be the most likely process since it is sufficiently exothermic to produce OH* in the second vibrational level and has been found by Zeegers and Alkemade (42) to be the cause of OH chemiluminescence in the burned gas region of premixed oxygen–acetylene flames. A similar mechanism is responsible for excitation of metallic atoms in flames.

In hydrocarbon flames, marked abnormalities in the rotational distribution are found in the reaction zone. In these flames there is good evidence that the reaction proposed by Gaydon (43)

$$CH + O_2 \rightarrow CO + OH^* \tag{23}$$

produces the strong OH chemiluminescence which is a characteristic of the reaction zones of these flames and also favors the production of OH with high rotational energies. High rotational temperatures are found in low pressure flames and also at atmospheric pressure. In the latter, Kane and Broida (38) find the effect becomes more pronounced with dilution by an inert gas, presumably because the "normalizing" effect of the underlying thermal excitation is reduced. This chemiexcitation reaction and the rotational distribution anomalies are confined to the reaction zone, since the reactant CH does not survive into the burned gas region, and only the weaker chemiluminescence and vibrational anomalies described above persist in this region.

For CH and C_2 nonequilibrium rotational distributions are also found in the reaction zone. The observations for these species, and the earlier work referring to OH, have been described by Gaydon (43). Naturally, the CH and C_2 anomalies are entirely confined to the reaction zones since these species do not survive beyond it.

A question that is often posed is whether delays in obtaining vibrational equilibria may have significant effects on the rate of combustion reactions.

For example, oxygen molecules moving toward the reaction zone of a flame will have a vibrational temperature lagging somewhat behind the translational temperature. If the vibrational energy of O_2 contributes appreciably toward the activation energy of the reaction $H + O_2 \rightarrow OH + O$, the over-all rate will be slower than if vibrational temperatures were able to keep up with the translational temperatures. Schott and Kinsey (44) suggested slow vibrational relaxation as an explanation of trends in their measurements of induction time in shock-heated H_2–O_2 mixture, and a similar effect has been suggested by Voevodsky and Soloukhin (45). However, this possibility has been investigated specifically by Asaba et al. (46) and Belles and Lauver (47). Both groups find that the effect of O_2 relaxation of induction periods is insignificantly small so that this effect is probably of little importance in flames.

D. NATURAL IONIZATION IN FLAMES

The reaction zones of some flames are the seats of extensive ionization involving various positive ions and electrons. The latter give rise to high electrical conductivities. Such ionization is negligible for hydrogen and carbon monoxide flames (with oxygen or air) and even then appears to be owing to impurities, but it is very pronounced with hydrocarbon flames.

At equilibrium it is possible to calculated the degree of ionization of a substance A

$$A \rightleftharpoons A^+ + e^-$$

since the equilibrium constant of this reaction is a known function of the temperature and the ionization potential of A (i.e., the heat of reaction). The higher this ionization potential the lower is the ionization. The values of ionization potential for flame gas constituents are quite high (generally > 8 eV) and are quite incompatible with the large amounts of positive ions and electrons found in reaction zones of hydrocarbon flames.

This phenomenon is, therefore, ascribed to chemi-ionization—i.e., nonequilibrium ionization which occurs because of the absence of chemical equilibrium in the reaction zone. If radicals are present in amounts of several orders of magnitude above the equilibrium, then corresponding excess ionization may occur, and suitably stable products are formed. A very important step of this kind in hydrocarbon flames is

$$CH + O \rightarrow CHO^+ + e^-$$

This reaction is only slightly endothermic (by about 20 kcal/mole) because of the stability of CHO^+, which has the structure $H—C \equiv O^+$, isoelectronic with H—C ≡ N. Subsequently, other positive ions may be formed by exchange reactions, such as

$$CHO^+ + H_2O \rightarrow CO + H_3O^+$$

The rapid disappearance of the ions and electrons on leaving the reaction zone is explained by the very fast reaction

$$H_3O^+ + e^- \rightarrow H_2O + H$$

and the absence of CH radicals to give fresh electrons. These three processes have been found to give a satisfactory account of many of the features of ionization in hydrocarbon flames. The absence of suitable radicals (CH) in hydrogen and carbon monoxide flames explains the absence of chemi-ionization.

Very rich, soot-containing hydrocarbon flames show high electronic conduction even in the burned gas. This arises from a new phenomenon— the evaporation of electrons from the graphite particles of soot—and is comparatively near equilibrium.

If substances of low ionization potential such as alkali metals, are added, significant amounts of ionization occur both in the reaction zone and the burned gases. This is discussed briefly in a later section.

E. The Equilibrium State

The final equilibrium state of a mixture of hot reactive gases is a hypothetical state never achieved by normal flames. In this state a flame would emit a continuous spectrum of intensity given by the Planck expression and would have no heat losses. The equilibrium state may be approached by large soot-containing flames in refractory lined enclosures but not by unenclosed small flames. These will always have below-equilibrium emission intensities and uncompensated radiative heat losses, which must be restored by kinetic processes within the gas.

Nevertheless, the equilibrium state is a very valuable concept; the effect of the nonequilibrium effects referred to earlier on the over-all composition of flame gas mixtures is generally small because the fraction of the total energy of the gas that resides in excited states or in free radicals is very small. Of course, effects such as heat losses to the burner, air entrainment, or the addition of significant amounts of liquid droplets may have a large effect on the composition, either directly or through effects on the temperature. These effects must either be avoided or taken into account in accurate calculation of the equilibrium compositions.

In the absence of these effects, the theoretical equilibrium composition and temperature of a flame are fully determined by the input gas composition and temperature. The problem of calculating these properties is generally difficult because of the dependence of equilibrium constants on the temperature, and reiterative methods are necessary. Details of methods of calculating equilibrium compositions and adiabatic temperatures have been discussed in several books and papers, for example, by Penner (*48*) and by Gaydon (*49*). Where a large number of such calculations are needed, the method can be readily adapted for digital computers. If the flame temperature has been measured, the problem is a simple one of solving a set of equations expressing the relationships between equilibrium constants and concentrations and the equations for conservation of elements. This is often more useful than a completely theoretical calculation since heat losses, etc., make the actual temperature different from the theoretical one.

Figures 5–7 show the adiabatic temperatures and equilibrium composition at 1 atm (expressed as mole fractions) of various proportions of three fuels and oxidants commonly used in spectrometry. The equivalence ratio ϕ is defined as the ratio

$$\frac{([fuel]/[oxidant])}{([fuel]/[oxidant])_{st}}$$

expressed as volume proportions. The subscript refers to the stoichiometric mixture. (For the acetylene flame, $\phi = 1$ gives complete combustion to CO_2 and H_2O.)

Thermodynamic data for the chemical constituents of most common flames are accurately known and documented (*8, 50*). When such data are not available, values of equilibrium constants can be derived by statistical mechanical methods, detailed descriptions of which may be found in standard text books (*51*).

III. Flames Containing Metal Additives

The amount of metal commonly added to flames for spectrometric purposes is sufficiently small as that the metal can be regarded as a trace additive. While the metal participates in the chemical processes in the flame, the main chemical characteristics of the flame are not altered. The flame can, therefore, be regarded as a "solvent" whose characteristics are reasonably well known. Against this background the chemistry of the metal may be examined.

Discussed elsewhere in this book are the manner in which the metal is introduced into the flame, the physical processes of droplet evaporation, and metal compound sublimation or boiling—all occur before the metal

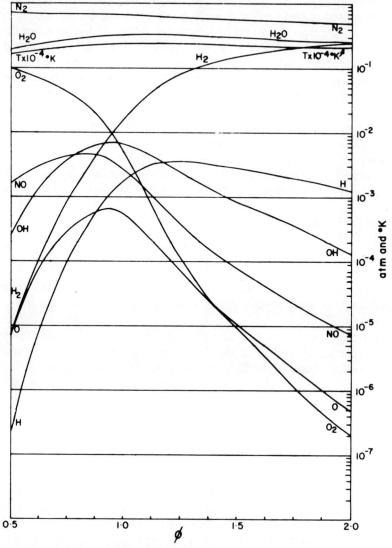

Fig. 5. Equilibrium composition and adiabatic temperatures of air–H_2 flames. $T_{initial} = 300°K$. Thermodynamic data from (8).

appears in the vapor phase. In this chapter we are primarily concerned
with the subsequent reactions of the metal. We shall regard the metal as
if it, or its compounds, has been introduced in the vapor phase with the
flame gas supply.

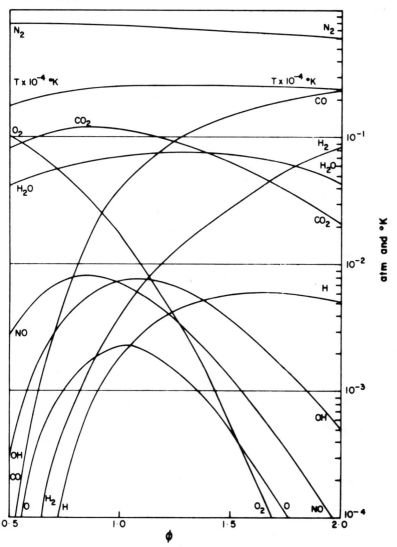

Fig. 6. Equilibrium composition and adiabatic temperatures of air–acetylene flames.
$T_{initial} = 300°K$. Thermodynamic data from (8).

It is expedient here to reverse the order of the previous section and
consider the equilibrium state first. The equilibrium relationships, which
relate the concentrations of the metal and its compounds and ions to the

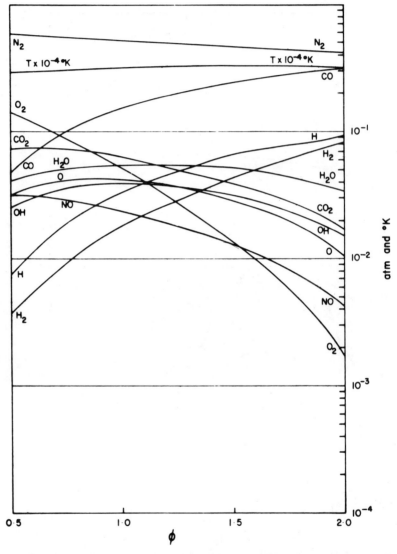

Fig. 7. Equilibrium composition and adiabatic temperatures of nitrous oxide-
acetylene flames. $T_{Initial} = 300°K$. Thermodynamic data from (8).

flame gas compositions, will describe the actual state in the burned gas region far away from the reaction zone quite well in many flames, particularly the hotter ones. When the equilibrium state is not reached—because of slow recombination of excess radicals—many of the equilibrium relationships are still applicable, since the reactions which they describe will be balanced and these relationships serve to link together the reasonably well-known chemistry of the flame to the less well-known chemistry of the metal.

A. THE EQUILIBRIUM STATE

1. No Compound Formation (ionization)

For metals which form no compounds under flame conditions the only process which affects the concentration of the metal in the flame is ionization. Irrespective of the way in which the metal atom M is ionized, the equilibrium ionization is given by

$$K = [M^+][e^-]/[M] \tag{24}$$

where the ionization constant K is given by the Saha equation

$$\log K = \frac{-5040E_i}{T} + \frac{5}{2}\log T + \log \frac{g_{M^+}g_{e^-}}{g_M} - 6.49$$

where E_i is the ionization potential (in eV) and the g's are statistical weights. If the total concentration $[M]+[M^+]$ is $[M]_0$ then

$$[M] = \frac{[M]_0}{1+K/[e^-]} \tag{25}$$

If other equilibria, such as ionization of a second metal or flame gas molecules, or negative ion formation, occur as well, then these must be included in determining $[e^-]$. However, for a flame containing one easily ionized metal, such as one of the alkali metals, it is probably sufficiently accurate away from the reaction zone to equate $[e^-]$ to $[M^+]$ since the ionization potentials of flame gas molecules are much higher (at least for nonsooting flames) and mass spectrometric work (52) suggests that negative ion formation (in particular OH^-) is unimportant in flames at atmospheric pressure. Putting $[M^+] = [e^-]$ in Eqs. (24) and (25) gives

$$[M]+(K[M])^{\frac{1}{2}}-[M]_0 = 0 \tag{26}$$

The solution to Eq. (25) gives the dependence of $[M]$ on $[M]_0$. The limiting cases for high and low concentrations are, respectively:

$$[M]_0 \gg K; [M] = [M]_0, [M^+] = [e^-] = (K[M]_0)^{\frac{1}{2}}$$
$$[M]_0 \ll K; [M] = [M]_0^2/K, [M^+] = [e^-] = [M]_0 \qquad (27)$$

These equations explain the well-known observations that when the added metal is the principal source of electrons, such as at high values of $[M]_0$, the metal is present mostly as free atoms, whereas at low values of $[M]_0$, the metal is mostly in the ionized state. This causes upward concavity on the curve of growth.

As may be seen from Eq. (25) the presence of significant amounts of natural ionization or the addition of other metals to the flame lowers the value of $[M]_0$ at which ionization effects becomes significant, and may suppress ionization of M almost completely. Consider, for example, the addition of caesium to a flame at $2260°K$ containing sodium. At this temperature the ionization constant $K_{Cs} = 1.6 \times 10^{-7}$ atm and $K_{Na} = 2.5 \times 10^{-10}$ atm. If the contribution of sodium and of background ionization to $[e^-]$ is neglected, when $[Cs]_0 \ll K_2$, $[e^-] \sim [Cs]_0$ and $[Cs]_0 \gg K_2$, $[e^-] \gg K_2$ it can be seen from Eq. (24) that the ionization of sodium is negliglble ($< 1\%$) when $[Cs]_0 \gg 2.5 \times 10^{-8}$ atm. Small amounts of easily ionized metals are therefore very effective in preventing the ionization of others, a fact which is widely used in spectrometric determination of the alkali metals.

2. Compound Formation

For many metals the occurrence of compound formation is evident from the emission of band spectra by the compounds which have been formed. For all cases of fairly extensive compound formation the effect is also apparent from comparison of the intensity of emission of the atomic lines with those of metals which are known not to form compounds under the prevailing conditions.

The intensity of emission of an atomic resonance line of frequency v is given, in the absence of self-absorption, by

$$I = Ahv[M](g'/g_0) \exp(-hv/kT) \qquad (28)$$

where A is the transition probability, g' and g_0 are the statistical weights of the upper and ground states, respectively, h is Planck's constant, and k is Boltzmann's constant. If two metals, M_1 and M_2, the latter of which is known not to form any compounds in the flame (e.g., sodium in fuel-rich flames), are added to a flame then the ratio of the concentrations of the elements is given by

$$\frac{[M_1]}{[M_2]} = \frac{I_1}{I_2} \frac{A_2 \nu_2}{A_1 \nu_1} \left(\frac{g_0}{g'}\right)_1 \left(\frac{g'}{g_0}\right)_2 \exp\left(-\frac{h(\nu_2 - \nu_1)}{kT}\right) \tag{29}$$

If the element M_1 forms a compound $M_1 X$ and the ratio $[M_1 X]/[M_1]$ is called ϕ then

$$\frac{[M_1 X] + [M_1]}{[M_2]} = \frac{[M_1]}{[M_2]} (1 + \phi) = \frac{[M_1]_0}{[M_2]_0} \tag{30}$$

where the subscript 0 denotes total concentration of metal added. Hence ϕ may be deduced from the measured line intensity ratio and the concentration ratio of the solutions in the atomizer (assuming equal delivery rates). This method of determining the extent of compound formation has been widely used. No atomizer calibration is required and the limitation of the accuracy in most cases is probably set by the accuracy of the values used for the transition probabilities. Examples of the use of this method may be found in (53–55).

The absolute concentration of M in a flame can be determined by fitting experimental curves of growth, i.e., log (intensity) versus log (atomizer solution concentration), to the theoretical curves. If the concentration of sodium, which forms insignificant amounts of compounds, is similarly determined under the same conditions, ϕ can be deducted from Eq. (30). This method is discussed in detail in (55–57).

The occurrence of compound formation may also be inferred from the intensity of emission of atomic resonance lines in flames of differing temperatures and compositions. If no significant amount of compound is formed (under conditions of thermal excitation and negligible self-absorption), a plot of log (intensity) versus $(1/T)$ will give a straight line of slope $(-E/R)$, where E is the excitation energy of the line. If significant amounts of a compound are formed, however, the amount of free metal atoms, and hence the intensity, will, in general, be dependent on the flame composition. This dependence will be reflected in the plot. Figure 8 shows such a plot (58) for gallium, indium, and thallium. Thallium shows no composition effect and hence the bulk of the added thallium must be present as free metal in the flames used. The slope of the line gives $E = 76.5$ kcal mole^{-1}, agreeing well with the theoretical value of 75.5 kcal mole^{-1}. The marked composition, or "family," effect for the other two metals indicates extensive compound formation. Hydroxides of InOH and GaOH are significant. This method and variations of it have been used quite extensively since they not only demonstrate the occurrence of compound formation but can also give information about the nature of the compound formed. Further examples of this technique may be found in (59).

The methods described above enable the amount of added metal which

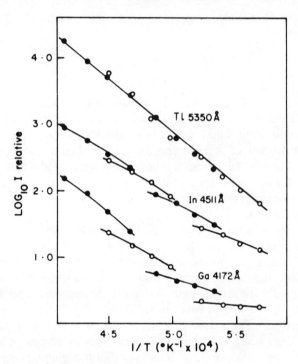

Fig. 8. Relative intensities of Ga, In, and Tl lines in flames of different compositions and temperatures. Each "family" of four points connected by a line (clearly separated for Ga and In) refers to flames with the same $[N_2]/[O_2]$ (unburned) composition. This ratio (by volume) took the values 3.0, 4.0, 5.0, 6.0 in the four families depicted. $[H_2]/[O_2]$ is varied within a family, taking values (for unburned gas, by volume) of 2.5, 3.0, 3.5, 4.0, respectively, in the direction of decreasing temperature. (Reprinted from (58) by courtesy of The Faraday Society.)

is converted into compounds to be determined fairly accurately when this occurs to an appreciable extent. Generally, these methods are not sufficiently sensitive and/or the transition probabilities not known with sufficient accuracy to enable conversions into compounds of less than about 20% of the added metal to be detected. Cases of weak compound formation can sometimes be studied by measurements of the compounds themselves where these give rise to suitably placed emission spectra.

More difficult than finding out how much of a compound has been formed is the problem of discovering its identity. Generally, the most important compounds to be expected are the simple oxides, hydroxides, and hydrides, though higher valent compounds may also be present, particularly in cooler flames. The simplest cases are those which only form one compound, such as the alkali metals in fuel-rich hydrogen flames which form only MOH. An example of a more complex case is that of barium, which in hydrogen-containing flames is believed to form appreciable amounts of BaO, BaOH, and Ba(OH)$_2$ (59).

The identification of compounds has been carried out by analyses of their emission spectra [for a comprehensive list of references for such analyses see Pearse and Gaydon (60), and for tables and recordings of flame spectra see (61–62)] or by measurements of the dependence of the concentration of the compound or free metal atoms on flame composition.

At equilibrium, relationships such as

$$MO \rightleftharpoons M+O$$
$$MOH \rightleftharpoons M+OH$$
$$MH \rightleftharpoons M+H$$

serve to relate $[MX]$ and $[M]$ to flame gas concentrations. If, for example, a compound formed is assumed to be the hydride MH, then

$$\phi = [MH]/[M] = [H]/K \tag{31}$$

where K is the equilibrium constant. This assumption may be checked and, if valid, the value for K obtained, by plotting measured values of ϕ versus calculated equilibrium values for [H]. Similar procedures may be used to examine for the formation of other compounds, MOH, MO, etc. This technique has also been widely used in the burned gas region of flames before equilibrium is reached. In this case, however, not only must the flame species concentration be determined experimentally but the relationship between ϕ and the flame composition must be determined, since equilibrium relationships such as Eq. (31) may not be applicable. This point is discussed more fully below.

Far less reliable thermodynamic data are available for equilibria involving metal compounds than for equilibria between natural flame gas species. Where values for the dissociation energies of the compound are known, K can be calculated from a statistical mechanical calculation for the entropy change, ΔS, and hence from $\Delta G^0 = -\mathscr{R}T \log K$ and $\Delta G^0 = \Delta H^0 - T\Delta S^0$. The main uncertainties in these calculations are in the values for vibrational frequencies and electronic statistical weights of the compounds. Examples of such calculations may be found in (63, 64) and values for bond dissociation energies in (65–68).

Direct experimental determinations of K have been made by effusion mass spectrometry and by flame photometric methods. The merits and disadvantages of both methods have been discussed by Schofield (69). In the flame photometric method K is either measured at one temperature and a general expression for K as a function of temperature obtained from a calculation of ΔS, or it is measured directly at several temperatures. Generally, the accuracy is good if one compound predominates, as for the alkali metals, but is less satisfactory when this is not the case, as for the alkaline earths in hydrogen-containing flames.

B. NONEQUILIBRIUM STATE IN THE BURNED GAS REGION

In a chemically interacting system, departures from chemical equilibrium in the concentrations of flame gas molecules and radicals will be reflected by corresponding disturbances in the relative amounts of metal atoms and compounds present. Where reactions between the metal and flame gas species are very fast, the concentration of metal atoms and compounds can be related to the flame gas composition; however, the reactions which enable these relationships to be deduced are less readily discernible than for a state of equilibrium where any relevant chemical reaction will serve this purpose.

The reactions of metals to form compounds in flames fall into two general types—bimolecular exchange and termolecular recombination. For the formation of the hybride MH, for example, these are,

$$\text{Type 1:} \quad M + H_2 \rightleftharpoons MH + H \tag{32}$$

$$\text{Type 2:} \quad M + H + X \rightleftharpoons MH + X \tag{33}$$

where X is a third body. Other reactions, such as

$$M + OH \rightleftharpoons MH + O$$

$$M + H_2O \rightleftharpoons MH + OH$$

are not distinguishable from (32) when reactions (2) and (3) are balanced. Similar reactions for (32) and (33) may be written for MOH and MO.

Sugden has shown (70) that the relaxation time for both reactions proceeding simultaneously is short compared with the rate of approach to complete equilibrium in flames and that one or other of the two types of reaction will become effectively balanced and link the ratio ϕ with the flame gas composition. It is important to note that, generally, only the reaction with the shorter relaxation time will tend to balance. Although alternative reactions may have short relaxation times, the over-all response time of the system to changes in composition will be closer to that of the faster reaction and this one will largely determine the value of ϕ. If reaction (32) predominates then ϕ for a hydride will be given by $\phi = K_{32}[H_2]/[H]$; if reaction (33), then by $\phi = K_{33}[H]$. Since, in the burned gas region, H may differ greatly from $[H]_{eq}$ the alternative expressions for ϕ may differ by a large factor.

The relative relaxation times for the two types of reactions in any particular case depend mainly on the stability of the compound involved. If the bond dissociation energy exceeeds about 70 kcal mole^{-1} then the bimolecular exchange (Type 1 reaction) will predominate, since balancing of the termolecular reaction is hindered by the large activation energy. If the bond dissociation energy is less than about 50 kcal mole^{-1} then Type 2 will predominate, since the balancing of this reaction is not hindered as much by the activation energy of the reverse reaction as much as reaction (32) is by the small values of [H] relative to [X]. For dissociation energies lying between 50 and 70 kcal mole^{-1} neither reaction is necessarily dominant and an intermediate value of ϕ may be obtained.

Examples of each kind of behavior are afforded by lithium and copper. Lithium forms a hydroxide with a Li-OH bond dissociation energy of 101 kcal mole^{-1}, and copper forms the hydride, CuH, with a bond energy of 66 kcal mole^{-1}

For Li, bimolecular exchange,

$$Li + H_2O \rightleftharpoons LiOH + H, \quad K_{34} \tag{34}$$

should predominate over termolecular recombination

$$Li + OH + X \rightleftharpoons LiOH + X$$

If this is the case, the function $\log (\phi[H]/[H_2O])$, which is $\log K_{34}$, will give a straight line of slope $-\Delta H/R$ when plotted against $1/T$, whereas $\log (\phi/[OH])$ will not. Figure 9 shows this to be the case. For copper, however, the plots in Fig. 10 show that balancing occurs by reaction (33) and not (32).

Above-equilibrium concentrations of free radicals in the burned gas region, therefore, affect the distribution of added metal between free atoms and compounds in different ways, depending on the bond energy and the type of compound. For the alkali metal hydroxides, for example, the bond energies, as determined by Jensen and Padley (71), are 101, 91, 83, 81, and 77 kcal mole^{-1} for Li, Cs, Rb, K, and Na, respectively. For each metal, therefore, ϕ is given by

$$\phi = K_{34}[H_2O]/[H]$$

where K_{34} is the equilibrium constant appropriate for each metal, and $[M]$ by

$$[M] = [M]_o(1+K_{34}[H_2O]/[H])^{-1}$$

Excess concentrations of [H], therefore, give rise to higher than equilibrium amounts of M. This is illustrated in Fig. 11, which shows the

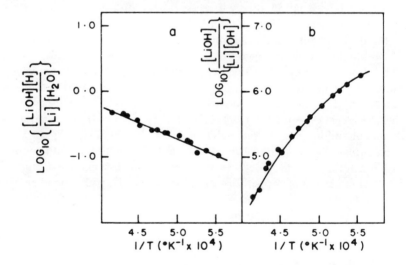

Fig. 9. (a) log ([LiOH][H]/[Li][H$_2$O]) against $1/T$. (b) log ([LiOH]/[Li][OH]) against $1/T$, establishing the dominance of the reaction Li+H$_2$O $\rightleftharpoons$ Li+OH in controlling the [LiOH]/[Li] ratio. (Reprinted from (70) by courtesy of The Faraday Society.)

[Li] profile for the hydrogen flame of Fig. 3(b). The effect is smaller for the other alkali metals in the order of decreasing bond energies, and for sodium the bond strength corresponds with values of $K_{34}[H_2O]/[H]$ which are $\ll 1$, and hence $[M] \approx [M]_0$ at all distances above the reaction zone.

The hydrides MH are usually unstable compounds and are balanced by Type 2 reactions. Therefore,

$$\phi = K_{33}[H]$$

and

$$[M] = [M]_0(1 + K_{33}[H])^{-1}$$

Excess values of [H] therefore give lower values for [M]. However, since compounds which are balanced by reaction (33) have low values of bond dissociation energies, $K_{33}[H] \ll 1$ for all values of [H] found in flames,

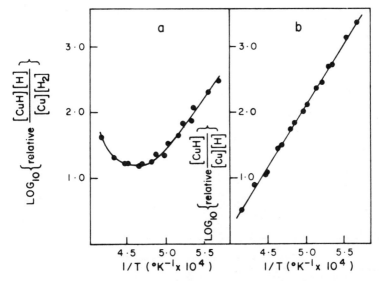

Fig. 10. (a) log (relative [CuH][H]/[Cu][H$_2$]) against $1/T$. (b) log (relative [CuH]/[Cu][H]) against $1/T$ establishing the dominance of the reaction Cu + H + $X \rightleftharpoons$ CuH + X in controlling the [CuH]/[Cu] ratio. (Reprinted from (70) by courtesy of The Faraday Society.)

and the effect on M is small. Measurement of [MH] provides a direct relative measure of [H], since [MH] = [M]K_{33}[H] $\approx$ [M]$_o K_{33}$[H] and the intensity of the CuH bands has been frequently used for determining relative [H] profiles in flames, for example, in (72).

Oxides are generally stable compounds and would be expected to be equilibrated in fuel-rich flames by reactions such as

$$M + H_2O \rightleftharpoons MO + H_2, \; K_{35} \tag{35}$$

$$M + OH \rightleftharpoons MO + H, \; K_{36} \tag{36}$$

which are indistinguishable when Eq. (3) is balanced. These give

$$\phi = K_{35}[H_2O]/[H_2] = K_{34}[OH]/[H]$$

and

$$M = M_o(1+K_{35}[H_2O]/[H_2])^{-1}$$

As $[H_2O]/[H_2]$ is essentially constant in the burned gas region, ϕ is independent of height and equal to the equilibrium value, ϕ_e. This assumes

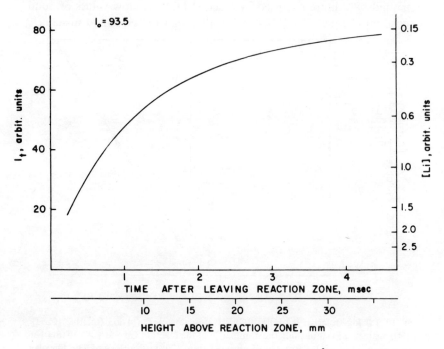

Fig. 11. Traced recording of intensity of light, from a Li 6707 Å hollow cathode lamp transmitted through a lithium-containing premixed laminar flow H_2–O_2–N_2 flame of unburned volume proportions 3.12/1/4.76, respectively, and relative [Li] as functions of distance and time from reaction zone. This flame is the same as that in Fig. 3(b).

that all the oxide formed is present in the gaseous phase. Many elements, however, and in particular the transition elements, form nonvolatile oxides; therefore, much of the added metal is present in the solid phase. In this case, if we assume that the MO in the gaseous phase MO_g is equilibrated with the solid phase MO_s, that is,

$$MO_s \rightleftharpoons MO_g, K_{37} \qquad (37)$$

and considering the case where the bulk of the added metal is present in the solid phase, then

$$[M][H_2O]/[M]_o[H_2] = K_{37}/K_{35}$$

This shows that, in fuel-rich flames, the temperature dependence of log $[M]$ is proportional not to ΔH_{35}, as in the case of volatile oxides, but to the term $\Delta H_{35} -$ (molar heat of evaporation), and the rate of increase of atomic emission with temperature is therefore generally larger for elements forming nonvolatile oxides than for those which form gaseous oxides.

REFERENCES

1. B. Lewis and G. von Elbe, *Combustion, Flames and Explosions of Gases*, 2nd ed., Academic, New York, 1961.
2. G. J. Minkoff and C. F. H. Tipper, *Chemistry of Combustion Reactions*, Butterworths, London, 1962.
3. V. N. Kondrat'ev, *Chemical Kinetics of Gas Reactions*, Oxford, London, 1964.
4. R. R. Baldwin and L. Mayor, *Trans. Faraday Soc.*, **56**, 80, 103 (1960).
5. C. P. Fennimore, *"Chemistry in pre-mixed flames"*, The International Encyclopaedia of Physical Chemistry and Chemical Physics, Topic 19 (A. F. Trotman-Dickenson, ed.), Vol. 5, Pergamon, London, 1964.
6. R. M. Fristrom and A. A. Westenberg, *Flame Structure*, McGraw-Hill, New York, 1965.
7. G. Dixon-Lewis, *Proc. Roy. Soc. (London)*, **A298**, 495 (1967).
8. Joint Army Navy Air Force, *Thermochemical Tables* prepared by Dow Chemical Company distributed by Clearing House for Federal Scientific and Technical Information, *PB 168370* (1965).
9. N. N. Semenov, *Some Problems of Chemical Kinetics and Reactivity*, Vol. 2, Pergamon, Oxford, 1958, pp. 48–49.
10. P. J. Padley, Ph. D. Thesis, Cambridge Univ., Cambridge, 1959.
11. K. N. Bascombe, *Symp. Combust. 10th, Univ. Cambridge, Cambridge, Engl., 1964*, The Combustion Institute, Pittsburgh, 1965, p. 55.
12. G. Dixon-Lewis, M. M. Sutton, and A. Williams, *Symp. Combust. 10th, Univ. Cambridge, Cambridge, Engl., 1964*, The Combustion Institute, Pittsburgh, 1965, p. 495.
13. A. Dixon-Lewis and A. Williams, *Nature*, **196**, 1309 (1962).
14. C. P. Fennimore and G. W. Jones, *Symp. Combust. 10th, Univ. Cambridge, Cambridge, Engl., 1964*, The Combustion Institute, Pittsburgh, 1965, p. 489.
15. R. W. Getzinger and G. L. Schott, *J. Chem. Phys.*, **43**, 3237 (1965).
16. M. A. A. Clyne and B. A. Thrush, *Proc. Roy. Soc. (London)*, **A275**, 559 (1963).
17. M. A. A. Clyne and B. A. Thrush, *Symp. Combust. 9th, Cornell Univ., Ithaca, N.Y., 1962*, Academic, New York, 1963, p. 177.
18. C. P. Fennimore and G. W. Jones, *J. Phys. Chem.*, **62**, 1578 (1958).
19. R. M. Fristrom and A. A. Westenberg, *Symp. Combust. 10th, Univ. Cambridge, Cambridge, Engl., 1964*, The Combustion Institute, Pittsburgh, 1965, p. 473.

20. C. P. Fennimore and G. W. Jones, *J. Chem. Phys.*, **39**, 1514 (1963).
21. C. P. Fennimore and G. W. Jones, *Symp. Combust. 9th, Cornell Univ., Ithaca, N.Y., 1962*, Academic, New York, 1963, p. 597.
22. R. M. Fristrom, C. Grunfelder, and S. Favin, *J. Phys. Chem.*, **64**, 1386 (1960).
23. C. P. Fennimore and G. W. Jones, *J. Phys. Chem.*, **63**, 1834 (1959).
24. U. Bonne, K. H. Homann, and H. G. Wagner, *Symp. Combust. 10th, Univ. Cambridge, Cambridge, Engl., 1964*, The Combustion Institute, Pittsburgh, 1965, p. 503.
25. G. L. Schott, *J. Chem. Phys.*, **32**, 710 (1960).
26. W. E. Kaskan, *Combust. Flame*, **3**, 39 (1959).
27. M. J. McEwan and L. F. Phillips, *Combust. Flame*, **11**, 63, (1967).
28. W. E. Kaskan and G. L. Schott, *Combust. Flame*, **6**, 73 (1962).
29. K. Schofield, *Planet Space Sci.*, **15**, 643 (1967).
30. C. P. Fennimore and G. W. Jones, *J. Phys. Chem.*, **62**, 178 (1958).
31. R. L. Taylor, M. Camac, and R. M. Feinberg, *Symp. Combust. 11th, Univ. of California, Berkeley, 1966*, The Combustion Institute, Pittsburgh, 1967, pp. 49–65.
32. D. R. White and R. C. Millikan, *AIAA J.*, **2**, 1844 (1964).
33. B. Widom and S. H. Bauer, *J. Chem. Phys.*, **21**, 1670 (1953).
34. R. C. Millikan and D. R. White, *J. Chem. Phys.*, **39**, 98 (1963).
35. M. Camac, *Avco Everett Research Laboratory, Research Rep. 194*, Oct. 1964.
36. J. H. Kiefer and R. W. Lutz, *Symp. Combust. 11th, Univ. of California, Berkeley, 1966*, The Combustion Institute, Pittsburgh, 1967, pp. 67–76.
37. A. G. Gaydon and H. G. Wolfhard, *Proc. Roy. Soc. (London)*, **A199**, 89 (1949).
38. W. R. Kane and H. P. Broida, *J. Chem Phys.*, **21**, 347 (1953).
39. E. C. Hinck, T. F. Seamans, M. Vanpee, and H. G. Wolfhard, *Symp. Combust. 10th, Univ. Cambridge, Cambridge, Engl., 1964*, The Combustion Institute, Pittsburgh, 1965, p. 21.
40. F. E. Belles and M. R. Lauver, *J. Chem. Phys.*, **40**, 415 (1964).
41. W. E. Kaskan, *J. Chem. Phys.*, **31**, 944 (1959).
42. P. J. T. Zeegers and C. T. J. Alkemade, *Symp. Combust. 10th, Univ. Cambridge, Cambridge, Engl., 1964*, The Combustion Institute, Pittsburgh, 1965, p. 33.
43. A. G. Gaydon, *The Spectroscopy of Flames*, Chapman and Hall, London, 1957.
44. G. L. Schott and J. L. Kinsey, *J. Chem. Phys.*, **29**, 1177 (1958).
45. V. V. Voevodsky and R. L. Soloukhin, *Symp. Combust. 10th, Univ. Cambridge, Cambridge, Engl., 1964*, The Combustion Institute, Pittsburgh, 1965, p. 279.
46. T. Asaba, W. C. Gardiner, Jr., and R. F. Stubbeman, *Symp. Combust. 10th, Univ. Cambridge, Cambridge, Engl., 1964*, The Combustion Institute, Pittsburgh, 1965, p. 295.
47. F. E. Belles and M. R. Lauver, *Symp. Combust. 10th, Univ. Cambridge, Cambridge, Engl., 1964*, The Combustion Institute, Pittsburgh, 1965, p. 285.
48. S. S. Penner, *International Series of Monographs on Aeronautical Sciences and Controlled Flight* (Chairmen, T. von Kármán and H. Dryden), Division III: *Propulsion Systems including Fuels* (E. R. Sharp and A. D. Baxter, eds.) Vol. I, *Chemistry Problems in Jet Propulsion*, Pergamon, London, 1957.
49. A. G. Gaydon, *Flames, Their Structure Radiation and Temperature*. 2nd ed. revised, Chapman & Hall, London, 1960, Chap. XII.
50. *Selected Values of Chemical thermodynamic properties*, Natl. Bur. Std. (U.S.A.). Circ. 500, 1952.

51. R. H. Fowler and E. A. Guggenheim, *Statistical Thermodynamics*, Cambridge University Press, London, (1962).

52. P. F. Knewstubb and T. M. Sugden, *Nature*, **196,** 1311 (1962).

53. P. J. Kalff, T. Hollander, and C. T. J. Alkemade, *J. Chem. Phys.*, **43,** 2299, (1965).

54. C. G. James and T. M. Sugden, *Proc. Roy. Soc.* (*London*), A**227,** 312 (1955).

55. T. Hollander, Ph.D. Thesis, State Univ., Utrecht, 1964.

56. C. G. James and T. M. Sugden, *Nature*, **171,** 428 (1953).

57. E. Hinnov and H. Kohn, *J. Opt. Soc. Am.*, **47,** 156 (1957).

58. E. M. Bulewicz and T. M. Sugden, *Trans. Faraday Soc.*, **54,** 830 (1958).

59. T. M. Sugden and K. Schofield, *Trans. Faraday Soc.*, **62,** 566 (1966).

60. R. W. B. Pearse and A. G. Gaydon, *The Identification of Molecular Spectra*, 3rd ed., Chapman and Hall, London, 1963.

61. R. Mavrodineanu and H. Boiteux, *Flame Spectroscopy*, Wiley, New York, 1965.

62. R. Herrmann and C. T. J. Alkemade, *Chemical Analysis by Flame Photometry* (P. T. Gilbert, Jr., transl.), Interscience, New York, 1963.

63. P. W. J. Boumans, *Theory of Spectrochemical Excitation*, Plenum, New York, 1966.

64. G. Herzberg, *Infra-red and Raman Spectra of Polyatomic Molecules*, Chap, 5, Van Nostrand, New York, 1945.

65. G. Herzberg, *Spectra of Diatomic Molecules*, Van Nostrand, New York, 1950.

66. A. G. Gaydon, *Dissociation Energies*, 2nd ed., Chapman and Hall, London, 1953.

67. P. G. Wilkinson, *Astrophys. J.*, **138,** 778 (1963).

68. M. G. Inghram, W. A. Chupka, and J. Berkowitz, *Mem. Soc. Roy. Sci. Liege*, **18,** 513 (1957).

69. K. Schofield, *J. Chem. Phys.*, to be published.

70. T. M. Sugden, *Trans. Faraday Soc.*, **52,** 1465 (1956).

71. D. E. Jensen and P. J. Padley, *Trans Faraday Soc.*, **62,** 2132 (1966).

72. E. M. Bulewicz and T. M. Sugden, *Trans. Faraday Soc.*, **52,** 1475 (1956).

6 Flames for Atomic Absorption and Emission Spectrometry*

Richard N. Kniseley

INSTITUTE OF ATOMIC RESEARCH
DEPARTMENT OF CHEMISTRY
IOWA STATE UNIVERSITY
AMES, IOWA

I. Introduction

The purpose of the flame in atomic emission and absorption spectrometry is to provide a stable, noise-free system to convert the sample into

* Contribution No. 2283. Work was performed in the Ames Laboratory of the U.S. Atomic Energy Commission.

free atoms, and in the case of atomic emission, to provide energy to excite spectral lines. In fulfilling these requirements the flame must perform many functions in the analytical process. Table 1 lists the processes which may occur when a solution of a metallic salt is sprayed into a flame. These are not necessarily all the processes which occur nor is it necessary that all of these occur in a stepwise manner. This table merely illustrates the complexity of the reactions which must occur in order to produce free atoms from the solution droplets. Because of this complexity, the reactions must occur in rapid succession, the total time being as short as 5 msec in some instances. Thus, the reactions are probably kinetically controlled and in most cases probably do not go to completion. The extent to which they are complete depends on many factors involving both the flame and the

TABLE 1

Processes Occurring in the Flame

1. Vaporization of solvent
2. Dehydration of residual salt particles
3. Vaporization of residue or its reaction product
4. Decomposition of vaporized species
5. Dissociation of molecules
6. Excitation and ionization
7. Emission of line radiation
8. Absorption of incident radiation by ground state atoms

nebulized solution. In the case of the flame, the major considerations are the temperature and the chemical environment within the flame gases. These will, of course, vary in different parts of the flame and thus the flame position sampled also becomes important (1).

The maximum temperature which can be attained in a flame is principally determined by the fuel and the oxidant. The actual effective temperature under analytical conditions depends on many factors including the fuel-to-oxidant ratio, the type of burner, the nature of the solvent and the amount nebulized into the flame, the heat capacity of flame combustion products, the geometry of the flame, the position observed within the flame, the amount of air entrainment, etc. Table 2 lists the maximum theoretical adiabatic temperatures (3) for several flames assuming stoichiometric gas mixtures for the reactions listed. Actual measured temperatures and burning velocities are also included in this table. The measured temperatures are, in general, somewhat lower than the theoretical ones, principally due to the factors just listed. Also, it is appropriate to note that these measured values are only representative and may vary among experimenters, depending on the exact flame conditions and the method of measurement. However, measured temperatures do provide a general indication of the relative temperature of various flames.

If the excitation of free atoms is the only consideration and if the excitation is purely thermal in nature, the optimum sensitivity in flame emission spectrometry is usually obtained with the flame of the highest temperature. Likewise, high temperature flames often provide a more efficient source of free atoms for atomic absorption spectrometry. However,

TABLE 2

Temperatures and Burning Velocities of Common Premixed Flames

Fuel	Oxidant	Temperature (°C) Theoret.[a]	Meas.	Burning velocity[b] (cm/sec)	Ref.[c]
Acetylene	Air	2050	2125–2400	160–266 (160)	(2–4)
Acetylene	Oxygen	3110	3060–3135	800–2480 (1100)	(3–4)
Acetylene	Nitrous oxide	—	2600–2800	160	(5–6)
Hydrogen	Air	2115	2000–2050	320–440	(3–4)
Hydrogen	Oxygen	2690	2550–2700	900–3680 (2000)	(2, 3, 7)
Methane	Air	1955	1875	70	(3)
Methane	Oxygen	2720	2670	5502 (?)	(3)
Natural gas	Air	1840	1700–1900	55	(3)
Natural gas	Oxygen	2800	2740	—	(3)

[a] From (3).
[b] Values in parentheses are probably the ones most applicable to laboratory burners.
[c] References refer to experimental values of temperature and burning velocity.

in both flame emission and flame absorption spectrometry, one must also consider ionization and chemical reactions. Ionization will deplete the neutral atom population and eventually lead to a decrease in the atomic line emission or absorption signal. The so-called "chemical interferences" are the result of a reduction in the number of free atoms available for excitation due to the formation of relatively stable molecular species. The use of high-temperature flames favors the dissociation of these compounds and minimizes the chemical interferences (8, 9). Thus, one must often compromise between the optimum excitation of atomic lines, the optimum dissociation of chemical compounds, and minimal ionization.

It is important to note that while high-temperature flames decrease the problems associated with chemical interferences, they also introduce other problems into the analytical process. Ionization, as already mentioned, tends to decrease the atomic emission and absorption due to a decrease in the number of neutral atoms present within the flame. In addition, high temperatures increase the population of the upper excited states and

TABLE 3

Dissociation Energies of Some Stable Metal Monoxides

Molecule	Dissociation energy (eV)	Molecule	Dissociation energy (eV)
AlO	5.98[a]	NdO	7.4[b]
BO	7.5–9.37[a]	PrO	7.8[b]
BaO	5.46–5.85[a]	ScO	7.1[b]
BeO	4.82–5.70[a]	SmO	6.1[b]
CeO	8.3[b]	TaO	8.4[b]
DyO	6.5[b]	TbO	7.4[b]
ErO	6.6[b]	ThO	8.7[a]
GdO	7.4[b]	TiO	6.9[c]
HfO	7.9[a]	TmO	6.0[a]
HoO	6.5[b]	UO	7.8[a]
LaO	8.2[b]	VO	6.4[a]
LuO	7.2[b]	WO	6.68–7.2[a]
NbO	7.5[a]	YO	7.3[b]
		ZrO	7.8[a]

[a] From (3).
[b] From L. L. Ames, D. N. Walsh, and D. White, *Report AD-651562* (Defense Documentation Center, Arlington, Va.), May 1967.
[c] From G. Herzberg, *Spectrum of Diatomic Molecules* 2nd ed., Van Nostrand, New York, 1950.

therefore add to the complexity of the emission spectra. In the case of elements which have relatively simple spectra, this is not a serious problem. However, in the case of elements such as the transition elements, which have very complicated arc and spark spectra, the increase in temperature may well produce exceedingly complex spectra which require large, high-dispersion spectrographs in order to separate the spectral lines. One of the major advantages of flame emission spectrometry is the simplicity of the spectra, which allows determination of most metallic elements using a low-dispersion table-model spectrometer. The use of extremely high-temperature flames may well negate this advantage. Within certain limits the complexity of the flame emission spectrum is not an important consideration in atomic absorption spectrometry.

The chemical environment within the flame also influences the production of free atoms. This is most apparent in the case of elements which form relatively stable monoxides at ordinary flame temperatures. Some of

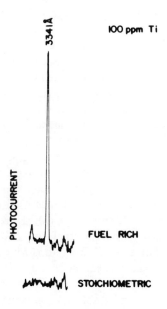

Fig. 1. Short wavelength region of the titanium spectrum emitted by a stoichiometric and fuel-rich flame.

these elements, along with their MO dissociation energies, are listed in Table 3. Changes in the chemical environment as a result of changes in flame stoichiometry produce large differences in the efficiency of free atom production. Atomic line spectra of the elements which form stable monoxides are only weakly observed in normal oxygen–hydrogen and oxygen–acetylene flames. However, the fuel-rich, oxygen–acetylene flame is capable of producing intense atomic line spectra from these elements (*10, 11*). This is well illustrated in Fig. 1 for the case of titanium. These spectra were run under identical conditions except for a change in the acetylene flow rate. Only weak atomic line emission is observed in the stoichiometric flame. However, in the fuel-rich flame, intense atomic line emission is observed when an ethanolic solution of titanium perchlorate is introduced into a fuel-rich oxygen–acetylene flame. Similar results are obtained with a nitrous oxide–acetylene flame (8, 12). These increases are readily attributed to an increase in the free atom population as a result of a decrease in the number of MO molecules. This may occur through reduction of MO molecules by carbon-containing species which are present in high concentrations in the fuel-rich flame, and through a decrease in the rate of formation of MO molecules due to the deficiency of atomic oxygen within the fuel-rich region (10). The effect cannot be primarily related to temperature because the fuel-rich flame is approximately 150° K cooler than the normal stoichiometric flame. The observation that the fuel-rich flames are more efficient in producing free atoms in the elements listed in Table 3 has been confirmed by atomic absorption studies (8, 12–15). These studies on the production of free atoms from MO molecules illustrate the necessity of compromising between flame temperature and flame environment.

Flames are generally divided into the broad types of premixed and diffusion flames (16). However, for the flames used in analytical atomic spectrometry, the classes would better be called premixed and surface-mixed flames. In premixed flames the fuel and oxidant are thoroughly mixed prior to combustion at the burner top. Many types of premixed burners have been used for atomic emission and absorption spectrometry. One of the most commonly used premixed burners is the ordinary Bunsen burner wherein the oxidant (air) is thoroughly mixed with the fuel (natural gas) within a long cylindrical chamber prior to combustion. The same principle is utilized in numerous emission and absorption burners used in ordinary analytical spectrometry. In the case of surface-mixed flames the fuel and the oxidant are conducted to the burner surface through separate channels, and are mixed at the burner surface during, or just prior to, the combustion process. The surface-mixed burner is best characterized, as far as normal analytical spectrometric burners are concerned, by the ordinary Beckman-type sprayer-burner which utilizes separate ports to conduct the fuel and oxidant to the burner surface. The fuel and the oxidant are mixed within the combustion zone by turbulence which is created at the burner tip. An internal nebulizer introduces the solution into the center of the very turbulent flame. The advantage of the surface-mixed burner over the premixed burner lies principally in the problem associated with the burning velocity and explosive nature of many gas mixtures. In the case of the premixed burner, since the fuel and oxidant are intimately mixed within a chamber, the danger of explosion always exists. However, in the surface- or turbulent-mixed burner the oxidant and fuel are separated until they

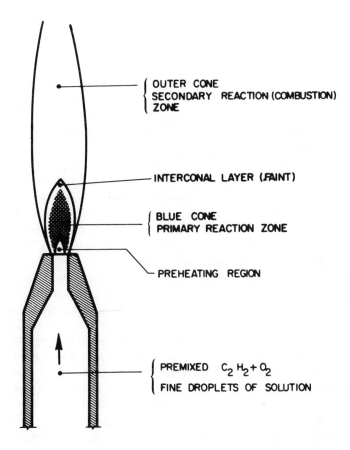

OUTER CONE
SECONDARY   REACTION (COMBUSTION)
ZONE

INTERCONAL LAYER (FAINT)

BLUE CONE
PRIMARY REACTION ZONE

PREHEATING REGION

PREMIXED $C_2 H_2 + O_2$
FINE DROPLETS OF SOLUTION

Fig. 2. Schematic diagram of a stoichiometric oxygen–acetylene flame.

reach the actual combustion zone. Thus, in the latter case, the danger of flashback is negligible as compared with the premixed burner.

In addition to the question of gas mixing, one must also consider the nature of gas flow when designing a burner for atomic emission or absorption spectrometry. Gas flow is normally divided into two general categories: laminar flow and turbulent flow (16). Differentiation between the two is often difficult and has been defined according to several different criteria. However, one may define laminar flow within a burner as flow which is generally directed perpendicular to the flame front. In the case of turbulent flow, the gas flow direction is not well defined and often flows in many directions with respect to the normal of the flame front. Turbulent flow is used in most surface-mixed burners since the turbulence is necessary for thorough mixing of the gases within the combustion zone. However, in premixed burners, since the gases are mixed prior to entering the combustion zone, turbulence is not necessary and the gases may be better directed with respect to the combustion front. This results in a "better behaved" flame which usually has a lower flame noise and an improved atomization efficiency. Also, the premixed, laminar-flow flame usually exhibits a lower spectral background than that encountered when using turbulent-mixed flames. The problems associated with the high burning velocity of several gas mixtures such as oxygen–hydrogen, oxygen–acetylene, and other similar mixtures have tended to make turbulent-mixed flames more popular in certain applications. However, if burners of both types are available, it is usually preferable to use premixed, laminar-flow burners for the optimum signal-to-noise ratio in both atomic emission and atomic absorption spectrometry.

Flames are not homogeneous sources; rather the temperature and chemical environment vary from area to area. In surface-mixed or turbulent-mixed flames this is not as readily apparent since no well-defined zones are observed. However, in premixed flames four definite zones can be observed, as illustrated in Fig. 2. The first (or innermost) is the preheating zone where the combustion mixture is heated to the ignition temperature. The second zone is the primary reaction zone which is characteristically a blue cone surrounding the preheating zone. The primary reaction zone is the seat of very complex reactions which are basic to the combustion process. Since the reactants and products are not in thermodynamic equilibrium, chemiexcitation is often observed within this zone (7, 17). Immediately beyond the primary reaction zone lies the interconal zone. In stoichiometric hydrocarbon flames this zone is extremely small, usually a millimeter or less in height. However, in fuel-rich hydrocarbon flames, particularly oxygen–acetylene and nitrous oxide–acetylene flames, this zone increases greatly in height and may reach a size of several centimeters before a "sooty", ill-defined flame results. The interconal region is very important in the production of free atoms in fuel-rich acetylene flames. It is within this zone that the chemical environment is most conducive to the production of free atoms from those elements which form stable monoxide molecules (*10*). The outermost zone is the secondary reaction zone or flame plume. Within this zone the products of the combustion processes are burned to stable molecular species by the air which is entrained from the atmosphere.

Since chemical equilibrium is probably not attained within the primary reaction zone, in most cases the areas above the primary reaction zone are of prime analytical interest. The environment above the primary reaction

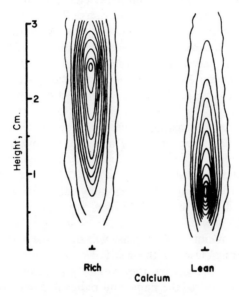

Fig. 3. Distribution of atoms in an air–acetylene flame. Contours are drawn at intervals of 0.1 absorption unit, with maximum absorbance in the center. (Courtesy of *Analytical Chemistry*.)

zone is usually more conducive to the production of free atoms provided that proper flame stoichiometry has been achieved. Likewise, the maximum temperature within the flame is usually achieved just beyond the tip of the blue cone, and this higher temperature favors both the production of free atoms and maximum excitation for atomic emission spectrometry. The higher one proceeds in the flame the longer is the time that nebulized material has spent within the flame, thus improving atomization efficiency. However, at higher points in the flame, the atomized material is diluted by flame gases, thereby lowering the sensitivity of detection. Likewise, the cooling effect of the entrained air lowers the flame temperature and may decrease the efficiency of atomization. Thus, the selection of the proper position within the flame for optimum emission or absorption is dependent on a careful compromise among the above factors. This is shown in Fig. 3, which illustrates the distribution of calcium free atoms in a fuel-rich and a fuel-lean flame.

In selecting and designing burners, the burning velocity of the combustion mixture is also a very important parameter. The burning velocity of a flame can be conveniently defined as the rate of flame propagation through a homogeneous gas mixture. The exact value of the burning velocity will vary, depending on the exact experimental conditions used for the measurement (16). It is not uncommon for the reported burning velocity to vary by a factor of 2 or more for the same combustion mixture, but again it is a convenient relative parameter for the selection of combustion mixtures.

Table 2 also lists the maximum burning velocities reported for several common flames. The propagation of a stable, stationary flame requires that the velocity of the gas mixture, normal to the flame front, must be at least equal to, and preferably higher than, the burning velocity. In premixed burners, if this condition is not fulfilled, flashback will occur. In properly designed surface-mixed burners, the danger of flashback is remote but, if the flow does not exceed the burning velocity, the flame is difficult to maintain and the flame base will sit on the burner top, thereby causing overheating. Usually the gas flows are adjusted to exceed the burning velocity of the gas by approximately a factor of 5, thereby increasing the "stiffness" of the flame and reducing flame noise. The exact flow velocities necessary for the production of a useful flame must be experimentally determined for the particular burner and the combustion mixture utilized. Fiorino, Kniseley, and Fassel (15) have discussed the factors involved in burner design.

When using unfamiliar gas mixtures for the production of a flame, it is well to remember that the danger of flashback and explosion always exists. Therefore, one must always be extremely cautious when using premixed burners in these situations, particularly if the volume of premixed gases is large. When the particular characteristics of a combustion mixture are unknown or uncertain, it is usually preferable to use surface-mixed burners for preliminary studies and later change to premixed burners if the flames seem well behaved and if the necessary flow rates can be achieved.

II. Common Flames for Emission and Absorption Spectrometry

A. HYDROCARBON FLAMES

At the present time, hydrocarbon flames are the ones most widely used in both atomic emission and absorption spectrometry. The hydrocarbon flames offer a wide range of temperatures, the air–natural gas flame being as low as 1900° K and the oxygen–acetylene flame reaching temperatures in excess of 3000° K. The air–natural gas flame is often used for the determination of alkali elements by atomic absorption spectrometry. The low temperature of this flame tends to minimize ionization and thereby increase sensitivity. However, in low-temperature flames, chemical interferences are more prevalent and therefore the utilization of these flames is somewhat limited. The problem of ionization of alkali and alkaline earth elements in higher-temperature flames can usually be overcome by the addition of an ionization suppressor to the solutions, thereby minimizing the advantages of low- temperature flames for these elements. The hotter acetylene flames are the ones most extensively used in both atomic emission and absorption spectrometry.

Three oxidants, air, oxygen, and nitrous oxide, are normally used with acetylene. These flames provide a range of temperatures from about 2400°K for air–acetylene up to approximately 3200°K for oxygen–acetylene flames. These higher temperatures favor improved atomization, elimination of chemical interferences, and improved atomic emission detection limits due to the higher excitation levels achieved.

The air–acetylene flame is extensively used in atomic absorption and is quite satisfactory for metals which are relatively easy to atomize and do not form molecular species which are stable at the temperature of this flame. The air–acetylene flame is more transparent and has less intense emission compared with the nitrous oxide–acetylene and oxygen–acetylene flames and thus often provides an improved signal-to-noise ratio in instances where higher flame temperatures are not necessary. The air–acetylene flame is, however, less suitable for atomic emission spectrometry since the lower temperature is less effective in populating excited states. Therefore, its use as an emission source is restricted to those elements which easily form free atoms at lower temperatures and whose excited states lie at very low energies.

The advantages of the oxygen–acetylene flame for both emission and absorption spectrometry have been known for several years (*10*) and the more recently described nitrous oxide–acetylene flame (*12*) shares these attributes. The higher temperatures of these two flames increase the efficiency of free atom production and also provide higher populations of upper excited states. In addition, the higher-temperature flames have been shown to be very effective in eliminating many of the common "chemical interferences" in both atomic emission and atomic absorption flame spectrometry. The fuel-rich, oxygen–acetylene and nitrous oxide–acetylene flames can efficiently produce free atoms of those elements which form stable monoxides in ordinary flames. Fassel and Golightly (*18*) have given detection limits for the flame atomic emission of most metallic elements utilizing a premixed oxygen–acetylene flame. Likewise, Pickett and Koirtyohann (*19*) have published emission detection limits for many metallic elements utilizing the nitrous oxide–acetylene flame. In almost all cases these detection limits are superior to those obtained with other types of flames. The principal exceptions are the elements with extremely high excitation potentials, such as arsenic, tin, and antimony, which have been observed with improved detection limits in special flames that exhibit chemiexcitation (*17, 20*). Thus, with few exceptions, the oxygen–acetylene and nitrous oxide–acetylene flames are the flames of choice for atomic emission spectrometry. Atomic absorption studies (*12, 21*) have shown that the oxygen–acetylene and nitrous oxide–acetylene flames are also superior for the atomic absorption determination of many metallic elements.

One disadvantage of the nitrous oxide–acetylene and oxygen–acetylene flames is the relatively intense background which is emitted within certain spectral regions. This background spectrum is the result of radicals and molecules which are present in the flame gases in large quantities. The strongest emission arises from the CH, OH, CN, and C_2 molecules. Several tabulations of flame band systems are available (*3, 22–24*) and these are very useful to investigators who utilize flames.

The bands which can be attributed to the CH radical lie in the region from 3870 to 4385 Å. The 4315 Å system is the strongest and is degraded to shorter wavelengths. The systems at 3870 and 3980 Å appear quite strong and are degraded to the red. The system at 3140 Å is somewhat obscured by the very prominent OH band systems within this region.

The OH radical emits very prominent bands in the 2800–2950, 3060–3200, and 3400–3480 Å regions. The strongest systems have their band heads at 3064, 3067, and 3089 Å and all bands are degraded to the red. The bands attributable to the CN molecule have their heads at 3600, 3900, 4200, and 6100 Å. The lower three bands are degraded to the violet while the upper band is degraded to the red. The most prominent of these bands is the 3900 Å band.

The C_2 molecules emit the well-known Swan bands which are all degraded to the violet. The outstanding band heads are at 5636, 5165, 4600, and 4780 Å. At certain positions in the flame the much weaker Fox–Herzberg system is observed in the region from about 2850 to 2990 Å. This is obscured to some extent by the OH band systems in this region.

The intensities of the various band systems will vary greatly with the flame stoichiometry. Usually the C_2 and CH systems become more prominent as the flame is made more fuel-rich. The OH bands reach their maximum intensity near a stoichiometric mixture and remain strong in fuel-lean mixtures. Likewise, the relative intensities of these bands vary between the nitrous oxide–acetylene and oxygen–acetylene flames. The CN band systems are very prominent in the nitrous oxide–acetylene while the C_2 and CH bands are considerably lower in intensity. The converse is true for the oxygen–acetylene flame. In the latter flame the C_2 and CH systems are very prominent compared with the relatively weak and limited CN system. The background of the flame is, of course, quite important because high background flame emission will often contribute noise in both atomic emission and atomic absorption spectrometry. This noise, if excessive, will lead to much poorer detection limits and lower precision of analysis. Thus, since the backgrounds of these two flames are considerably different and the strong emission occurs in different regions, the two flames tend to complement one another. If nitrous oxide–acetylene cannot be used because of high emission within certain spectral regions, the oxygen–acetylene flame can usually be substituted. The same is true if one wishes to make measurements in regions where the oxygen–acetylene flame has excessively high background. In these instances the nitrous oxide–acetylene flame can usually be substituted.

The major difficulty with oxygen–acetylene flames is their high burning velocity, which complicates burner design. Nitrous oxide–acetylene mixtures, with their lower burning velocity, are more easily handled in premixed burners. For this reason, the nitrous oxide–acetylene flame is more widely used for atomic absorption and is becoming more popular for atomic emission. With both flames the danger of flashback is always present and care should be taken to prevent this occurrence, particularly when large-volume burners are used. Flow rates must be adjusted to provide a gas velocity at the exit port which exceeds the burning velocity of the flame by a factor of two or more. The safest procedure is to light the burner with air–acetylene mixture and then carefully add the alternate oxidant until the proper flame stoichiometry is attained. Likewise, return to air–acetylene mixture before extinguishing the flame. Care should also be taken to keep the burner orifice clean since interruptions in the gas flow pattern may lead to flashback.

B. HYDROGEN FLAMES

Hydrogen is normally burned using either air or oxygen as an oxidant. The hydrogen flames are relatively transparent and thus useful for the atomic emission and atomic absorption determination of many metals. The background radiation from the flame is weak with the exception of the OH bands, which are relatively strong. The temperatures of hydrogen flames are somewhat lower than those of the corresponding acetylene flames. Likewise, even under fuel-rich conditions, hydrogen flames do not exhibit the strong reducing properties which are characteristic of fuel-rich acetylene flames. Thus, when compared with the corresponding acetylene flames, the hydrogen flames ordinarily are less efficient in atomization, exhibit more chemical interferences, and are less efficient in excitation. The major advantage of hydrogen flames apparently lies in the improved signal-to-noise ratio for some elements due to the low background intensity of this flame. However, in most instances, the advantages of the acetylene flames outweigh this advantage of the hydrogen flames and therefore, for most elements, the acetylene flames are preferable for flame spectrometry.

Oxygen–hydrogen flames also have a very high burning velocity and thus only a few premixed burners have been designed which can safely handle a mixture of oxygen and hydrogen. Nitrous oxide–hydrogen mixtures should have a much lower burning velocity and N_2O is a preferable oxidant where high-temperature, premixed hydrogen flames are desired. Although the nitrous oxide–hydrogen flame has not been extensively studied, its characteristics should be very similar to those of oxygen–hydrogen flames and thus should be a suitable, more easily handled substitute for the latter flame. Dagnall et al. (*24a*) and Willis et al. (*5*) have recently studied the nitrous oxide–hydrogen flame. These investigators found the flame easy and safe to use with conventional premixed burners. In general the flame was found useful for the determination of a limited number of easily atomized metals.

An interesting application of hydrogen flames lies in the over-excitation emission from several elements with relatively high excitation potentials. Gilbert (*17*) has studied the chemiexcitation in the air–acetylene flame supplied with a solution of a hydrocarbon solvent. The emission detection limit for several elements can be improved by an order of magnitude or more using overexcitation phenomena in this flame to provide excitation energy. Interestingly enough, atomic absorption studies have shown that the air–hydrogen flame is more efficient in producing free atoms for some elements. The most striking example is the case of tin, where the atomization efficiency is improved by at least a factor of 3 or 4 in the air–hydrogen flame as compared with the air–acetylene flame. These phenomena are at present not well understood.

Gilbert (25) also has studied a "split" air–hydrogen flame for the detection of chlorine by observing the chloride band emission. The method is capable of detecting low concentrations of chlorine in organic compounds and probably would be satisfactory for the detection of chloride in solution. Zacha and Winefordner (26) have described an argon–hydrogen–air flame which they found useful for atomic fluorescence and flame emission analyses.

III. Exotic Flames

The area of "exotic" flames usually encompasses flames in which an oxidant other than oxygen is used, a fuel other than hydrogen or a hydrocarbon is consumed, or a combination of an unusual fuel and oxidant is utilized. One or two of these exotic flames have found use in atomic emission and absorption spectrometry but, for the most part, they have not been extensively studied. The nitrous oxide–acetylene flame is an excellent example of an exotic flame which has recently come into common use. In most other cases the exotic flames have not been used for analytical spectroscopy. Several of the more interesting flames are discussed briefly, and Table 4 summarizes this information.

A. Perchloryl Fluoride Flames

Perchloryl fluoride, ClO_3F, combines the three most electronegative elements into a chemically active but physically stable compound. When dry, the gas shows little reactivity toward common metals. Damp perchloryl fluoride, on the other hand, is very corrosive toward most metals. The perchloryl fluoride–hydrogen flame has a temperature of about 3300°C and has been used for the determination of calcium, strontium, magnesium, lithium, and sodium (27, 28). A Beckman-type spray-burner was used for these studies. The perchloryl fluoride–acetylene flame has extremely high background in the 4500–7000 Å region and this greatly limits the analytical application of this flame. No special precautions other than good ventilation appear necessary when using perchloryl fluoride.

B. Nitric Oxide Flames

Nitric oxide readily supports the combustion of a wide variety of fuel, but in some cases these flames are difficult to ignite (*6, 29*). For example

TABLE 4

Summary of Exotic Flames

Oxidant	Fuel	Temperature, °K	Ref.
ClO_3F	H_2	3550	(*27, 28*)
NO	H_2		
NO	CH_4		(*6, 29*)
NO	NH_3		
NO	C_2N_2		(*35*)
NO_2	H_2		(*29*)
NO_2	Hydrocarbon		(*29*)
NO_2	C_2N_2	> 5000	(*35*)
O_2	NH_3	2010	(*36*)
O_2	C_4N_2	5250	(*37*)
O_2	$(CN)_2$	4800	(*30–33*)
O_2	HCN	3050	(*38*)
O_2	C_2N_2	> 5000	(*35*)
ClF_3	H_2		
ClF_3	CO		
ClF_3	CS_2		(*39*)
ClF_3	H_2O		
ClF_3	NH_3		
F_2	H_2O		(*40*)
F_2	NO		(*41*)
F_2	H_2	4000	(*38*)
Cl_2	H_2	2500	(*42*)
NF_3	H_2	3760	(*43*)

the addition of nitric oxide to a hydrogen diffusion flame burning in air will extinguish the flame. Apparently, the temperature of the air–hydrogen diffusion flame is not sufficiently high to initiate the nitric oxide–hydrogen reaction. Another oxidant, such as nitrous oxide or ammonia, must be added to the gas mixture until combustion is established. The nitric oxide–ammonia and nitric oxide–hydrocarbon flames, in contrast, are easy to ignite and maintain.

Emission from the nitric oxide–methane flame includes weak C_2 and ammonia–α bands and strong CH, CN, NH, OH, and NO bands. Other nitric oxide–hydrocarbon flames have a similar type of emission, lacking the ammonia–α bands and having much stronger C_2 bands. Oxygen emission is always observed in both the reaction zone and in the burned gases when the flame is fuel-lean. Fuel-lean flames have an "interconal" zone above the primary reaction zone which coincides with an increase in OH radiation. This apparently corresponds to an increase in flame temperature due to the decomposition of excess NO.

C. Nitrogen Dioxide Flames

Nitrogen dioxide flames are very different from the flames produced by the other oxides of nitrogen and appear to have interesting properties. The reaction between hydrogen and nitrogen dioxide does not go to completion and the NO_2 decomposes to NO and O_2 with the hydrogen reacting only with the latter. This particular flame does not appear to offer any advantages over more conventional flames. Premixed nitrogen dioxide–ammonia flames are not possible because the gases react immediately upon mixing. Surface-mixed nitrogen dioxide–ammonia flames do not appear to have been extensively studied.

Nitrogen dioxide–hydrocarbon flames provide an interesting set of properties. Two distinctive reaction zones are observed, especially if slightly fuel-rich conditions are used (29). In this case the two zones are quite distinct and appear to be separated by about 2 mm. The first zone emits a yellow continuum while the second zone emits strong CH radiation and weaker radiation from OH, NH, NO_2, CH, and C_2. Absorption studies show that the NO_2 disappears in the first zone and only NO is present in the intermediate area. The NO is consumed in the second zone.

Studies of the nitrogen dioxide–hydrogen flames using a Smithells separator (29) showed that the first cone resembles the nitrogen dioxide–hydrogen flame both visually and chemically. It differs in that its products can support a second zone while those of the nitrogen dioxide–hydrogen flame cannot. The red halo which is observed with the nitrous oxide flame can also be seen in the nitrogen dioxide–hydrocarbon flame when the flame is operated under fuel-rich conditions (29). In addition, the fuel-rich flames often have a bright carbon zone in the area between the two reaction zones. Again, the major difficulties with handling nitrogen dioxide appear to make the flame undesirable for routine analytical purposes. Since nitrogen dioxide is a liquid near room temperature, one must provide heat to vaporize the nitrogen dioxide, and the tubing for conducting the gas must be kept warm to prevent condensation. Likewise, nitrogen dioxide is corrosive to many materials and special precautions must be taken in the fabrication of burners.

D. Cyanogen Flames

The oxygen–cyanogen flame is one of the hottest known chemical flames being about 1500°K hotter than oxygen–acetylene. This flame has been studied by Gilbert (30), Vallee and Bartholomay (31), Robinson (32), and Baker and Vallee (33). The flame is narrow and has a very bright, bluish-white primary reaction zone surrounded by a blue secondary reaction zone. The C_2 and CN bands are observed in the dry flame, but when aqueous solutions are introduced the OH, CH, NH, and NO bands also appear. The flame provides an almost arc-like spectrum for a large number of metals, particularly zinc, vanadium, molybdenum, beryllium, bismuth, and other elements which have comparatively weaker emission in other flames. However, the enthalpy of the flame is low and the temperature is lowered when solutions are introduced into the flame. In general, the results obtained with the oxygen–cyanogen flame are disappointing when compared with the results which can be obtained in more conventional flames. The disadvantages of the high toxicity of cyanogen, the high cost of cyanogen, and the need for special burners seem to preclude the extensive use of cyanogen flames.

E. Fluorine Flames

Fluorine has been used as an oxidant for several fuels including hydrogen, water, nitric oxide, and hydrogen cyanide. The fluorine–oxygen flame was studied by Collier (34) as a source for flame emission spectrometry. The maximum temperature is about 4000°K and the flame is effective in producing atomic line emission. Metal fluoride band emission is also observed; emission from metal monoxide band systems is generally absent. The major difficulty in utilizing fluorine flames comes from the highly corrosive nature of fluorine and the necessity of completely disposing of the combustion products. Since these present serious problems, it is doubtful that these flames will be extensively used in analytical spectrometry.

F. OTHER FLAMES

In addition to the flames discussed, a number of combinations have been suggested for use in analytical flame spectrometry. Some of these are: oxygen–carbon subnitride, ozone–cyanogen, nitrous oxide–cyanogen, ozone–carbon subnitride, nitrogen trifluoride–hydrogen, and nitrogen trifluoride–ammonia. For the most part, these combinations are aimed at maximizing flame temperature and have not been studied as analytical sources.

IV. Flame-like Plasma Sources

A. ATOMIC HYDROGEN FLAMES

Langmuir (44) first described the use of an electric arc to dissociate hydrogen molecules into hydrogen atoms which subsequently recombined in accordance with the reaction:

$$2H \rightarrow H_2 \qquad \Delta H = 106.7 \text{ kcal} \qquad (1)$$

The hydrogen molecules burn as they come into contact with the surrounding air, giving rise to the so-called atomic hydrogen torch. Several authors (45–47) have studied this flame, and maximum flame temperatures ranging from approximately 3650 to 4100°K have been reported. The high temperature of this flame combined with the reducing properties of atomic hydrogen should make the atomic hydrogen torch useful for both atomic emission and atomic absorption spectrometry. The background spectrum of the flame consists mainly of atomic hydrogen lines, which are principally emitted from the inner zone, and OH emission which is principally confined to the outer zone of the flame. In certain torch arrangements, the spectrum of the electrode material, usually tungsten, also appears in the main flame. However, in the case of tungsten electrodes, only the most intense lines of tungsten are observed. Van den Bold (47) and Cueilleron (48) have described suitable "burners" for the laboratory use of atomic hydrogen flames.

B. AUGMENTED FLAMES

Karlowitz (49) has described methods augmenting flames with the electrical energy from a diffuse discharge. This augmented flame can have a heat content more than double the enthalpy resulting from the combustion of the fuel and oxidant. By varying the electrical augmentation, the temperature of an ordinary natural gas flame can be varied from about 2000 to 5000°K. The temperature of the augmented flame can be varied independent of the flame composition and thus highly reducing or oxidizing environments can be maintained at high temperatures. This is a major advantage for both atomic absorption and emission spectrometry since the flame and the chemical environment can be varied independently over a very wide range. Although these flames have not been studied in detail spectroscopically, they could have very definite advantages as spectroscopic sources.

C. Plasma Jets

The plasma jet is a form of constricted arc in which the arc tail flame is blown free of the major portion of the arc discharge and appears as a flame-like plasma source beyond the cathode region. The basic plasma arc has an atomizer within a water-cooled anode, separated from a cathode (ordinarily graphite) which is placed above it (50, 51). The cathode has a hole in the middle through which a plasma jet emerges. The arc discharge between the anode and the cathode operates in a current range between 10 and 20 A. The supporting gas, ordinarily argon, usually operates the sprayer which introduces the solution. Often a coolant gas such as helium is blown tangently into the arc chamber. The temperatures measured within the plasma jet usually range between 6000 and 8000°K. Metals which are introduced into the plasma jet usually emit a spark-like spectrum. The detection limits for elements within the plasma jet are usually comparable to, or better than, those obtained by porous cup or rotating disk excitation (50). The plasma jet source has primarily been studied as an atomic emission source and has not been extensively utilized in atomic absorption spectrometry. The very high temperature which is achieved via this source seems to offer very little in the general improvement of atomic absorption spectrometry.

D. Electrodeless Plasma Discharges

Electrodeless discharges are useful for producing both high- and low-pressure plasma for spectrometric uses. One of the earliest uses of these particular sources was for the analysis of low concentrations of impurities in gases. In most instances the source used was a very high-frequency source, usually within the kilocycle to megacycle range.

Mavrodineanu and Hughes (52) have extensively described electronic torches which operate at microwave frequencies. These discharges are flame-like and, in diatomic gases, are very hot, owing to the recombination of the dissociated atoms. The power introduced into these discharges is relatively low (0.5–5 kW). The reported temperatures for these discharges range from about 3000 to 5000°K. However, the heat capacity appears to be relatively low and the introduction of samples into the plasma flame causes a large decrease in the effective temperature. At the present time this type of discharge appears to offer few advantages over the simpler and more conventional-type flame.

E. INDUCTION COUPLED PLASMAS

One of the newest sources for atomic emission and absorption spectrometry is the induction coupled plasma. Wendt and Fassel (53) and Greenfield, Jones, and Berry (54) have demonstrated the usefulness of these plasmas as spectroscopic sources. They may offer distinct advantages over flames both as emission sources and absorption media for atomic absorption spectrometry. The high-temperature core region (approximately 8000–15,000°K) through which the sample passes, combined with the oxygen-free enviroment, leads to a high degree of conversion of the aerosol to free atoms even in the case of elements which form highly stable monoxides. In addition, these sources minimize the depressant effect of chemical interferences which occur in many flames. By sampling the plasma at various positions from the hot central core region out to the relatively cool tail flame region, one may select the source temperature which is most suitable for a particular determination. On the basis of published information, these flame-like plasma sources should be very useful for atomic emission and absorption analysis.

REFERENCES

1. C. S. Rann and A. N. Hambly, *Anal. Chem.*, **37**, 879 (1965).
2. A. P. Dronov, A. G. Sviridov, and N. N. Sobolev, *Opt. i Spektroskopiya*, **5**, 490 (1958).
3. R. Mavrodineanu and H. Boiteux, *Flame Spectroscopy*, Wiley, New York (1965).
4. E. Bartholomé, *Z. Elektrochem.*, **54**, 169 (1950).
5. J. B. Willis, J. O. Rasmuson, R. N. Kniseley, and V. A. Fassel, *Spectrochim. Acta*, in press.

6. W. G. Parker and H. G. Wolfhard, *Symp. Combust. 4th, Cambridge, Mass., 1952*, Williams and Wilkins, Baltimore, 1953, p. 420.
7. H. P. Broida and K. E. Shuler, *J. Chem. Phys.*, **27**, 933 (1957).
8. J. B. Willis, *Applied Optics*, **7**, 1295 (1968).
9. V. A. Fassel and D. A. Becker, Paper presented at XIII Colloquium Spectroscopicum Internationale. Ottawa, Canada, 1967.
10. V. A. Fassel, R. H. Curry, and R. N. Kniseley, *Spectrochim. Acta*, **18**, 1127 (1962).
11. V. A. Fassel, R. H. Curry, R. B. Myers, and R. N. Kniseley, *Spectrochim. Acta*, **19**, 1187 (1963).
12. M. D. Amos and J. B. Willis, *Spectrochim. Acta*, **22**, 1325 (1966).
13. V. A. Fassel and V. G. Mossotti, *Anal. Chem.* **35**, 252 (1963).
14. V. G. Mossotti and V. A. Fassel, *Spectrochim. Acta*, **20**, 1117 (1964).
15. J. A. Fiorino, R. N. Kniseley, and V. A. Fassel, *Spectrochim. Acta*, **23B**, 413 (1968).
16. A. G. Gaydon and H. G. Wolfhard, *Flames, Their Structure, Radiation and Temperature*, (2nd ed.) Chapman and Hall, London, 1960.
17. P. T. Gilbert, *Proceedings Xth Colloquium Spectroscopicum Internationale*, Spartan, Washington, D.C., 1963, pp. 171–215.
18. V. A. Fassel and D. W. Golightly, *Anal. Chem.*, **39**, 466 (1967).
19. E. E. Pickett and S. R. Koirtyohann, *Spectrochim. Acta*, **23B**, 235 (1968).
20. L. Capacho-Delgado and D. C. Manning, *Spectrochim. Acta*, **22**, 1505 (1966).
21. V. A. Fassel, V. G. Mossotti, W. E. L. Grossman, and R. N. Kniseley, *Spectrochim. Acta*, **22**, 347 (1966).
22. R. W. B. Pearse and A. G. Gaydon, *The Identification of Molecular Spectra* (3rd ed.). Wiley, New York, 1963.
23. A. Gatterer, J. Junkes, E. W. Salpeter, and B. Rosen, *Atlas of Molecular Spectra of Metallic Oxides*, Specola Vaticano, Vatican City, 1956.
24. W. Jevons, *Report on Band Spectra of Diatomic Molecules*. University Press, Cambridge, 1932.
24a. R. M. Dagnall, K. C. Thompson, and T. S. West, *Analyst*, **93**, 153 (1968).
25. P. T. Gilbert, *Anal. Chem.*, **38**, 1920 (1965).
26. K. Zacha and J. D. Winefordner, *Anal. Chem.*, **38**, 1537 (1966).
27. G. E. Schmauch and E. J. Serfass, *Anal. Chem.*, **30**, 1161 (1958).
28. G. E. Schmauch and E. J. Serfass, *Appl. Spectr*, **12**, 98 (1958).
29. H. G. Wolfhard and W. G. Parker, *Symp. Combust. 5th, Pittsburgh, 1954*, Reinhold, New York, 1955, pp. 718–728.
30. P. T. Gilbert, *Oxycyanogen Flame Photometry*, Beckman Instruments, Fullerton, California, 1958.
31. B. L. Vallee and A. F. Bartholomay, *Anal. Chem.*, **28**, 1753 (1956).
32. J. W. Robinson, *Anal. Chem.*, **33**, 1226 (1961).
33. M. R. Baker and B. L. Vallee, *J. Opt. Soc. Am.*, **48**, 576 (1958).
34. H. E. Collier, *Mechanism of Spectral Excitation of Metallic Ions by a New High-Temperature Source*, Ph.D. Thesis, Lehigh University, 1955.
35. A. V. Grosse and C. S. Stokes, *P.B. Report 161460*, 1960. (Off. Tech. Serv., U.S. Dept. Comm.).
36. E. E. Bell, P. B. Burnside and F. P. Dickey, *J. Opt. Soc. Am.*, **50**, 1286 (1960).
37. A. K. Kirshenbaum and A. V. Grosse, *J. Am. Chem. Soc.*, **78**, 2020 (1956).
38. C. S. Stokes and A. V. Grosse, *Ind. Eng. Chem.*, **49**, 1311 (1957).

39. G. Skinow and H. G. Wolfhard, *Proc. Roy. Soc. (London)*, **A232**, 78 (1955).
40. A. G. Steng, *Combust. Flame*, **6**, 89 (1962).
41. D. Rapp and H. S. Johnston, *J. Chem. Phys.*, **33**, 695 (1960).
42. C. Barthel, *Genic Chim.*, **77**, 34 (1957).
43. C. S. Stokes, *Ind. Eng. Chem.*, **51**, 1494 (1959).
44. I. Langmuir, *Ind. Eng. Chem.*, **19**, 667 (1927).
45. D. Séfèrian, *Chaleur Ind.*, **19**, 76 (1938).
46. L. Hackspill and J. Cueilleron in *High Temperatures and Their Use in Chemistry* (in French). P. Lebeau (ed.), Masson et Cie, Paris, 1950.
47. H. J. Van den Bold, Thesis, University of Utrecht, 1945.
48. J. Cueilleron, *Ann. Chimie*, **19**, 459 (1944).
49. B. Karlowitz, *International Science and Technology*, (June 1962) pp. 36–41; U.S. Patent 663065, June 3, 1957.
50. M. Margoshes and B. F. Scribner, *Spectrochim. Acta*, **15**, 138 (1959).
51. L. E. Owen, *Appl. Spectry*, **15**, 150 (1961).
52. R. Mavrodineanu and R. C. Hughes, *Spectrochim. Acta*, **19**, 1309 (1963).
53. R. H. Wendt and V. A. Fassel, *Anal. Chem.*, **37**, 920 (1965).
54. S. Greenfield, I. Jones and C. T. Berry, *Analyst*, **89**, 713 (1964).

7 The Measurement and Calculation of Flame Temperatures

W. Snelleman

FYSISCH LABORATORIUM
RIJKS-UNIVERSITEIT, UTRECHT
THE NETHERLANDS

I. Equilibrium in Flames

The concept of temperature is rigidly derived in thermodynamics. It is possible to set up a temperature scale which is based upon a Carnot cycle. The efficiency of such a cycle is equal to the difference of the two temperatures used in the cycle, relative to the higher one. No use is made of any material property of the system involved (in contrast to other scales which are derived, for example, from the expansion of liquids or gases). The scale thus defined is called the Thermodynamic Temperature Scale (TTS). One fixed point for the numerical definition of the scale is to be prescribed; the triple point of water (273.16°K) has been chosen as such.

In the kinetic theory of gases the temperature has been introduced as a quantity proportional to the mean translational energy of the particles; this concept yields the perfect gas temperature scale. Also, the theory of black body radiation can be used to develop a temperature scale according

to Planck's radiation formula. It has been shown that the latter temperature scales are equivalent to the thermodynamic scale.

For practical use a system of fixed points, together with methods of
temperature interpolation and extrapolation, has been set up, which is
called the International Practical Temperature Scale (IPTS). The aim of
the IPTS is twofold. In the first place it should establish a system of temperature measurements with methods which are more easily applicable than
those used in absolute measurements, such as gas thermometry. In the
second place the IPTS should equal, as closely as possible, the temperatures obtained directly on the TTS.

The highest fixed point of the IPTS is the freezing point of gold, for
which a value of 1063°C has been accepted. Above this temperature the
procedure prescribed in the IPTS is to compare the radiation from a
black body at the higher temperature with the radiation from a black
body at the gold point, and to calculate this higher temperature with the
aid of Planck's formula for black body radiation [see Eq. (5)], using the value
$c_2 = 1.438$ cm°K where $c_2 = hc/k$. Recent discussions indicate that the
value of the gold point is too low. A correction of about $+1.5$°K yields a
value which is in better agreement with the TTS. (This means that at
present a flame temperature measured in the IPTS, as is done in reversal
measurements, is about 5°K lower than when measured in the TTS, as
is done when line intensities are used.) An official change of the IPTS
is still under consideration.

The assumption underlying the assignment of a temperature to a
system is that the system is in a state of thermodynamic equilibrium. Such a
state can be characterized by the fact that it satisfies a number of conditions
with the use of a single value of a quantity T, which then represents the
temperature of the system. For a gaseous system these conditions are:

1. A velocity distribution of the particles according to the Maxwell
equation

$$f(v)\, dv = 4\pi \left(\frac{m}{2\pi kT} \right)^{3/2} v^2\, e^{-mv^2/2kT}\, dv \qquad (1)$$

where $f(v)\, dv$ is the fraction of the particles with velocities between v and v
$+ dv$, m is the mass of the particles, and k is the Boltzmann constant.

2. A population of the atomic and molecular energy levels according
to the (simplified) Boltzmann formula

$$\frac{N_i}{N_o} = \frac{1}{Q} g_i \exp\left[-\frac{E_i}{kT} \right] \qquad (2)$$

where N_o is the total number of a kind of particles, Q is the partition function, g_i is the statistical weight of level i, and E_i is the energy of the level.

3. An ionization of a kind of atoms according to the Saha equation

$$K_i = [M^+] [e^-]/[M] \tag{3}$$

where K_i is the equilibrium constant, with $[M^+]$, $[e^-]$, and $[M]$ standing for the concentrations of ions, electrons, and atoms, respectively. (See Chapter 4.)

4. A dissociation of the molecular species according to the law of mass action. For example, for the reaction $A + B \rightleftarrows AB$ one has:

$$K_p = \frac{[A] [B]}{[AB]} \tag{4}$$

in which K_p is the dissociation constant. (See Chapter 4.)

5. A density of the radiation between the wavelengths λ and $\lambda + \Delta\lambda$ according to Planck's radiation formula

$$E_\lambda \, d\lambda = \frac{8\pi hc\lambda^{-5}}{e^{hc/k\lambda T}-1} \, d\lambda \quad \text{erg/cm}^3 \tag{5}$$

where c is the light velocity and h is Planck's constant. For the emission from a "black" surface in a unit solid angle, the formula becomes

$$E'_\lambda \, d\lambda = \frac{2hc^2\lambda^{-5}}{e^{hc/k\lambda T}-1} \, d\lambda \quad \text{erg/cm}^2 \text{ sec ster} \tag{6}$$

As will be shown, flame gases approach equilibrium in certain aspects, but in other aspects finite differences remain. To answer the question of equilibrium experimentally, many investigators have determined the initially formal "temperatures" that correspond to different aspects of a system, which have been listed. The better these "temperatures" coincide, the better the state of equilibrium can be assumed to be attained and the more physical meaning the "temperature" of such a system possesses. To avoid confusion the "temperatures" are named after the special process to which they apply, such as translational temperature, excitation temperature, etc. Although there is no a priori reason to prefer one "temperature" to another, the translational temperature is often considered the most realistic one, from which the others may deviate. The reasons are that the translational energy is very soon (after less than 10 collisions, i.e., are 10^{-8}

sec at standard pressure) equipartitioned to a good approximation and that consequently there is only one translational temperature in one place in the gas. In contrast, to every pair of energy states of every type of particle an excitation temperature (rotational, vibrational, or electronic) can be attributed. The methods to determine the various temperatures are described in Section II. In this section we consider the state of the gases in a flame by starting from a state of thermodynamic equilibrium.

A state of thermodynamic equilibrium eventually exists, for example, in a closed cavity in which a gas is present and whose walls are at a uniform temperature T. To make an optical measurement possible, a hole is made in the wall of the cavity small enough not to disturb the equilibrium state appreciably. The radiation emerging from this hole is Planckian and is independent of the material of the wall and of the gas inside the cavity and only depends on the temperature of the wall. The radiation from the gas inside the cavity does not show up in the spectrum since the gas absorbs exactly the same amount of radiation from the walls as it emits itself. This is an example of the "principle of detailed balancing," which states that in a system in equilibrium the rate of a process and the rate of the reverse process are equal even when there are parallel processes (such as collisional and radiative) which yield the same products. When a second, equally small, hole is made in the wall opposite the first one, there is an area outside the cavity in which only radiation from the gas (and not from the walls) is received. This radiation is comprised in the spectral lines and/ or bands of the atoms and molecules that are present in the cavity. This situation exists with ovens designed for spectrographic use. The population of the atoms in the various energy levels still corresponds to the Boltzmann distribution, but now the intensities and the wavelengths of the radiation yield a vast amount of information on the amount and the properties of the particles involved. However, it should be stressed that these discontinuous spectra can only be observed because of a lack of radiative equilibrium in the solid angle of viewing, because of the absence of a radiating and reflecting wall behind the gas. It is only by virtue of the smallness of the holes, which means that from almost all directions light can be absorbed by the particles, that the population of the energy levels is still close to the value given by Boltzmann's equation. The intensity of the spectral lines is governed by this population and by the transition probabilities. A deviation that does occur in this situation is that emission stimulated by radiation from the walls is lacking. However, at the temperatures and wavelengths of light encountered in flames, stimulated emission can be neglected.

In the case of a flame, the walls at equal temperature with the flame gases are absent. This causes a disturbance of those partial equilibria in which radiation from the walls was involved. Atoms and molecules are de-excited by emission and by inelastic collisions, but the excitation only occurs through inelastic collisions, since absorption of radiation from the wall is now absent. As a consequence, a depopulation of the upper levels with respect to the lower levels occurs. The extent to which the higher energy levels will be depopulated depends, therefore, upon the ratio of the rates of de-excitation by emission and by inelastic collisions (1). Chapter 4 deals with this problem in more detail. Measurements of fluorescent radiation efficiency show that in most flames only a few percent of the atoms are de-excited by emission of radiation. The bulk is de-excited by inelastic collisions, for example, with CO_2 and N_2 molecules. Because of the principle of detailed balancing, the same holds true for the reverse process of excitation. For example, the fraction of the sodium atoms in an air–acetylene flame, de-excited by radiation, is 3 % (2). Since the number of atoms per second that are excited must be equal to the number of atoms that are de-excited, the result is a lower population of the $3p$ level, which can be described by a temperature in the Boltzmann formula which is 7°K lower than the translational temperature of the gas. When the sodium concentration is such that self-absorption occurs, the radiation equilibrium is partly restored and a deviation of only 1 or 2°K remains. However, in flames consisting predominantly of atomic gases such as the stoichiometric $Ar–O_2–H_2$ flame, in which collisional de-excitation is far less probable, radiative de-excitation as high as 58 % has been measured, involving depressions of the excitation temperature up to 160°K (1). As a conclusion one might state than in an open gas system at atmospheric pressure, such as arcs and flames (except for the reaction zone), the Boltzmann distribution, as calculated with the translational temperature, generally is closely realized because of the dominance of collisional over radiative processes.

Another more technical consequence of the absence of walls around a flame is the inhomogeneity of the temperature caused by turbulent or diffusive mixing of the flame gases with the surrounding atmosphere. This mixing occurs at first near the edge of the flame and at greater heights through its entire cross section. When the gas mixture to be burned is rather fuel-lean, the mixing will result in a decrease of the temperature toward the edge of the flame. When the mixture is fuel-rich and the atmosphere contains oxygen (or more generally a gas that reacts with the flame gases), the edges of the flame may be hotter than the center (Fig. 1). The influence of such gradients can best be discussed together with the temperature history of the flame gases on their way through the flame.

As was discussed in more detail in Chapter 5, one can hardly speak of a temperature in the reaction zone of a flame. Too much of the energy

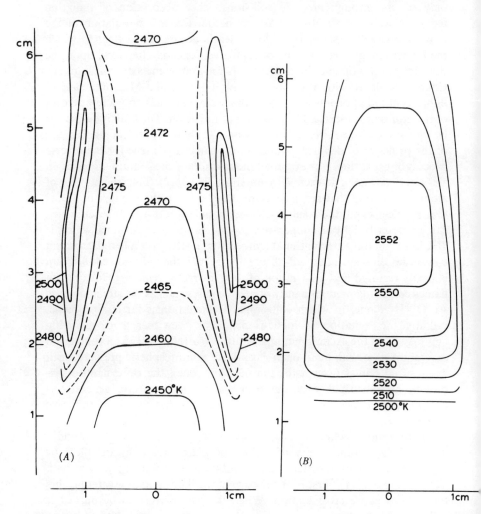

Fig. 1. The distribution of the (reversal) temperature in a premixed air–acetylene flame. The rectangular flame base, 2×3 cm^2, consisted of 10 rows of holes. Sodium was only introduced in the two middle rows, perpendicular to the optical axis. (A) Fuel-rich nonluminous flame. (B) Flame of optimum mixing ratio.

released is not yet equilibrated, as is shown visually by the excessive radiation from that zone and by measurements of various "temperatures" in the reaction zone. For example, Gaydon and Wolfhard (*3*) reported a number of reversal temperatures obtained with sodium and iron lines which range from 2000 to 3400°K in the reaction zone of a premixed air–C_2H_2 flame at 24 mm pressure. Broida and Shuler (*3a*) reported rotational temperatures in the reaction zone of a flame up to 10,000°K. Such chemiluminescent radiation decreases rapidly above the reaction zone but remains a possible source of error as long as the energy is not completely equilibrated.

Emphasis should be laid on the difference between flames produced with premixed gases, which generally have a laminar flow pattern, and flames in which the gases mix by diffusion and turbulence. In the last type, the reaction zone virtually spreads through the whole flame body, and a quantitative or even qualitative description of the processes in terms of height in the flame is impossible. Also, temperatures measured in such flames are ill defined and unreliable quantities. The following discussion will, therefore, pertain mainly to premixed, laminar-flow flames.

As already mentioned, the translational temperature is established almost immediately above the reaction zone. Then the rotational (after about 10^3 collisions), vibrational and electronic (after about 10^5 collisions), and ionization and dissociation (after about 10^7 collisions) temperatures follow. With a collision rate of about 3×10^9 per sec at 1 atm and 2000°K, and a velocity of the burned gas of 5–10 m/sec, there is hardly an excitation lag above the reaction zone, but lagging ionization (*4*) and radical recombination are noticeable in the larger part of premixed flames. Therefore, ionization and dissociation phenomena are not used as a thermometer in flames. In terms of the influence on the translational temperature, ionization does not play a role. Assuming an ion concentration of 10^{12} cm^{-3}, an ionization energy of 5 eV, and a specific heat of the flame gases of 30 J per mol °K, the temperature drop is found to be about 0.01°K. In contrast, dissociative phenomena do have a marked influence on the translational temperature. Some particles are formed in the reaction zone in excess of their equilibrium concentration, e.g., atomic hydrogen and atomic oxygen. These gases recombine with other flame components until the equilibrium value is reached. Since heat is liberated in these processes, the flame temperature keeps rising above the reaction zone. In air–acetylene flames this increase varies from 30°K in fuel-rich flames to about 100°K in lean flames (Fig. 1).

Still, the flame gases continuously lose energy by radiation. In non-

luminous flames this radiation mainly occurs in the infrared part of the
spectrum in the bands of molecular species such as CO_2, H_2O, and CO.
Since the intensity of this radiation is fairly constant with height, one can

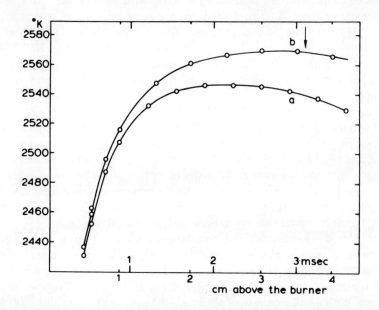

Fig. 2. Curve a: The (reversal) temperature of a "shielded" air–acetylene flame versus
height in the flame. Curve b: The same data after correction for the (measured) losses,
due to infrared radiation. The arrow indicates the onset of self-reversal.

describe the temperature profile of a flame as a function of the time t
(or of height in the flame) as:

$$T = T_0 + (T_{max} - T_0)(1 - e^{-\alpha t}) - \beta t \tag{7}$$

in which T_0 is the temperature just above the reaction zone and T_{max} is
the equilibrium flame temperature in the absence of radiative losses.
Furthermore α stands for the decay rate of the recombination reaction(s)
and β is a radiation coefficient. Figure 2 shows such a profile in an air–
acetylene flame. In relatively simple cases, such as the air–hydrogen flame,
α can be calculated, the main reaction being the recombination of H and
OH (5). In air–hydrocarbon flames in which the recombination of CO and
O is also involved, the situation is much more complicated. The radiation

coefficient can be obtained from the abundances and the emissivities of the molecular vapors, together with the specific heat of the flame gases. (See Section IV.)

This model of the temperature profile holds up to the height where intermixing becomes noticeable. It is evident that the height at which this will occur depends on the geometry of the flame. In thin flames (e.g., on a slot burner) there will be no region of the flame which is reasonably free both from recombination reactions and from intermixing with the surrounding gases, whereas in flames with a cross section of say 2×2 cm^2 or larger this region will be of the order of 3–10 cm height in the middle of the flame. When intermixing becomes noticeable, the temperature will vary over the cross section of the flame, and, although the composition of the gases may lag somewhat behind the actual local temperature, the rate of population and depopulation of the energy levels is fast enough to follow the changes. The value of the temperature measured by optical means will generally be some weighted mean over the cross section of the flame. One may avoid this difficulty by introducing the species that is used in the measurement in the isothermal center of the flame only. However, outward diffusion of this species and inward diffusion of, for example, nitrogen from the surroundings will again cause inhomogeneities at a greater height in the flame. A "peeling" procedure can still yield the real temperature distribution, if needed.

In summary, the deviations from equilibrium in the "reaction-free" area of nonluminous flames are:

1. Large deviations of the radiation density.

2. A small depopulation of the energy levels.

3. A residual lag in the equilibration of ionization and dissociation phenomena.

Outside this favored area, or in flames where this area hardly exists, one has to deal with two additional deviations:

1. In the lower parts of the flame (but above the reaction zone) the various "excitation" temperatures may agree with the translational temperature, but the composition of the gas is not in agreement with this temperature.

2. In the higher parts of the flame, which will have a well-established temperature locally, the temperature will vary considerably over a cross section of the flame.

From a standpoint of measuring temperatures, any deviation from equilibrium is a hazard to the concept of temperature and, therefore, to the accuracy of the measurement. Yet it should be remembered that one needs such a deviation to be able to measure any rate constant of an atomic process at all.

II. Methods of Temperature Measurement

In principle, any of the equilibrium conditions given in Section I may be used to determine the temperature of a flame. The foregoing discussion stressed the caution with which the measured temperature of a flame has to be considered. However, very reliable results have been obtained with various methods, and the practical situation is quite satisfactory.

The group of methods used most often is the one based on the Boltzmann formula. The intensity of a spectral line is given by

$$I = N_n A_n h v_n \tag{8}$$

or with Eq. (2)

$$I = N_o \frac{1}{Q} g_n A_n \exp\left[-\frac{E_n}{kT}\right] h v_n \tag{9}$$

in which A_n is the transition probability of the transition and v_n is the frequency of the radiation in the spectral line. A calculation of T would require the measurement of the absolute intensity I and the number of particles N_o. The use of more than one line avoids these absolute measurements. By measuring the intensity ratio of two or more spectral lines, the relative populations of the upper levels of these transitions can be obtained as follows: When the upper levels have energies E_n and E_m, etc., with respect to the ground level of the particle, the intensity ratio of the spectral lines is given by

$$I_n/I_m = N_n A_n h v_n / N_m A_m h v_m \tag{10}$$

and, with Eq. (2),

$$\frac{I_n}{I_m} = \frac{A_n g_n}{A_m g_m} \exp\left[-\frac{E_n - E_m}{kT}\right] \frac{v_n}{v_m} \tag{11}$$

when no self-absorption occurs. Thus, a knowledge of the (relative) transition probabilities and the measurement of the intensity ratio yield a value of the temperature, in this case called the excitation temperature. The main sources of error in this method are the uncertainties of the A-values and the occurrence of self-absorption. The latter is especially likely when the lower level of a transition is the ground level (with a resonance line) or an energy level very near to the ground level. When self-absorption occurs, the intensity ratio is not proportional to the population ratio any more, and the resulting temperature is seriously in error. Therefore, when resonance lines are employed, the concentration of the species used should be kept sufficiently low. Still, some additional arguments may influence the choice of the pair of lines. It is seen from Eq. (11) that the larger the difference between E_n and E_m, the more sensitive the intensity ratio is to a change in T, while from a practical standpoint the lines should not be too different either in intensity or in wavelength. Some of these requirements are contradictory, but they might be of some help in the choice of a pair of lines. Among the elements that have been used for this type of measurement are iron (3) and cesium (8521 and 8943 Å) (6), while copper (e.g., 5219 and 5106 Å) and zinc (3072 and 3076 Å) have been used extensively in electric arcs and might be usable in hot flames. A full discussion has been given by Boumans (7).

Apart from atomic lines, lines and bands from molecular spectra have also been used for temperature determinations. A detailed discussion has been given by Gaydon (8). The rotational temperature is obtained when the intensity ratios of the spectral lines in one particular band are used. In that case, the number of lines available partly makes up for the poor precision that one would expect due to the small energy difference between the upper levels of the transitions. In most cases, the transition probabilities are not known, but the relative transition probabilities of the rotational part can be calculated, while the vibrational and the electronic part are equal (to the first approximation) for all transitions in the band. The expression for the intensities of the lines in a band is

$$I = aA_{rot}v^4 \exp[-E/kT] \tag{12}$$

in which a is a constant, A_{rot} is the rotational transition probability, and E is the energy of the rotational level. A plot of $\log I - \log A_{rot} v^4$ versus E yields a straight line of slope $-1/kT$ if equilibrium prevails within the band. Bands of OH, C_2, and CH have been mostly used in these measurements, yielding reasonable temperatures in air–acetylene and hydrogen–air flames above the reaction zones, but very high temperatures in the reaction zones, although the plot yielded a straight line. Evidently, the excitation is equilibrated within the band but not in comparison with the translational temperature. Transition probabilities for the OH band at 3064 Å have been reported extensively by Dieke and Crosswhite (9).

The vibrational temperature is obtained in the same way as the rotational temperature by comparing the intensities of a sequence of bands in a molecular spectrum. The intensity of the band can be measured using either the band head or the total profile. The method has often been used with the CN bands in electric arcs (7, 10, 11) and also in the hot cyanogen-oxygen flame (12). In the infrared, the bands of CO_2 and CO have been employed (13).

A different way to obtain excitation temperatures is the method of line reversal. Because of its wide use and different technique it is considered separately in Section III.

The translational temperature, based on the distribution of the velocity of the particles, would be the first choice if one wishes to measure the intuitively "real" temperature of a flame. Optically, it can be obtained from the profile of a spectral line, if that profile is mainly determined by Doppler broadening. Then the full halfwidth of the line is given by

$$\Delta\lambda = 7.2 \times 10^{-7} \lambda(T/M)^{1/2} \tag{13}$$

where λ is the wavelength of the spectral line, T is the temperature, and M is the atomic or molecular weight of the particle. For the sodium D-lines at 2500°K this yields a value of 0.04Å. The measurement of such a width requires an instrument of high resolving power ($\sim 10^6$). However, in flames at atmospheric pressure another process of line broadening, namely Lorentz broadening, is of the same order of magnitude as Doppler broadening (see the discussion of line profiles in Chapter 3), which virtually rules out the use of line profiles as a tool for temperature measurements in atmospheric flames.

As discussed in Section I, the radiation density in a nonluminous flame is lower than the density given by Planck's formula at the flame temperature by some orders of magnitude. Consequently, a radiation temperature derived from this formula would generally give erroneous results. However, it is still possible to measure the intensity in the center of a strong, heavily self-absorbed spectral line, but a high resolving power would be required. A modified method has been used with success in cases where a continuum spectrum was available, such as in luminous flames, and also by using the infrared bands of, for example, CO_2 (13). Apart from the emission measurement, an additional absorption measurement is performed to determine (Kirchhoff's law) the emissivity of the gas. By inserting the emissivity factor into Planck's formula, one allows for the fact that the flame does not radiate as a black body at the wavelength considered. Such emission–absorption measurements are related to the method of line reversal, as discussed in Section III.

The methods discussed are all optical methods. Their advantage is that the flame is not disturbed by the measurement. However, it is laborious to measure local temperatures in this way. If a small disturbance does not influence the flame noticeably, as in most industrial flames, methods employing a wire in the flame can be used. This field, covering thermocouples, resistance thermometers, and pyrometers, is only mentioned here but is dealt with extensively in the literature (14).

It is hard to assess, in general, the accuracy and precision of the various methods without doing injustice to some precise measurements. However, it can be stated that the accuracy and precision of the methods decrease from about 25°K for the two-line method to 100°K or even more for the measurement of vibrational temperatures. The errors are mainly due to inaccuracy of the A values and to the occurrence of self-absorption. The line reversal method, discussed in the next section, is independent of the A values and is not influenced by self-absorption.

III. The Method of Line Reversal

Instead of using the intensity of two or more emission lines of an element, as described in Section II, one may employ the comparison of emitted light and absorbed light pertaining to the same transition between two energy levels of a particle. One advantage of the latter procedure over the former is that, instead of the ratio of the transition probabilities of the emission lines [Eq. (11)], the ratio of the transition probabilities for emission and absorption of the same transition is needed. This ratio is known by definition from the Boltzmann distribution and the application of the principle of detailed balancing, which states that in equilibrium the number of downward radiative transitions should equal the number of upward radiative transitions (see below). A second advantage is that the "intensities" of both the emission line and the absorption line are affected by self-absorption in exactly the same way, so that self-absorption does not interfere with the measurement. In fact, this "pair" of lines fulfills all requirements put forward in the preceding section. A final important advantage is that the comparison of the lines is made as an optical addition of emitted and absorbed light so that a null method results. These advantages of the method of line reversal are somewhat countered by the following experimental requirements:

1. In order to generate an adequate absorption line one normally needs a calibrated reference light source of a (radiation) temperature at least equal to the flame temperature. [With a special modification, flame

temperatures which are some 500°K higher than the reference source can be measured (*15*).]

2. The requirements of optical alignment and quality are increased, as will be discussed.

This comparison of the two methods shows the close link between them; the method of line reversal also determines the ratio of the population of two levels, viz., the upper and the lower level of one transition.

The relation between the intensity of the auxiliary light source and the flame temperature can be explained as follows. In equilibrium the principle of detailed balancing requires that in a given volume per unit time the number z_{mn} of absorbed quanta equals the number z_{nm} of emitted quanta:

$$z_{nm} = z_{mn} \tag{14}$$

or

$$N_n g_n \left(A_{nm} + B_{nm} U_\lambda(T)\right) = N_m g_m B_{mn} U_\lambda(T) \tag{15}$$

in which N_n and N_m are the numbers of atoms in the upper and the lower levels, g_n and g_m are the statistical weights, A_{nm}, B_{nm}, B_{mn} are the Einstein coefficients for spontaneous emission, stimulated emission, and absorption, respectively, and $U_\lambda(T)$ is the radiation density given by Planck's radiation formula. The ratio of the populations N_n and N_m in Eq. (2) is governed by an excitation temperature T_E, and the radiation density in Eq. (15) by a radiation temperature T_R. In thermodynamic equilibrium, $T_E = T_R$.

In a flame where no radiation equilibrium exists, T_E and T_R generally are not equal and Eq. (15) does not hold. Yet one may restore the validity of Eq. (15) in a restricted solid angle by installing outside the flame a radiation source of variable radiation temperature T_R. When T_R is adjusted until Eq. (15) is satisfied, equality of T_E and T_R is again obtained.

The use of a restricted solid angle does not restrict the validity, but the possibility exists of coherent scattering of the incident light beam. However, in nonluminous flames this type of scattering is quite negligible.

The possibility of equalizing T_E and T_R experimentally is the basis of the method of line reversal: one observes the radiation of a reference light source in a given solid angle and in a small spectral range which should contain a spectral line of the gas under investigation. We now may admit this gas intermittently into the optical path between the light source and the observer and adjust the reference light source to an intensity at which a difference between the two situations is no longer observed. Then the excitation temperature T_E of the transition, which corresponds to the observed spectral line of the gas, equals the radiation temperature T_R of the light from the reference source for the wavelength considered. In practice, the gas remains in the light path all the time and the comparison is made with the intensity of the continuum, adjacent to either side of the line.

With the method of line reversal, an image of the reference light source is formed in the flame, and a second image of the reference light source and the flame is formed on the slit of a spectrograph. Generally, a salt is introduced into the flame to generate the spectral line, but a band of the flame gases, such as the OH band at 3064 Å, also can be used. The usual way to give equal weight to emitted and absorbed radiation is to overfill the collimator of the spectrograph with light of both sources and, for photoelectric measurements, to stop down the slit height of the spectrograph so that only the part of the slit that is illuminated by both light sources is used. If the solid angle or the area viewed from the flame is larger than that viewed from the reference source, the measured reversal temperature will be too high. On the other hand, if the reverse is true, no systematic error results, but a larger random error occurs. Other lens arrangements are still possible. For example, one may omit the first lens from the setup, form an image of the reference source on the slit, and place the flame in front of the lens. Errors due to the lens before the flame (e.g., in wavelength-dependent measurements) can thus be avoided. However, the flame is no longer imaged on the slit, and a temperature value averaged over the width of the light beam in the flame is obtained.

The reference source most often used is the tungsten strip lamp. The calibration of the lamp (in the IPTS) is sometimes given in terms of real temperature versus current through the lamp and sometimes in terms of the radiation temperature at a certain wavelength versus current. Since the emissivity of tungsten is dependent on the wavelength (and to a lesser degree on the temperature), one usually has to make corrections to obtain the radiation temperature at the real temperature and the wavelength used. Also, one has to allow for light losses at the window of the lamp and at any optical surface in front of the flame. Generally, it suffices to allow for reflection losses of 4 % per surface. (As a rule of thumb, 1 % in energy is equivalent to 0.1 % in temperature in the visible region and for normal flame temperatures, as can be calculated from Planck's formula.) However, with composite and/or coated lenses this estimate does not suffice and separate measurements must be made. For example, the transmission of a coated lens with eight surfaces was measured and found to be 91 % at 6000 Å. The measurements by DeVos (16) of the emissivity of tungsten are recommended for these calculations. Tungsten strip lamps can be used up to about 2800°K real temperature (about 2500°K radiation temperature). Recently, a lamp has been designed (17) consisting of a bundle of fine tungsten wire, viewed end-on. Since the brush structure increases the emissivity from about 0.44 (of flat tungsten) to 0.95, and furthermore the structure of the lamp allows the use of higher real temperatures, radiation temperatures of about 3000°K can be obtained. For still higher temperatures the anode of a carbon arc (3800°K) and high-pressure discharges in Hg and Xe (up to 6000°K) (18) can be used with an appropriate filter to control the intensity. The accuracy of the calibration of these sources is about 5°K for tungsten lamps, 20°K for the carbon arc anode, and 100°K for the discharges. With the exception of the carbon arc, one has to be aware of possible aging effects. With strip lamps it is a good practice to keep one lamp as a standard and another one for actual measurements, and make periodic comparison measurements at not too high a temperature.

The adjustment to the "reversal point" is made by varying the intensity of the image of the reference source in the flame until neither an emission line nor an absorption line is observed in the spectrum. This observation can be made visually, photoelectrically, or photographically.

Visual observation is quick, holds little risk of systematic errors, and is quite precise. A lens is useful for observing the spectrum as to precision, since one can match the apparent width of the spectral line to the resolving power of the eye. Too large a magnification decreases the precision, since the brightness of the spectrum becomes too low. The sodium lines are very well suited for visual observation and a precision of about 5°K in some 10 measurements can usually be obtained with instruments of medium resolving power.

Photoelectric detection of the spectrum yields, of course, more possibilities in regard to the spectral line used, time-dependent phenomena, integration of the signal, and also the quantitative treatment of the obtainable precision, which is considered first.

Generally, the precision obtainable with the line reversal method is determined by the marginal detectability of a weak signal (the absorption line or the emission line) in the presence of a large background signal (the continuum). When the line is present all the time, one compares the averages of the intensity of the continuum on either side of the line with the intensity at the wavelength of the spectral line. The question of the temperature difference between the flame and the background when the line is "just" distinguishable from the background can be answered by statistical arguments. Let the number of photons per second that are detected in a small spectral range, determined by the resolving power of the instrument, be P. This number is subject to (at least) statistical variations that are equal to the square root of the number of detected photons and therefore can only be measured as $\bar{P} \pm P^{1/2}$. Shifting the detection from the adjacent continuum to the line should therefore give a difference in intensity of at least $kP^{1/2}$ photons per second, in order that the line be detectable. Here, k is a factor which determines the reliability of the conclusion. The complete expression for this "contrast threshold," $\Delta I/I$ (15), contains the parameters of the reference source, the apparatus, and the spectral line, and is

$$\Delta I/I = k(\Delta\lambda)^{-1} (I_{\lambda,T} \frac{H}{f} DSa \, \phi_e t)^{-1/2} \qquad (16)$$

in which $\Delta\lambda$ is the equivalent width of the spectral line [i.e., the width of a line with a rectangular profile, the height of which corresponds to black body radiation (at the temperature of the hot gas) and the area of which equals the area under the real line profile], $I_{\lambda,T}$ is the number of photons per cm^2 steradian sec and per unit of wavelength, H is the slit height, f is the focal length of the monochromator, D is the angular dispersion in radians per unit of wavelength, S is the effective area of the dispersing element, a is the transmission factor of the apparatus, ϕ_e is the efficiency of the photocathode (in electrons per photon), and t is the measuring time. Still the assumption is that the square root fluctuation in P is the dominating noise source. For tungsten strip lamps with well-stabilized power supplies, this assumption is certainly justified.

For a medium glass spectrograph, a source of 2500°K at 6000Å, and a detector with $\phi_e = 0.01$, we find $\Delta I/I = 2.4 \times 10^{-3}$, equivalent to a temperature difference of two black bodies of 0.6°K. This value was confirmed by experiments. In Eq. (16) we used the equivalent width of the spectral line in the flame, estimated at 0.05Å. The spectral range actually transmitted is generally larger, of the order of 1Å. The result is a smoothing of the spectral line (by a factor of 20), but also a decrease (i.e., an improvement) of the contrast threshold by the same factor, due to the square root character of the fluctuations. This is the reason that in photoelectric measurements the minimum detectable temperature difference does not depend upon the actual resolving power, i.e., upon the slit widths, but only upon the square root of the angular dispersion [Eq. (16)]. For visual observation the latter argument does not hold, since the contrast threshold in the eye has a lower limit (of about 1 %). Therefore, the resolving power and the slit widths should be optimized in this case.

Photographic detection has the well-known advantage that a number of lines can be investigated simultaneously by taking a series of spectra with increasing radiation temperature of the reference source. As to precision, the same argument holds as did with visual observation, that is, that the resolving power (and here, of course, the exposure time) should be optimized.

One would prefer the oscillator strength of the spectral line to appear in Eq. (16), rather than the equivalent width. However, the lines are mostly used in the region of self-absorption, where the oscillator strength is not a satisfactory parameter. Generally, of course, resonance lines with large values of the oscillator strength are preferred. The influence of the wavelength and the flame temperature is implicit in the use of Planck's formula, which determines the number of quanta available. Some elements used in reversal measurements are the alkali metals, Cr, Fe, Pb, Sr, and Tl.

The emission–absorption measurements, mentioned in Section II, differ from a reversal measurement in that emission and absorption are measured consecutively in the former method, while in the latter they are measured simultaneously. The reversal method is superior in precision because of the null procedure, but it is normally limited in range to the maximum radiation temperature of the background source. This limitation does not exist in the emission–absorption method.

The risk of systematic errors in the method of line reversal due to the apparatus is rather small. The main error that may occur stems from the use of a smaller solid angle of light from the reference source than from the flame, as discussed previously. Another erroneous increase of the reversal temperature may occur when light in the spectral line from the relatively large flame is scattered by the second lens into the spectrograph. On dusting this lens with some powder, we once found an increase of 40°K in the reversal temperature. The error will normally amount to about 10°K and can be avoided by placing a diaphragm between the flame and the second lens. Still another error is caused by reflection of light from the flame by the first lens or by the reference source (especially when a strip lamp is used). The effect is that the continuum spectrum that enters the flame already contains the spectral line to be used in emission. Again this leads to too high a reversal temperature. One can avoid this error, which may amount to 10–15°K (15), by placing the reflecting surfaces of the components before the flame not quite perpendicular to the optical axis. However, care should be taken that other conditions (solid angles, calibration of the source) are not violated. A general check on the occurrence of these errors (except the last one) is made by a series of measurements in which the solid angle of light is decreased, e.g., by stopping down the second lens. This should not change the reversal temperature. Since all errors tend to increase the reversal temperature, one may say that the lower the temperature of a given flame is measured to be, the smaller are the residual errors.

Systematic errors due to the flame are of a different kind. The possible deviations from complete equilibrium were discussed earlier. Local deviations seem only to be of practical importance in the reaction zone and in flames with little quenching of radiation, e.g., flames of stoichiometric O_2–Ar–H_2 mixtures, that are favored for measurements of fluorescence. The major source of error is the inhomogeneity of the temperature through the flame. For reasons of sensitivity one has to use high atom concentrations and therefore strongly self-absorbed lines. This implies that it is predominantly atoms in an outer zone of the flame, facing the detector, that contribute to the emission line and that the temperature of this outer zone, generally cooler than the center of the flame, is measured. Under high resolution the emission line would show a self-reversal dip in its center. To avoid this error the flame can be shielded with an identical flame in which no vapor is introduced. Yet it is impossible to contain the metal vapor in the inner flame. The metal atoms will diffuse outward and reach the cooler outer layers of the flame at a greater height. One can demonstrate that this effect is actually diffusion (and not turbulence) by examining a slightly luminous flame. The soot particles, too heavy to diffuse noticeably, form straight luminous trails, whereas an added metal vapor shows a plume-like pattern. Indeed, measured diffusion coefficients (e.g., for Na in an air–C_2H_2 flame at 2500°K: 10 cm^2 sec^{-1}) agree well with values calculated from transport theory (19). An elegant way to suppress self-reversal in the cool outer layer of a flame is the following (20): With the introduction of a strontium salt into a N_2O–C_2H_2 flame, the emitting atoms are mainly confined to the hot center of the flame, and at the lower temperatures in the outer parts of the flame, strontium is mainly present as an oxide. A general check on the occurrence of self-reversal is made by a series of measurements in which the concentration of the metal vapor is decreased stepwise. The decrease in self-absorption shifts and broadens the zone of the flame in which the average reversal temperature is obtained. No change of the reversal temperature should occur. More generally still, one may compare the reversal temperatures of different lines. (The variation in the radiation temperature with wavelength should be allowed for.) Table 1 gives some measurements for the alkali metals.

TABLE 1

Reversal Temperatures of Various Spectral Lines in a Premixed, Shielded Air–Acetylene Flame

Element	Wavelength, Å	Real temp. of strip lamp, °K	Radiation temp. of strip lamp, °K
Li	6708	2722	2432 ± 2
Na	5890	2677	2435 ± 1
K	7665	2789	2436 ± 1
Rb	7948	2801	2436 ± 1

IV. The Calculation of Flame Temperatures

Methods for calculating compositions and temperature in chemical
equilibria are well established. Wilkins (21) has given a very thorough
treatment of these calculations, dealing with the calculation of the required thermodynamic properties from molecular structure data, through
the actual calculation of equilibria and temperatures and applying the
results to a discussion of the performance of chemical propellants in
rocket engines. Gaydon and Wolfhard (3) have given a very clear description of the calculations, particularly aiming at spectrochemical
flames, including numerical examples and a set of thermochemical data
for the components of normally used flames. A large compilation of
thermochemical data can be found in the JANAF Interim Thermochemical Tables (22). A brief outline of the method of calculation is given
here, together with some results of calculations that were made by P. J. T.
Zeegers in our laboratory.

The calculation of the equilibrium composition is made by an iterative
method using the equilibrium equations and the equations of mass conservation and pressure conservation. For an air–hydrocarbon flame the
main equilibria involved are: $H_2 + \frac{1}{2}O_2 \rightleftarrows H_2O$, $OH + \frac{1}{2}H_2 \rightleftarrows H_2O$,
$H + H \rightleftarrows H_2$, $O + O \rightleftarrows \frac{1}{2}O_2$, $CO + \frac{1}{2}O_2 \rightleftarrows CO_2$, and $NO \rightleftarrows \frac{1}{2}N_2 + \frac{1}{2}O_2$.
One makes a reasonable assumption for the flame temperature, for a
partial pressure (H_2O), and for the ratio of the partial pressures of another
two (CO_2 and CO) and then calculates, with the use of the equations
mentioned, the partial pressures of the other components. Two equations

remain to check and revise the assumptions and a new calculation is made, starting from these revised assumptions. This process is repeated until a fit is obtained within a properly chosen tolerance. Thus, the composition is obtained at a chosen temperature.

The equilibrium temperature is found from the equation of heat conservation. From the heats of formation and the partial pressures of both the initial and the final components, one calculates the heat, ΔH, released in the reactions, assuming that the temperature remains constant. Next, one calculates from the specific heats, integrated from the initial temperature to the assumed temperature, the heat $\Delta H'$ needed to raise the final mixture from the initial to the assumed temperature. The difference between ΔH and $\Delta H'$ is used to make a new assumption for the temperature. Again, this procedure is repeated until ΔH and $\Delta H'$ are equal within a properly chosen tolerance. Heat losses can be simulated by diminishing ΔH by some chosen heat loss.

TABLE 2

Equilibrium Compositions and Temperatures of Stoichiometric
Air–Acetylene and Air–Hydrogen Flames

	Air–C_2H_2	Air–H_2
H_2O	7.01%	32.35%
O_2	1.66	0.47
H_2	0.38	1.53
OH	0.72	0.70
CO	4.12	—
CO_2	11.57	—
NO	0.69	0.27
N_2	73.43	64.43
O	0.22	0.06
H	0.18	0.18
Temperature	2537°K	2385°K

Table 2 gives the composition and temperature of two flames that also have been calculated by Gaydon and Wolfhard (3). Our compositions agreed with theirs within 1%, while the temperatures are 13°K higher in our calculations for both flames. It was ascertained that the remaining error is a few hundredths of a percent in the partial pressures and about

3°K in the temperature. It was also found that the thermochemical data given by Gaydon and Wolfhard and those given in the JANAF tables yielded equal temperatures within 1°K.

Figure 3 shows the influence of the mixing ratio and of heat losses on

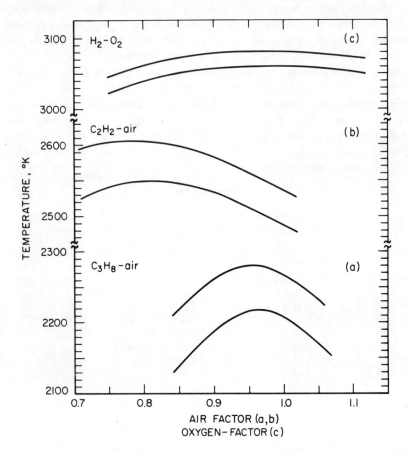

Fig. 3. Calculated flame temperatures for varying mixing ratio. (*a*) Air–propane. (*b*) Air–acetylene. (*c*) Oxygen–hydrogen. The numbers indicate the ratios of air/fuel and oxygen/fuel, respectively, relative to the stoichiometric ratio. The upper curves were calculated without heat losses, the lower curves with 5% heat losses.

the temperature of some flames. It demonstrates the fact that the use of stoichiometric mixing ratios in actual flames as well as in calculations has no physical meaning. Since the basis of stoichiometry, namely the ratio required for complete combustion, e.g., to H_2O and CO_2, is not realized in most flames, a stoichiometric mixture does not yield the maximum flame temperature. It can be seen from Fig. 3 that the optimum mixing ratio, yielding the maximum temperature, does come closer to stoichiometry when the heat losses are increased. Table 3 gives calculated tempera-

TABLE 3

Calculated Flame Temperatures (°K) for Stoichiometric and Optimum Mixing Ratios

	Oxidant						
	Air[a]				Oxygen		Nitrous oxide
			With 5% heat loss				
	Stoichiometric	Optimum	Stoichiometric	Optimum	Stoichiometric	Optimum	Stoichiometric
			A[b]			A[b]			O[b]	
H_2	2385	2401	0.94	2324	2337	0.94	3080	3081	0.98	2960
CO	2382	2417	0.83	2333	2364	0.86	2971	2973	0.91	2872
C_2H_2	2537	2606	0.78	2488	2547	0.82	3343	3430	0.70	3148
C_3H_8	2267	2279	0.95	2207	2216	0.96	3094	3103	0.88	2932

[a] Composition of the air: 78.11% N_2, 20.93% O_2, 0.93% Ar, and 0.03% CO_2.
[b] The air factor (A) and the oxygen factor (O) are defined as the amount of air or oxygen used relative to the stoichiometric amount.

tures of the most common flames with 5% heat losses and without heat losses. The accuracy of these temperatures is 3–5°K. Finally, Fig. 4 gives the calculated influence of the oxygen content of the air, the acetone content of acetylene (which increases from about 1% to 10% with decreasing pressure in the tank), and the spraying of water on the temperature of an air–acetylene flame.

Another application of such calculations, rather outside the scope of this chapter, is the influence of the flame temperature and the mixing ratio on the dissociation of metal oxides. In such calculations the metal and its oxides are taken into the calculation of the composition. A variation of the air–gas mixing ratio then shows the advantage of fuel-rich and/or hot flames for the formation of atomic vapors of metals like vanadium and aluminum (23).

Consistent sets of thermochemical tables are the JANAF tables and Technical Notes 270–3 (24), 270–4, etc., edited by the National Bureau of Standards (U.S.).

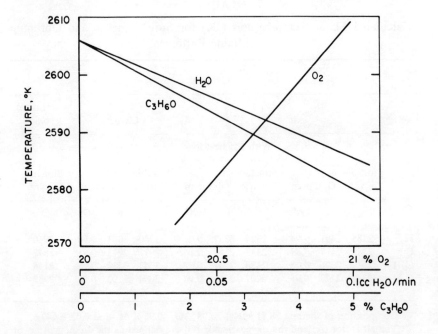

Fig. 4. The calculated influence of the oxygen content of air, the amount of water introduced (as liquid), and the acetone content of the acetylene gas on the temperature of an air–acetylene flame (50 liters/min air, optimum mixing ratio).

V. Obtainable Temperatures

To obtain a high temperature, the initial components of the gas mixture should have high endothermic heats of formation and the final components should have high exothermic heats of formation. Along this line a number of very hot flames have been obtained. (See Chapter 6.) However, the rise in temperature is often less than is expected since at high temperatures a considerable amount of heat can be consumed by the dissociation of a combustion product. For example, an oxygen–acetylene mixture, burning completely to CO_2 and H_2O, would yield a flame with a temperature of about 7000°K (3), whereas a calculation with the proper dissociation equilibria included yields a temperature of about 3400°K. Another practical limitation is that the safety hazards tend to increase with the use of highly endothermic gases. However, the recently increased use of N_2O (instead of air) in, for example, acetylene and hydrogen flames (increasing the temperature by some 500°K) is a good example of the progress that has been made.

Since the dissociative equilibria shift to the undissociated side with increasing pressure, one can increase the flame temperature by working at higher pressures. An increase of 500°K in an oxygen–hydrogen flame at 40 atm has been measured (25), as compared with the temperature of such a flame at 1 atm.

Another way to increase the flame temperature is by additional supply of thermal or electrical energy. Preheating of the gases does increase the flame temperature, but again the shift in the dissociative equilibria offsets the expected rise in temperature. For example, in an air–acetylene flame the specific heat of the burned gases (which includes the shift in the equilibria) at 2500°K is twice the specific heat of the unburned gases (26). For higher temperatures this ratio increases, and at about 3000°K the effect of preheating is for the main part consumed in additional dissociation.

The addition of electrical energy is discussed in Chapter 6.

VI. Comparison of Calculated and Measured Temperatures

Generally, calculated flame temperatures are higher than actual flame temperatures by one or more hundreds of degrees K. With laminar flames the main reason for this difference is the heat loss that an actual flame suffers through various mechanisms. In the first place, there is a conductive heat loss to the burner. A part of this heat is used to preheat the gases flowing through the burner and thus is restored to the flame, but a considerable loss of 10% or more generally remains. Calculations for an air–acetylene flame showed that 1% heat loss was equivalent to a temperature drop of 12°K. Depending on flame size, flame speed, the area of the burner top in contact with the hot gas, and other features of burner design, the losses will vary considerably, but a temperature decrease of at least

100°K due to these losses is often encountered. With small flames on large burners (e.g., slot burners) the decrease is certainly larger.

Another loss is the radiation from the hot gases which occur mainly in the infrared. An amount of radiation equivalent to a drop of 10°K per msec (or 10–20°K per cm height in the flame), mainly due to CO_2, occurs in an air–acetylene flame. In an air–hydrogen flame the losses are probably less.

Finally, the question of equilibrium must be considered again. It has been mentioned already that the rise in temperature above the reaction zone is caused by slow recombination processes. Figure 2 showed that these processes are practically completed at the height of maximum temperature and that equilibrium is fairly closely attained. An effort was made to minimize the various losses, using a well-insulated burner. The losses at the height of maximum temperature still amounted to 27°K, of which 20°K was due to radiation. After correction of the reversal temperature for these measured losses, we found that the measured and calculated temperatures (26) agreed within 5°K.

With turbulent flames the heat losses to the burner are practically nil, due to the small burners and the large gas velocities used. The differences here are mainly caused by a lack of equilibrium and by entrainment of considerable amounts of gas from the surrounding. Also, the introduction of water with the sample has a large influence in these flames. Temperature drops of 500°K have been reported. The use of an organic solvent, which is burned itself, can decrease the effect considerably.

REFERENCES

1. H. P. Hooymayers and C. Th. J. Alkemade, *J. Quant. Spectry. & Radiative Transfer*, 6, 847 (1966).
2. W. Snelleman and J. A. Smit, *Metrologia*, 4, 123 (1968).
3. A. G. Gaydon and H. G. Wolfhard, *Flames, Their Structure, Radiation and Temperature*, Chapman and Hall, London, 1960.
3a. H. P. Broida and K. E. Shuler, *J. Chem. Phys.*, 27, 933 (1957).
4. T. Hollander, P. F. Kalff, and C. Th. J. Alkemade, *J. Chem. Phys.*, 39, 2558 (1963).
5. P. J. T. Zeegers and C. Th. J. Alkemade, *Combust. Flame*, 9, 247 (1965).
6. T. Hollander and H. P. Broida, *J. Quant. Spectry. & Radiative Transfer*, 7, 965 (1967).
7. P. W. J. M. Boumans, *Theory of Spectrochemical Excitation*, J. W. Arrowsmith, Bristol, 1966.
8. A. G. Gaydon, *The Spectroscopy of Flames*, Chapman and Hall, London, 1957.
9. G. H. Dieke and H. M. Crosswhite (1948), reprinted in *J. Quant. Spectry. & Radiative Transfer*, 2, 97 (1962).
10. L. S. Ornstein and H. Brinkman, *Physica*, 1, 797 (1934).

11. J. A. Smit, *The Production and Measurement of Constant High Temperatures, up to 7000°K*, Ph.D. Thesis, Utrecht, 1950.
12. N. Thomas, A. G. Gaydon, and L. Brewer, *J. Chem. Phys.*, **20**, 369 (1942).
13. R. H. Tourin, *Spectroscopic Gas Temperature Measurements*, Elsevier, Amsterdam, 1966.
14. A. I. Dahl, ed., *Temperature, Its Measurement and Control in Science and Industry*, Vol. III, Part 2, Reinhold, New York, 1961.
15. W. Snelleman, *Combust. Flame*, **11**, 453 (1967).
16. J. C. DeVos, *Physica*, **20**, 690 (1954).
17. T. J. Quinn and C. R. Barber, *Metrologia*, **3**, 19 (1967).
18. E. M. Kudryavtsev, E. F. Gippius, A. N. Pechenof, and N. N. Sobolev, *High Temperature*, **1**, 60 (1963).
19. W. Snelleman, *A Flame as a Standard of Temperature*, Ph.D. Thesis, Utrecht, 1965.
20. J. B. Willis, J. O. Rasmuson, R. N. Kniseley, and V. A. Fassel, *Spectrochim. Acta.* **23B**, 725 (1968).
21. R. G. Wilkins, *Theoretical Evaluation of Chemical Propellants*, Prentice Hall, N.J., 1963.
22. Dow Chemical Co., *JANAF Interim Thermochemical Tables*, 1960.
23. C. H. Anderson, *Pittsburgh Conf. Anal. Chem. Appl. Spectry.*, Cleveland, Ohio, March 1968.
24. D. D. Wagman, W. H. Evans, V. B. Parker, I. Halow, S. M. Baily, and R. H. Schumm, *N.B.S. Tech. Note 270–3*, January, 1968.
25. J. Diederichsen and H. G. Wolfhard, *Proc. Roy. Soc. (London)*, **A236**, 89 (1956).
26. W. Snelleman, *Metrologia*, **4**, 117 (1968).

8 Distribution of Atomic Concentration in Flames

A. N. Hambly and C. S. Rann

CHEMISTRY DEPARTMENT
AUSTRALIAN NATIONAL UNIVERSITY
CANBERRA, AUSTRALIA

I. Introduction

Diagrams which show the variation in concentration of normal or excited atoms in the cross section of a flame, or along the vertical central line of a flame, are often called concentration profiles. The dictionary meanings of profile are "a silhouette," "a cross section of a fortification," or, more recently, "a character sketch." A consideration of the techniques used to obtain the common distribution diagrams shows that these do not conform to any of these meanings of profile. One must be extremely careful in giving meaning to the published patterns of atomic distribution in flames since the pattern is often dependent on the optical system used in its measurement. This is not always important for the analyst who, in using a standard set of flame conditions in a fixed optical arrangement, is concerned with the apparent or "practical" distribution observed with that arrangement, rather than with the absolute meaning to be attached to each measurement.

The ambiguities can be illustrated with examples from emission and absorption measurements. Many flame photometers used for emission measurements employ Meker-type burners in which there is a gradient in temperature from the center of the flame to the outside. If light emitted at the center line of the flame is focused on the slit of the monochromator, the radiation recorded will be diminished to some extent by reversal as it passes through the cooler outer zone of the flame and so is not truly representative of conditions along the center line. Some workers who are interested in atomic concentrations have sought to avoid this difficulty by surrounding the central region of the flame, into which the solution is sprayed, by a sheath flame so that the emitting atoms are in a region of uniform temperature. Even with this precaution errors due to self-absorption can arise if the concentration of metal atoms is high. Similar difficulties of interpretation occur in atomic absorption measurements with a beam of small cross section. The exact path followed by the beam, when passing through the flame with its varying refractive index due to changing composition and temperature, cannot be specified. Fortunately, the refractive indices are always close to unity so that the deviation from a straight path is small though it is readily demonstrated (1). In this chapter we will be concerned mainly with "practical" distributions as they appear to the analyst.

Atomic and molecular distribution studies may be made by measuring absorption, emission, or fluorescence in a flame containing dispersed atoms, when the flame is moved relative to the light path of the optical system. Studies have also been made by sampling various regions of the flame through a small orifice leading directly into a mass spectrometer. For optical measurements the burner is mounted on a stand equipped with traversing screws which permit vertical and horizontal movement relative

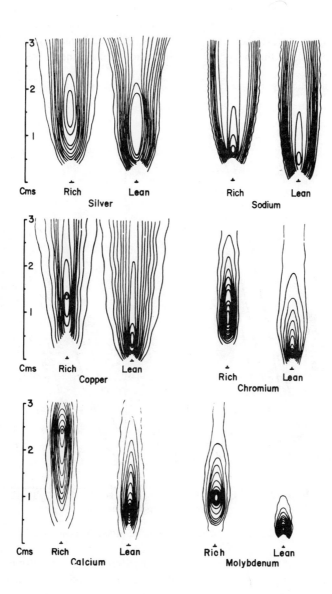

Fig. 1. Distribution of atoms in a 10-cm air–acetylene flame. Contours are drawn at intervals of 0.1 absorbance unit with maximum absorbance in center (*1*).

to the optic axis. In some cases the flame is placed relative to the optic axis so that a maximum reading is obtained, and this is taken to indicate coincidence with the center line of the flame. Measurements are taken by displacing the burner vertically, and a one-dimensional distribution

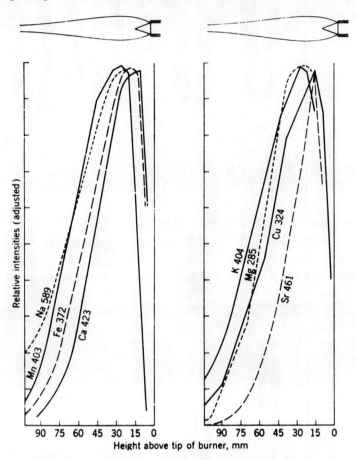

Fig. 2. Distribution patterns of atomic emission (2).

pattern is obtained. Concentration distributions in two dimensions are represented by contours of equal value of the measured quantity, e.g., absorbance, which is proportional to the concentration. The ordinate and abscissa give the coordinates of the point in the flame in a plane at right angles to the optic axis. The contours show relative, not absolute, concentrations (Fig. 1). When the distribution along the center line in the flame is represented, the usual convention is to present the quantity proportional to concentration along the ordinate and the height in the flame above the burner outlet along the abscissa. Because of the reluctance of the mind to translate a horizontal coordinate as a height, it is common to draw the outline of the flame parallel with the abscissa, as is shown in Fig. 2 which includes some of the earliest distribution diagrams reported by Lundegårdh (2).

II. Distribution Patterns of Absorbance

Measurements of distribution patterns by absorption methods are relatively easy to perform. The experimental arrangement used by Rann and Hambly (1) to measure the distribution of absorbance by the full length of the flame from a standard 10-cm slit burner is shown in Fig. 3.

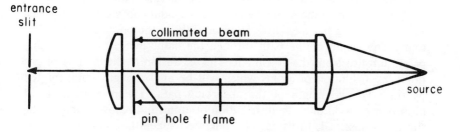

Fig. 3. Optical arrangement for measurement of atomic distribution patterns by absorption (1).

The incident radiation from a hollow cathode lamp was collimated by a lens so that a beam of approximately parallel rays passed through the flame. An aperture 1 mm in diameter selected the area of the emerging beam over which the absorption by the flame was measured. To obtain resolution in the distribution pattern, it is necessary to use a small area of measurement about each position coordinate in the flame. As limitation of the area reduces the strength of the signal to be recorded, a compromise has to be made. The signal is necessarily weak so that the reduction of noise is very important. A selected photomultiplier and a high-quality amplifier are needed. The flame is traversed horizontally and vertically, relative to the selected beam, by rotating the micrometer screws on the burner mounting. The hollow cathode source, chopper disk, mono-chromator, and photomultiplier detector are similar to those used for routine atomic absorption measurements.

The flame will be emitting light at the same wavelength as the source and as there is turbulence in the flame the light emitted will carry some modulation. A Fourier analysis of the flame noise from 100 to 50,000 cps showed an even distribution of noise power per unit band width so that there is no specially favored modulating frequency for the chopper. The narrower the pass band of the amplifier the less will be the effect of emis-sion from the flame. The Hewlett-Packard, Model 302A, wave analyzer, which was used as an amplifier in obtaining the distributions of Fig. 1, had a pass band of ± 3 cps and was tuned to the 300-cps modulating frequency of the chopper, which was located between the source and the collimating lens. If the modulating frequency changed because of a change in the rate of rotation of the chopper disk, an "automatic frequency control" circuit in the amplifier locked the latter to the modulated signal.

There are some minor difficulties of measurement and interpretation. In the outer part of the flame the entry of secondary air creates turbulence in the absorbing gas and there is uncertainty in the position of the con-tours. The length of the path through the flame increases as the flame passes upward from the 10-cm slit. The expansion in the volume of gas produces a dilution of atoms which will be only partially compensated by the increased length of the absorbing path. The measurements of absorbance reveal only the distribution of atoms in the lower state of the transition observed. In flames of moderate temperature, only transitions from the ground state will be effective in absorption if the atom has a singlet or a degenerate S ground state. For atoms with multiplet ground states, e.g., tin, lead (Fig. 11, Table 1), there will be appreciable concen-trations of atoms in low-lying excited states. The strongest absorption may even occur from one of these excited states either because of its high population, arising from a greater statistical weight, or because of a higher transition probability for excitation.

III. Factors Controlling Observed Absorbance Pattern

Some important factors which determine the pattern of absorbance which is observed are (a) the type of burner, (b) the fuel composition, (c) the rate of supply of solution to the flame, (d) the solvent in the solution

supplied [which will also affect (c)], (e) the rate of decompositi
solute particles to generate metal atoms, and (f) the rate of remo___ __
atoms by reaction with molecules or radicals in the flame.

A. BURNER TYPE

An extreme difference of absorption pattern occurs between the flame
of a standard 100mm × 1mm slit-type burner (Fig. 1) and a flame from a
Meker-type burner in which the solution is supplied to the central region
which is surrounded by a sheath of burning fuel gas [Fig. 4(a)]. For the
latter, the distribution of atoms (and of temperature) is much more uniform and the absorbance contours are consequently more widely spaced.
In those photometers which permit rotation of the 10-cm slit burner so
that the length of path through the flame can be varied, the proportion of
the path in a high-temperature region steadily decreases as the flame is
rotated until it is at right angles to the optic axis. This causes small but
appreciable changes in the distribution pattern. It may be necessary to
change the position of the burner relative to the optic axis if the maximum
of absorbance is to remain on the axis. There will be a greater variation of
absorption with height in some directions through the flame than in
others [Fig. 4(b)]. When solution is supplied only to the central region of a
sheathed flame, absorption does extend into the sheath; atoms are transported by diffusion and also by the explosive breakup of droplets of
solution or of small crystallites containing occluded solvent.

B. FUEL COMPOSITION

The flame gases perform a dual role in creating the high temperature
favorable to the formation of atoms and in providing reactants which by
reduction or oxidation control chemically the production and removal of
atoms in the flame. From Fig. 1 it can be seen that an increase in the air-to-
acetylene ratio in the fuel gases, which will affect both temperature and
chemical distribution in the flame, causes the region of maximum absorption to become smaller and to move downward. The region of maximum temperature is higher and more diffuse in the richer flame (1, 3). The
diminished oxidizing power of the fuel-rich flame will also delay the
oxidative removal of atoms. Where materials are difficult to decompose
into atoms, high-temperature flames can give enhanced absorption, but
when the atoms are easily excited or easily ionized, there may be a loss
of absorption of resonance radiation in the hottest region of the flame.

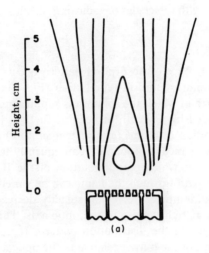

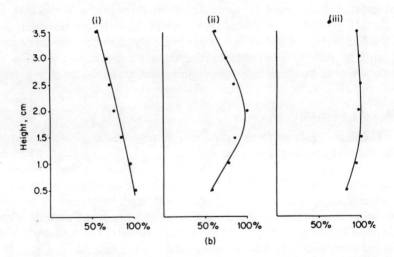

Fig. 4. (*a*). Distribution of copper atoms in a rich air–acetylene flame. The solution of a copper salt is supplied to the inner part only of the flame from a Meker-type burner. (*b*). Apparent vertical distribution of atoms in an air–acetylene flame from a 10-cm slit burner: (i) along the full length of the flame, (ii) flame at 45° to the optic axis, (iii) flame at right angles to the optic axis.

C. RATE OF SUPPLY OF SOLUTION

The conditions vary between the supply of an aerosol from which the coarse particles have settled out in the spray chamber, to the supply of much greater volumes of solution and larger droplets in a direct injection burner. The supply of large droplets delays the release of atoms into the flame so that the maximum of absorbance comes at a higher level in the flame when direct injection is used. Droplets can survive to quite high levels in such flames. In the total consumption burner the turbulence in the flame, and the scattering of the modulated light from the source by droplets and solid particles, cause noise that can be accepted by the amplifier and so give a false reading of the absorbance. Such sprays also produce large temperature changes in very hot flames of the oxygen–cyanogen type (4). The choice of solvent also modifies the rate at which the solute reaches the flame.

D. SOLVENT COMPOSITION

Gibson et al. (3), who used a direct injection burner, showed that the replacement of water by acetone as the solvent in the spray supplied to an oxygen–hydrogen flame displaced the position of maximum absorption by sodium atoms downward. This was partly due to the more rapid removal of solvent and partly to the higher temperature obtained in and just above the primary reaction zone. The enhancement of absorption, due to this displacement of the maximum, is great in the lower regions of the flame, but near the position where maximum absorption is obtained with aqueous solutions the enhancement is very small. In the experiments of Gibson the solutions in organic solvents and the aqueous solutions were fed to the flame at the same rate. When aerosols from a spray chamber are used, the lower surface tension of the organic solvent compared with that of water favors the supply of a greater quantity of solution per second to the flame, thus producing an enhancement of the measured absorption.

E. RATE OF RELEASE OF ATOMS IN THE FLAME

For many metals the same atomic distribution in the flame is obtained when equal concentrations of its various salts are supplied as solution to the nebulizer. For a majority of binary salts the energy of dissociation into atoms is of the order of 3 eV or less and at a temperature of 2500°K the value of kT is approximately 0.2 eV. The rate of decomposition is therefore expected to be high, but the extreme dilution of the products of dissociation in the flame will make the rate of recombination small. The rate of re-combination can be appreciable if the concentration of one of the products is enhanced; for example, Sugden and co-workers (5–7) have determined equilibrium constants and heats of dissociation for alkali halides by the addition of organic halogen compounds to flames into which salts of the alkali metal were sprayed. In these cases, however, the heats of dissociation have greater than average values. The survival of undissociated diatomic halides in flames is shown by the emission of the band spectra of CuCl or BaCl when solutions of $CuCl_2$ or $BaCl_2$ are supplied to the flame. Al-though it is commonly assumed that the salts supplied are completely decomposed by passage through the primary reaction zone of the flame, the distribution diagrams frequently show that the maximum conversion to atoms does not occur there. The progress of metallic atom formation may be followed by integrating the total absorption across the width of the flame at various heights (3). Suitable plots can be obtained by changing the values of the absorbance contours at a given flame height, such as those in Fig. 1, into corresponding ordinates and plotting these against the distance from the center of the flame as abscissa (Fig. 5). In some cases this reveals an initial growth in total absorption with distance from the reaction zone. When integrated absorption measured in this way reaches its maximum value and then stays constant for some distance upward in the flame (3), it may indicate complete dissociation of the salt into atoms. When integrated absorption decreases rapidly from the maximum, due to loss of atoms by combination, the latter process must have been appreci-able below the maximum so that the maximum absorption will not corres-pond to complete atomization of the salt supplied to the flame.

It has long been known that the absorption due to calcium is low when solutions which also contain phosphate are sprayed into the flame. Montgareuil (8) and later Alkemade and Voorhuis (9) have shown that this low absorption is due to a slow release of calcium from complexes already present in the solution supplied as spray. The maximum ab-sorption for calcium in such solutions occurs at quite high levels in the flame. Slow release of copper and magnesium atoms is indicated by the distribution diagrams for rich air–acetylene flames in Fig. 1, where the contours diverge above the center of maximum absorption.* For calcium

* A growth of integrated absorbance, with height in the flame, would occur if there was a reduction in the velocity of the flame gases. This would cause an increase in concentration of atoms, as with traffic slowing on a highway. Measurements of flame velocity (9a) show that this is not decreasing at the relevant height.

and chromium in the lean air–acetylene flame, on the other hand, the maximum production of atoms occurs near the level of the center of maximum absorbance.

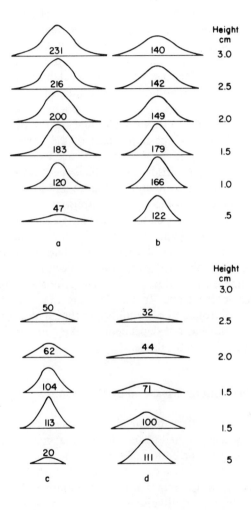

Fig. 5. Distribution of absorbance across the flame of a 10-cm burner at various heights. (*a*) Absorption due to Mg in a rich air–acetylene flame, (*b*) the same in a lean flame, (*c*) absorption due to Cr in a rich air–acetylene flame, (*d*) the same in a lean flame. The numbers show the relative area under the curve.

F. Depletion of Atoms in the Flame

The decrease in integrated absorption across the whole width of the flame, which occurs above a certain height, shows that atoms are being removed by combination or by diffusion from the flame. The height of maximum integrated absorption marks the level where the increased dissociation with height is just balanced by the rate of decrease in the concentration of atoms. The most likely compounds to be formed are the oxides and hydroxides, the former because of their great stability and because of the entrance of secondary air, and the latter because of the high concentration of hydroxyl radicals in the outer cone of oxygen–hydrocarbon and oxygen–hydrogen flames. Band spectra of oxides and hydroxides are often identified in the emission from the upper part of the flame. Band spectra of hydrides are also observed when some salts are fed into hydrocarbon or hydrogen flames, while nitride bands have been reported in oxygen–cyanogen flames. As the formation of oxides and hydroxides will be controlled by the temperature and the concentrations of oxygen and hydroxyl in the flame, it will be independent of the initial salt of the metal present in the aerosol, providing that this is at the low concentration usual in atomic absorption and that it decomposes readily. Uniformity in the distribution patterns obtained from equal concentrations of a number of salts of the same element does not therefore indicate that all the metal atoms are free in the flame. It may indicate that the concentration of metal atoms is controlled by an equilibrium that is independent of the salt in the original solution, but dependent on the composition of the flame gases at various points in the flame.

IV. Distribution Patterns Measured by Emission

The distribution pattern obtained in emission experiments is that of atoms in a particular excited state, whereas that measured by absorption is most commonly a distribution of atoms in the ground state. Frequently, the strongest emission is at the same frequency as that used in absorption. The recording of an accurate distribution pattern requires the collection of the emission from a small-volume element in the flame and the differentiation of the light emitted by the atoms of interest from that emitted by radicals and other atoms in the flame gases. Interference from the band spectra of radicals is least in the oxygen–hydrogen flame where the main molecular spectrum is the relatively weak emission of the hydroxyl radical in the ultraviolet. This is also the main interference experienced in the outer cone of oxygen–hydrocarbon flames, but in the inner cone, or primary reaction zone, not only are the hydroxyl bands present, but the Swan bands of C_2 and the bands of the CH radical cover a large portion of the visible spectrum. Because of these interfering emissions, analysts have avoided measurements in the primary reaction zone, but recently there has been considerable interest in the distribution of atoms in highly excited states in this region of the flame.

The interference from the band spectra in the primary reaction zone of hydrocarbon flames has been partially avoided by supplying the metal atoms, as compounds dissolved in an organic solvent, to an oxygen–hydrogen flame (14, 15). Dickey et al.(10) discriminated between the emission from atoms and that from flame constituents by pulsing the aerosol supply to the flame and using an amplifier tuned to the pulsing frequency. It seems certain, however, that there will be some modulation of the molecular emission due to this periodic change in the conditions in the flame. Most measurements have been made with a monochromator of high dispersion and with narrow slits to limit the background radiation reaching the detector. The intensity due to atomic emission is found by scanning across the emission wavelength and subtracting the mean of the background intensity on either side from the intensity at the maximum of emission.

In practical flames it is not possible to restrict the measured emission rigorously to that arising in a small volume element in the flame. Figure 6(a) shows an optical system that comes close to this requirement. To conserve the energy in the small radiation signal, the optical train should be designed to fill the angle of acceptance of the collimating lens or mirror in the monochromator. Most distribution patterns that have been published were obtained by using a lens or mirror to project an inverted image of the flame in the plane of the slit of the monochromator, and have obtained resolution by using a slit height of about 1 mm (Fig. 6(b)]. Although the origin of the light received by the detector cannot be accurately specified with this optical arrangement, the pattern recorded will correspond closely to conditions used in analysis. In either of these optical arrangements the whole area of the flame image is surveyed by moving the flame relative to the optic axis.

The same factors of burner type, fuel composition, rate of supply of solution, solvent employed, and rates of release and removal of atoms which govern distribution patterns of absorbance are also important in controlling intensity patterns in emission. If the excited and ground state atoms are in thermal equilibrium, it should be possible to calculate the distribution pattern of one state of the atom from that of the other. As the fraction of atoms in any excited state of high energy at a particular instant is very small, it is possible to have large relative changes in this small number without an appreciable effect on the concentration of the bulk of the atoms which are in the ground state. Gibson et al. (3) have shown that, if the temperature distribution is known for an oxygen–hydrogen flame, then the distribution pattern of emission by sodium atoms in the first excited, ^2P, state can be calculated from the distribution pattern for ground state atoms measured in absorption (Fig. 7). Sugden, however, has shown that this is not possible for emission from more highly excited states of atoms, some of which emit with an appreciable intensity although their concentration at thermal equilibrium is vanishingly small (11). For example, Bulewicz and Sugden (12) observed emission from the ^3S state of magnesium in oxygen–hydrogen–nitrogen flames at a much higher intensity than can be accounted for by the temperature of the flame. As they found that the intensity of this emission is constant over the region of the flame in which the product of hydrogen atom and hydroxyl radical concentrations is also constant, but falls when conditions reduce these concentrations, they suggest that chemiluminescence is induced by the reaction

$$H + OH + Mg \rightleftarrows H_2O + Mg^* \qquad (1)$$

Much stronger chemiluminescent effects are found in, and just above, the primary reaction zone of oxygen–hydrocarbon flames, but these occur in a region in which it is difficult to obtain accurate distribution patterns.

For atomic states in thermal equilibrium, the proportion of excited atoms increases steeply as the temperature rises, and the decomposition reactions which produce the atoms are more complete at higher temperatures also. We therefore expect a marked correlation between temperature distribution and emission distribution in the flame. Sheathed flames which have a considerable region of uniform temperature also show uniformity of emission in the same region. Oxygen–cyanogen flames which produce exceptionally high temperatures permit the determination of distributions of atoms which have very high excitation energies, though elements like the alkali and alkaline earth metals, which have low ionization energies, may have the concentrations of simple atoms reduced by ionization. We can then obtain distribution patterns for excited states of the ion (4), such as that shown for Ca^+ in Fig. 8. As in the case of absorption measurements, the change in fuel-to-oxygen ratio will affect the

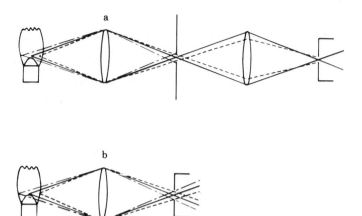

Fig. 6. Optical arrangements for measurement of distribution of atomic emission in flames. (*a*) Arrangement restricting the region from which emission reaches the detector. (*b*) A common arrangement which accepts emission from a more extensive region than in (*a*).

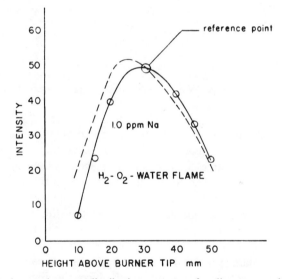

Fig. 7. Consistency between distribution patterns of sodium atoms determined by absorption and emission (*3*). (*Broken line*): Calculated distribution of emission with uniform distribution of atoms at the measured temperatures. (*Circles*): Calculated values of emission on atomic concentrations found by absorption and the measured temperatures. (*Solid line*): Observed distribution of emission.

distribution pattern by changing the rates of oxide and hydroxide formation, but the effect of temperature change will be especially important in
emission.

The increased rate of supply of solution to the flame, which is obtained
with direct injection burners, makes the emission distribution more uniform with height, by delaying the release and excitation of the atoms. The

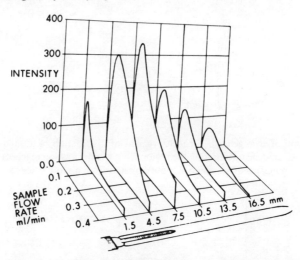

Fig. 8. Distribution of excited Ca^+ ions in an oxygen–cyanogen flame. The variation
of emission from the Ca^+, 3968.5 Å, line with height and rate of supply of solution was
measured (4).

large volume of aqueous solvent to be evaporated modifies the temperature
distribution in the flame and, in particular, reduces the emission intensities
in high-temperature flames such as that of oxygen–cyanogen. As the number of metal atoms supplied to the flame increases with the rate at which
the solution is fed, there will be an optimum rate of supply of solution for
emission measurements. This will occur when the effects of the increased
concentration of atoms in the ground state and of the lowering of flame
temperature just balance (13). Despite these effects, Fuwa et al. (4)
claim that the change in total emission which accompanies a change in
rate of supply of solution does not greatly affect the distribution patterns
for oxygen–cyanogen flames since the patterns are usually based on a
relative rather than an absolute intensity measurement (Fig. 8).

The solvent employed in supplying the salt to the flame can modify
the emission distribution by changing the flame temperature, by influencing

compound formation as with halogenated organic solvents, or by promoting nonequilibrium conditions which give rise to overexcitation (Fig. 9). Although the last effect occurs to some extent in oxygen–hydrogen flames supplied with aqueous solutions (6), it is greatly increased when combustible organic solvents are used (14). Emissions from ionized and other highly excited atomic states are then enormously enhanced in the region of the primary reaction zone and just above it; frequently, emissions that were not perceptible with aqueous solutions become easily measurable. There is no agreement regarding the specific reactions which are responsible for the overexcitation though correlations between the distribution patterns of an excited atomic state and that of emission by a particular radical have been regarded as useful evidence in this connection (14). Some of the enhancements of emission from less highly excited states are due to a change in the distribution pattern when an organic solvent is substituted for the aqueous solvent. The emission in the lower part of the flame is higher when organic solvents are used, but aqueous solutions give the greater emission in the upper region of the flame.

In absorption measurements the distribution pattern is frequently independent of the particular compound of the metal that is supplied. Apparently there are subtle effects in the combustion of metal-organic compounds which influence the distribution of emission. Buell (15) notes that the maximum intensity for the emission of the lead 4058 Å radiation occurs at different heights in the flame, and has different values, when equal concentrations of lead as lead tetramethyl, lead tetraethyl, and lead naphthenate are supplied in hydrocarbon solutions to the flame (Fig. 10). The relative intensities of emission for the three compounds are extremely different at lower heights in the flame, but their order is reversed in the upper part of the flame. The effects are probably somewhat more pronounced than those shown in Fig. 10, since Buell used a slit length of 6 mm which would give poor resolution with respect to height in the flame.

The concentration of excited atoms will fall more rapidly than the concentration of atoms in the ground state, when the pattern is measured at higher levels in the flame where the temperature is falling. The rate of this decrease will be modified by the composition of the flame gases and also by the nature of the excited state which is responsible for the emission. The probability that the atom will lose its energy of excitation by collision, rather than by radiation, depends on the nature of the colliding particles. This is usually represented by a "quenching cross section" which increases as the probability of deactivation increases (16).

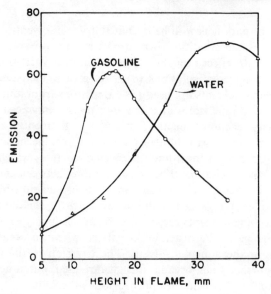

Fig. 9. Distribution of excited Pb atoms, determined by emission at 4058 Å, when supplied in gasoline and aqueous solutions (*15*).

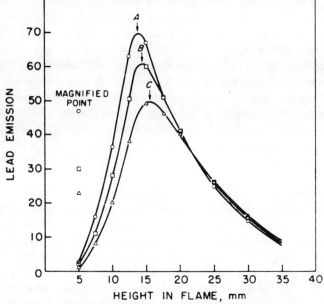

Fig. 10. Variation of distribution pattern of Pb 4058 Å emission when equimolar solutions of (A) lead tetramethyl, (B) lead tetraethyl, and (C) lead naphthenate are supplied to the flame (*15*).

V. Distribution of Fluorescent Emission

Observation of the pattern of fluorescent emission is made in a direction at right angles to that of illumination by the exciting source. The latter is usually a continuous source, such as a xenon arc, or a discharge through the particular metal vapor at low pressure. The fluorescent radiation is weak so that, when an image of the flame is focused onto the slit of the monochromator, the area observed cannot be kept at the ideally small value. The incident radiation is modulated by a chopper so that the fluorescent emission can be distinguished from the thermal radiation of the flame at the same frequency. The signal-to-noise ratio is poor because of the scattering of incident radiation by particles and inhomogeneities in the flame and by reflection from droplets of spray. This scattered light is modulated and is therefore accepted by the detector system. Veillon et al. (17) suggest that the effect of this scattering may be greatly reduced by placing a polarizing film between the illuminating source and the flame and a second such film, with its plane of transmission at right angles to the first, between the flame and the monochromator. The signal-to-noise ratio is greatly improved, though there is a considerable absorption of signal radiation by the polarizing films. In some cases where a discharge through the metal vapor is used as the source, excitation at one wavelength can be used to excite fluorescence at another. If the latter wavelength has been removed by filters from the incident radiation, there will be no scattered radiation to interfere. For example, the distribution of lead atoms in the $^3P_0$ ground state can be found by illuminating the flame with 2833 Å radiation and observing the emission at 4058 Å which involves a return of the excited atom to the $^3P_2$ state (Fig. 11). When a continuous source is employed for excitation, a correction can be made for background scattering by scanning across the wavelength of fluorescence and subtracting the mean background intensity from that at the maximum of fluorescent emission.

Although the distribution patterns of the fluorescence produced with a continuous source or a discharge in the metal vapor can be obtained directly, their interpretation in terms of the distribution of atoms in a particular energy state may be difficult. For atoms with a singlet ground state or a degenerate S ground state, the fluorescence and the excitation will, in general, involve the same frequency and will depend on the distribution of atoms in the ground state. In other cases where there is a multiplet of low-lying energy levels, as in the cases of tin and lead (Fig. 11), excitation from a number of initial states may lead to the same excited level. The contribution from each low level to populating the excited state will depend on the number of atoms in each of the initial states and on the transition probability for each of the excitation processes. The emitted fluorescence will depend only on the transition probability, so that a much higher fraction of the radiation may be emitted at a particular wavelength than was absorbed at that wavelength.

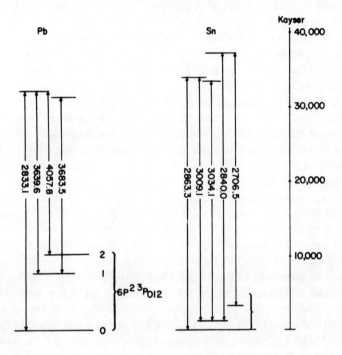

Fig. 11. Transitions between the lower energy states of tin and lead.

For tin atoms in a flame at 2800°K, the three lowest states are about equally occupied (Table 1) and all can be excited to the $^3P_1$ level at 34,914 cm^{-1} above the ground state. The return to the lower states is independent of the way in which the atom reached this upper energy level. In the case of lead the population of the $^3P_2$ state at 2800°K is less than 2% of the total lead atoms, but Veillon et al. (*17*) note that the fluorescence at 4058 Å, which involves return to this state, is quite as strong as that at 2833 Å, which arises from return to the $^3P_0$ ground state. The fractional contributions of the initial states to excitation will be very dependent on temperature, but the ratio of fluorescent emissions will be practically independent of temperature. If one is interested in particular initial states, excitation with monochromatic radiation is necessary.

TABLE 1

Populations of ^3P States of Lowest Energy for Sn and Pb at 2800°K

Element	$^3P_0$	$^3P_1$	$^3P_2$
	%	%	%
Sn	33.0	40.3	26.7
Pb	93.8	4.5	1.7

VI. Distribution Patterns for Molecules, Radicals, and Ions

The band spectra in flames are usually a source of interference rather than a help in analysis. The distribution patterns for the entities responsible for them can be found by absorption and emission measurements. In the former a wavelength where the absorption intensity is high and where the fine structure is crowded together near the band head, is usually employed. Emission at the same wavelength can be employed in studying the distribution of excited molecules. A typical distribution pattern is that for hydroxyl radical (1), shown in Fig. 12.

The emission bands due to CaF and BaF have been proposed as measures for the direct determination of fluorine (18). The distribution of this emission can be plotted when excess of a calcium (or barium) nitrate solution is added to a solution containing fluoride ion. A more refined measurement selects particular resolved radiations in a vibronic band and finds their relative intensities in different parts of the flame. From the measured intensity ratio a "rotational temperature" distribution may be plotted.

The use of the mass spectrometer in the study of the entities present in flames has been extensively developed. The distribution of a number of species at various heights in a low-pressure, premixed, oxygen–acetylene flame is shown in Fig. 13 (19). The sample is collected by allowing the flame

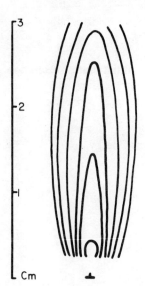

Fig. 12. Distribution of absorbance by hydroxyl radical in an air–acetylene flame (*1*).

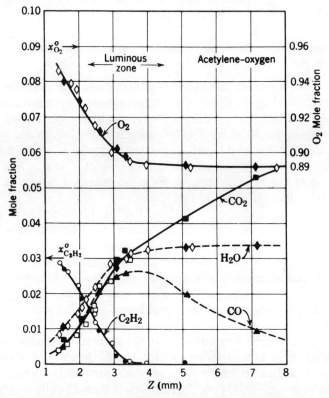

Fig. 13. Distribution of molecular species in an oxygen–acetylene flame, determined by mass spectrometry (*19*).

to impinge on a metal plate containing a minute orifice, through which a molecular beam passes into the ionization chamber of the mass spectrometer. The directness of the method is partially nullified by the disturbance to the distribution that must occur when the flame strikes the metal plate.

VII. Significance of Distribution Patterns

A. Position of Greatest Sensitivity

From the analyst's viewpoint the importance of a knowledge of the distribution of absorption, thermal emission, or fluorescent emission lies in obtaining greater sensitivity of measurement. The position of greatest intensity can be located along the optic axis, but if light from a large area of the flame is accepted by the monochromator the sensitivity will be diminished by the inclusion of areas where the measured effect is less intense. When using limited area techniques, even a minor change in one of the many factors which affect the distribution pattern may necessitate a readjustment of the position of the burner to keep the maximum on the optic axis. The flame photometer should therefore provide at least a simple movement of the burner in a horizontal direction to locate its center and a screw-drive for smooth adjustment in a vertical direction. An increase in the rate of flow of premixed fuel gases, without alteration in their ratio, has an effect similar to raising the burner, in displacing the distribution pattern relative to the optic axis. In those cases where the maximum intensity is found to be confined to a very small region, it may be preferable to use a wider collecting area, or a region in the flame where the distribution contours are more widely separated, in order to obtain greater stability in measurement despite minor fluctuations in the controlling variables.

B. Specification of Sensitivity and Enhancement

The limiting concentration, of a particular atomic species that can be detected by a form of flame spectrometry, will vary according to the portion of the distribution pattern that is accepted by the monochromator. For example, when the central contour encloses a very small area in absorption, detection will be more sensitive if a limited area within the central contour is employed rather than a wide beam which passes through areas where little absorption occurs. The specified sensitivity applies to a particular section of the flame. A study of distribution patterns shows that a change which produces enhancement of the measured quantity in one region of the flame may produce a reduction in that quantity in another region. Enhancement should always be specified in relation to its distribution.

C. Multiple Pass Technique

The spacing of the contours in the distribution pattern determines the utility of multiple pass techniques. Unless the contours are widely spaced the signal will increase by a factor much less than the number of passes. When the distribution pattern is compact, a single passage through a long flame will be more effective than multiple passes through a short flame.

D. Relationship to Chemical Processes in Flames

From the distribution patterns a beginning can be made on the interpretation of the processes occurring in the flame, in order to provide a scientific basis for the art of flame spectrometry. The study needs to be supplemented by observations with more specialized apparatus, such as sheathed flame burners which restrict some of the variation that is permitted in analytical apparatus. The attempts to account for activation of chemiluminescence by the correlation of distribution patterns have been mentioned (*14*).

E. Maximum Sensitivity or Freedom from Interference

When interference occurs due to the presence of an anion which forms a refractory compound, the study of the variation of the distribution pattern when the ratio of the cation concentration to that of the interfering anion is varied, enables the selection of the position in the flame where the measurement is least sensitive to variation in the amount of anion. This position, which will be the best to use in analysis, often occurs at a much higher level in the flame than that which gives maximum atomic concentration of the metal. It is also frequently at a much higher level than is commonly used in flame spectrometry.

REFERENCES

1. C. S. Rann and A. N. Hambly, *Anal. Chem.*, **37**, 879 (1965).
2. H. Lundegårdh, *Lantbruks-Högskol. Ann.*, **3**, 49 (1936).
3. J. H. Gibson, W. E. L. Grossman, and W. D. Cooke, *Anal. Chem.*, **35**, 267 (1963).
4. K. Fuwa, R. E. Thiers, B. L. Vallee, and M. R. Baker, *Anal. Chem.*, **31**, 2039 (1959).
5. E. M. Bulewicz, L. F. Phillips, and T. M. Sugden, *Trans. Faraday Soc.*, **57**, 921 (1961).
6. P. J. Padley, F. M. Page, and T. M. Sugden, *Trans. Faraday Soc.*, **57**, 1552 (1961).
7. A. N. Hayhurst and T. M. Sugden, *Trans. Faraday Soc.*, **63**, 1375 (1967).
8. P. G. de Montgareuil, *Contribution to the Study of Chemical Interactions in Flames*, Thesis, University of Paris (1954).
9. C. Th. J. Alkemade and M. H. Voorhuis, *Z. Anal. Chem.*, **163**, 91 (1958).
9a. C. S. Rann, *J. Sci. Instr.*, **44**, 227 (1967).
10. F. P. Dickey, S. Kopezynski, and G. Bell, *J. Chem. Phys.*, **25**, 180 (1956).
11. P. J. Padley and T. M. Sugden, *Symp. Combust.*, *7th, London, Oxford, 1958*, Butterworths, 1959, p. 235.
12. E. M. Bulewicz and T. M. Sugden, *Trans. Faraday Soc.*, **55**, 720 (1959).
13. M. R. Baker and B. L. Vallee, *Anal. Chem.*, **31**, 2036 (1959).
14. B. E. Buell, *Anal. Chem.*, **35**, 372 (1963).
15. B. E. Buell, *Anal. Chem.*, **34**, 635 (1962).
16. K. J. Laidler, *The Chemical Kinetics of Excited States*, Oxford, 1955, p. 102.
17. C. Veillon, J. M. Mansfield, M. L. Parsons, and J. D. Winefordner, *Anal. Chem.*, **38**, 204 (1966).
18. R. Ishida, *J. Chem. Soc. Japan*, **77**, 242 (1956).
19. R. M. Fristrom, W. H. Avery, and C. Grunfelder, *Symp. Combust.*, *7th, London, Oxford, 1958*, Butterworths, 1959, p. 304.

9 Spectral Interferences

B. E. Buell

UNION OIL COMPANY OF CALIFORNIA
BREA, CALIFORNIA

I. Introduction

Spectral interferences in flame spectrometry, as discussed in this chapter, are defined as any radiation which coincides with or overlaps that of the desired element (analyte), whether it stems from the sample or from the excitation source. Spectral interferences for atomic absorption are fewer and of a different nature and, therefore, will be discussed separately at the end of the chapter.

For flame spectrometry an attempt has been made to present some logical organization, first discussing types of interferences and then means of eliminating or compensating for them.

In discussing spectral interferences, some overlap of other areas such as instrumental parameters and flame emission spectra is unavoidable. In such cases discussion is restricted to their bearing on spectral interferences.

An exception is made for the unsalted flame emission, which is discussed thoroughly because it so frequently contributes background interference.

II. Flame Emission Spectrometry

A. METHODS FOR DETECTING SPECTRAL INTERFERENCES

Qualitative analysis of samples may be the only sure way of predicting interference where two lines coincide exactly. A reliable prior knowledge of sample composition will suffice but is not always available. In this case a qualitative analysis with a high dispersion spectrograph is very useful. Knowing sample composition, one can then refer to wavelength tables arranged by wavelengths for all of the elements. The tables listed by Herrmann and Alkemade (1), are excellent. Wavelength tables prepared primarily for the spectrograph (2–4) are also useful, particularly if they contain data which can be used in estimating flame sensitivities. If a given element is suspected as an interferent, then measurements of solutions containing only this element can be made at the analyte wavelength for verification and to determine the magnitude of interference.

A scanning technique is invaluable for detecting interferences where two lines do not coincide. A comparison of the adjacent wavelengths for both the sample and a pure standard can immediately reveal interferences from broad bands or continuum. Greater care must be used for detecting a nearby line which only partially overlaps another line or band. Diagrams of various types of spectral interferences are given in (1, p. 289).

B. MAGNITUDE OF SPECTRAL INTERFERENCES

The degree of spectral interference is governed by relative intensities and the amount of radiation overlap. The specificity factor, as discussed by Dean (5), is a good measure of interference. Specificity factors are calculated by dividing interferent concentrations by analyte concentrations that give equivalent intensities (ca 100% interference). They can also be calculated by dividing analyte relative intensity by interferent relative intensity. Table 1 gives factors calculated in this manner primarily from relative intensities (1). The table gives factors for only the most sensitive lines used for analysis and does not include data for many possible interferences that are extremely weak. The values are approximate and may

TABLE 1

Specificity Factors

Emitter	Wavelength Å	Interferent	Wavelength Å	Specificity factors	
				Concomitants[a]	Flame components[b]
Ag	3382.9	Ni	3381[d]	30	Weak
Al	3961.5	Ca	3968.5	1	
		CH	3872 series		Strong 30
As	2349.8	Be	2348.6	0.02	
Au	2676.0	OH	2609 series		Mild
BO_2	5180, 5476	Na	Continuum	10	
		C_2	5165, 5470		Strong 60
Ba	5535.6	CaOH	5540	0.1	
		C_2	5541		Strong 1
Ba II	4554.00	Cs	4555.3	1	
		Ca	Continuum	11	
BaOH	8730	CaO	8652	25	
		H_2O	9277		Weak
Be	2348.6	As	2349.8	200	
		CO	2338		Weak
Bi	3067.7	OH			Very strong
	2898.0	OH			Strong
Ca	4226.7	Sr	4215.5	Resolves	Weak 0.01
Cd	3261.1	Sn	3262.3	0.3	
		OH	3261		Mild 35
	2288.0	As	2288.1	10	
Co	3453.5	Ni	3452.9		Weak 1
			3458.5		
	3873.1	CH	3872		Strong 4
	3874.0	MgOH	3877	3	
		Fe	3872.5	100	
Cr	4254.3	Co	4252.3	60	
		CH	4249		Mild 0.3
Cs	8521.1	MnOH	8550	ca. 100	
Cu	3274.0	Ag	3280.7		
		OH	3274.2		Mild 0.05
Fe	3719.9	MgOH	3719	2	Weak 0.2
Ga	4172.1	BO_2	4180	300	
Ge	2651.2	Be	2650.6	2	
	2651.6	Be	2650.6	2	
In	4511.3	Mo	Continuum		
		BO_2	4530	100	
K	7664.9	PrO	7663, 7668	400	
Li	6707.8	SrOH	6720	200	

TABLE 1 Continued

Emitter	Wavelength Å	Interferent	Wavelength Å	Specificity factors	
				Concomitants[a]	Flame components[b]
Mg	2852.1	Na	2852.8	200	
		OH	2852.7		Strong 0.2
Mn	4030.8[t]	Ga	4033.0	5	
		CH	4034		Weak 0.1
Mo	3798.3	MgOH	3791, 3807	1	
		Ru	3798.9	0.2	
Na	5890.0	CaOH	5813, 5935	ca. 8000	
	5895.9	CaOH	5813, 5935	ca. 8000	
Ni	3524.5	Co	3526.8	5	
Pb	4057.8	Mn	4057[d]	10	
		Cu+CuH	4062	ca. 20	
		CH	4060		Weak 20
Pd	3404.6	Co	3405.1	5	
Rb	7800.2	CrO	7777, 7843	>100	
Rh	3692.4	Sn	3691.4	40	Weak 0.1
Ru	3726.9	MgOH	3729	5	
	3728.0	MgOH	3729	5	
Sb	2598.1	PO	2596	8	
Si	2516.1	PO	2519	0.5	
		Fe	2518.1	3	
Sn	3175.0	OH	3175		Strong 40
Sr	4607.3	Mn	4605.4	100	
		C_2			Weak 0.025
Tl	3775.7	Ni	3775.6	20	
		MgOH	3767	5	
V	3185.4[t]	OH	3185		Strong 125
VO	5737	Na	Continuum	ca. 1	
Zn	4810.5	Sr	4811.9	1	

[a] Specificity factor is the ratio of interferent to analyte concentration which contributes 100% interference using low dispersion.

[b] The mg/liter of analyte for which background contributes a 100% interference using high dispersion (4 Å mm). Specificity factors for low dispersion are about 30-fold greater.

[d] Doublet.

[t] Triplet.

vary by an order of magnitude. Interferences for bands originating from flame components cannot be calculated in the same way. The last column of Table 1 rates such interferences as strong, mild, or weak based on the relative intensities of the bands. This column may also contain a value, when it is available from (6), which is the amount (mg/liter) of analyte that gives an intensity equivalent to the background using high dispersion (4 Å/mm) and atomizing cleaner's naphtha into an oxygen–hydrogen flame (7, 8). The corresponding value for a low-disperson flame spectrometer will be on the order of 30-fold larger.

Because high dispersion, low dispersion, and the oxygen–hydrogen flame atomizing cleaner's naphtha will be referred to frequently, some clarification at this point will simplify further discussions.

Since the oxygen–hydrogen flame provides better sensitivity when atomizing organic solvents (partly through overexcitation from chemical

TABLE 2

Relative Intensities of Flame Bandheads

Flame	Relative emission from 10% (v/v) benzene–methanol		
	C_2 5165	CH 4315	OH 3090
Air–hydrogen	0.4	0.3	0.02
Oxygen–hydrogen	1^a	2	0.3
Oxygen–hydrogen–naphtha	5.8^b		

[a] Equivalent to emission from Mn 4031/4035 at concentration of 3 mg/liter in naphtha or benzene–methanol.

[b] Equivalent to emission from a manganese solution (18 mg/liter) in naphtha.

reactivity), it will henceforth be termed an oxygen–hydrogen–naphtha flame as described in (7).

Unless stated otherwise, any use of the terms high dispersion and low dispersion or their comparison will refer to the instruments compared by Buell (6) and his data, some of which are unpublished. The instruments referred to are a grating spectrometer with a dispersion of 4 Å/mm and a Beckman DU instrument with a variable, low dispersion (37 Å/mm at 3000 Å).

Because flame band interferences are governed by their relative intensities, data for C_2, CH, and OH bandheads are shown in Table 2. A Beckman DU instrument with oxygen–hydrogen and air–hydrogen flames was used to obtain the data. A 10% benzene solution in methanol was used because it produced OH intensities nearly equal to those produced by the flame alone. In each case the gas flows and burner height required to produce maximum intensity were employed. Since the bandheads measured are the most intense for each species, the intensities given represent the maximum possible interferences. To provide some measure of relating these intensities to those of metal emitters, the concentration of manganese required to produce an intensity equivalent to that for C_2 is shown. Intensity for cleaner's naphtha is given so it can be related to the data in Table 1.

To obtain an idea of the relative intensity for various flames given in absolute terms (W cm^{-2} sr^{-1} mμ^{-1}), see (9).

C. TYPES OF INTERFERENCES

1. Atomic Lines—High and Low Intensities

The most sensitive lines used for analysis are resonance lines involving transitions to the ground state. Emission lines with high intensity in flames arise from elements with low monoxide dissociation energies (D_o) and low excitation potentials (E_p). If instrumentation employing monochromators is used, interferences between high-intensity lines are infrequent. The following discussion of all interferences will assume the use of a low-dispersion monochromator such as a Beckman DU unless specified otherwise. Some examples of interference from moderately high intensity lines are:

(1) Mn 4030.8, 4033.1, and 4034.5, and Ga 4033.0.*

(2) Fe 3719.9 and Ru 3726.9 (a borderline example for low-dispersion monochromators. Cu 3274.0 and Ag 3280.3 are well resolved with a Beckman DU instrument).

(3) A classical example is the interference of all four of the most sensitive nickel lines by cobalt. Nickel, however, does not interfere with the most sensitive line of cobalt.

Interferences from low-intensity lines are possible more often than one might predict. They originate from lines with a larger E_p, a larger monoxide D_o, or from ion lines. Table 1 gives specificity factors for some of these and is excellent for predicting such interferences. The possibility of very

---

* As a short notation system for use only in this chapter, specific lines or bands will be designated by the element symbol immediately followed by the wavelengths in angstroms. All wavelengths will be given in angstroms with the Å indication omitted.

weak interferences from lines not listed should also be considered. For example, Buell (*10*) recorded approximately 200 very weak lines not listed by Gilbert. Fassel, Curry, and Kniseley (*11*) also recorded many lines of rare earth elements. Many of these extremely weak lines are encountered in the inner cone region of flames employed to produce overexcitation (rich acetylene flames, oxygen–hydrogen–hydrocarbon flames).

2. Bandheads Contributed by Concomitants

Interferences from bands are encountered more often than from atomic lines. Bands contributed by organic solvents or flame components are not discussed in this section. Bands emitted by metal species are usually found higher in the flame. Heights of maximum emission given by Buell (*7*) for an oxygen–hydrogen-naphtha flame range from 18 to 22 mm above the burner tip for various metal bands. Exceptions are BO_2 and CuH with heights of 17 mm, and CuOH with a height of 27 mm. (See Section II. D. 6).

The tables compiled by Pearse and Gaydon (*12*) are very useful for predicting interferences from bands.

Examples of specific band interferences are the following (examples of spectral interferences will be given in Section II. D.):

(1) MgOH 3600–4000 interferes with Fe 3719.9 (MgOH 3719) and Ru (3726.9, 3720.0).

(2) CaOH 5430–6220 interferes with Na (5890.0, 5895.9) and Ba 5535.6. (CaOH interference often prohibits use of this line.)

(3) SrOH 6000–7000 interferes with Li 6707.8.

(4) BO_2 4000–6200 interferes with MnO 5390 and Ba 5535.6.

(5) CuH 4000–4700 interferes with Mn 4030.8 and Pb 4057.8.

(6) Elements forming stable oxides in flames (monoxide D_o is larger than 5 eV).

Examples of several element oxides and their peak wavelengths are CeO 5300 (possibly a continuum rather than a bandhead), TiO 5167, and VO 5228, 5469. All of these bands gradually increase in intensity from about 4000 Å to their peak wavelengths and then gradually decrease becoming very faint at 6200 Å. They interfere with any element in the wavelength area 4500–6000 Å and in particular for In 4511.3 and Sr 4607.3.

3. Continuum

This type of interference is common and is most often contributed by high concentrations of alkali or alkaline earth elements. A reaction producing such continuum, as given by James and Sugden (13), is as follows:

$$M + OH \rightarrow MOH + h\nu \tag{1}$$

where M is an alkali element.

Solid, incandescent particles in the flame are also believed a cause of continuum. For example, MoO contributes a broad continuum in the area 4000–6500 Å with peak intensity at about 5000 Å. Sometimes it is difficult to differentiate such continuum from broad bandheads, although for our purpose (spectral interferences) it doesn't matter.

Continuum can also originate from flame components. Such continuum is weak compared with alkali continuum and only becomes apparent at high amplification. An example of a reaction producing such a continuum is given by Gaydon (14):

$$CO + O \rightarrow CO_2 + h\nu \tag{2}$$

4. Bandheads Originating from Flame Components or from Organic Solutions Sprayed into Flames

Because such bandheads are always present in flames and contribute a common and continual interference, they will be discussed in detail. With enough amplification, flame components radiate at almost any wavelength and may vary from continuum to sharp, rotational lines. In addition to the books already cited, that by Mavrodineanu and Boiteux (15) has a particularly good section devoted to flame bands. It also contains background spectra for acetylene flames obtained with a Bausch and Lomb medium quartz spectrograph.

Sometimes flame bands are not considered as spectral interferences but as blanks or background radiation. Since the spectra for organic solvents sprayed into hydrogen flames resemble the spectra for acetylene flames, organic solvents will be considered as flame components. Specificity factors for flame components are given in Table 1. They are only an approximate guide and may vary by orders of magnitude, depending on the type of flame and instrument used.

a. *OH Bands.* These bands occur in both hydrogen and acetylene flames. In hydrogen flames OH intensity increases more than 10-fold as oxygen content is increased (from air to a stoichiometric oxygen–hydrogen flame). In higher-temperature flames OH bands are quenched by spraying aqueous solutions. In other words, the OH flame background will decrease when water is sprayed into the flame—this will be the true blank.

An easy way to detect OH interferences (or any other flame components) is to simply scan the area of interest while spraying a blank solution. Prediction of OH interference is not possible from published information. Indeed, a complete listing of OH bands would be a large compilation since so many closely spaced lines are involved.

There are three distinct series of OH bands. The most intense series

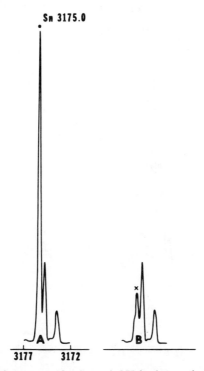

Sn 3175.0

3177   3172

Fig. 1. High-dispersion spectra for Sn and OH background. (A) 500 μg/ml Sn in cleaner's naphtha; (B) cleaner's naphtha blank coincidant OH radiation. (An *X* indicates the location of the analyte line on the blank spectrum.)

starts at 3063.7 Å where there is a sudden drop on the low-wavelength side. The 3089.9 Å bandhead is slightly more intense where the bands degrade to the red until their intensity decreases about 100-fold at 3300 Å. There is a slight intensity increase where they terminate near 3484 Å. This series interferes with Bi 3067.7 (severely), Sn 3175.0, V 3185.4, Cd 3261.1, Cu 3247.4 and 3274.0, and Ag 3280.7 and 3382.9. Figure 1 shows high-dispersion spectra for Sn and OH interference at low and high amplifica-

tion. An OH peak coincides with Sn 3175.0, contributing severe interference below 100 μg/ml Sn.

A second and less intense series of OH bands extends from 2811.3 to
3063 Å. There is a sudden intensity drop at 2811.3 Å and a degrading of
the series to the red. These OH bands are a serious interference for
Mg 2852.1. The least intense series extends from 2811 Å to the bandhead
at 2609 Å and may present some interference for Ge (2651.2, 2651.6).

b. *CH Bands*. These bands give intensity variations which are dependent

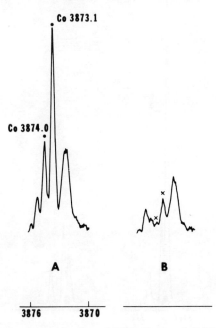

Fig. 2. High-dispersion spectra for Co and OH background. (A) 8 μg/ml Co in acetone;
(B) acetone blank showing a coinciding CH interference.

on the type of flame or the organic solvent. Relative intensities for the
main head (compared with C_2, OH, and Mn) are given in Table 2 for two
solvents. Height of maximum emission for CH in an oxygen–hydrogen–
naphtha flame is very low in the flame. (See Section II. D. 7.)

The most intense CH bandhead is at 4315 Å. It is degraded to the blue
and interferes mildly with Cr 4254.3. Fortunately, there are few sensitive
analytical lines in this region.

The CH series with a bandhead at 3872 Å is degraded to the red and extends to 4100 Å; it interferes with Co (3873.1, 3874.0), Mn 4030.8, and Pb 4057.8. Special data obtained for cobalt indicate that the specificity factor using high dispersion is about 4 mg/liter. The detection limit using high dispersion and an oxygen–hydrogen–naphtha flame is poor (about 1 mg/liter) due to exact coincidence of a CH peak. A secondary line using high dispersion gives better results (Section II. D. 4). High-dispersion spectra and CH spectra are shown in Fig. 2.

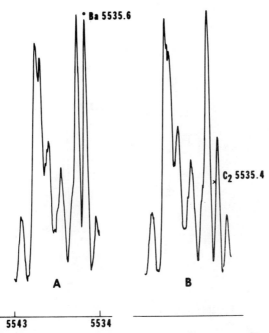

Fig. 3. High-dispersion spectra for Ba and C_2 background. (A) 2.2 μg/ml Ba in cleaner's naphtha; (B) cleaner's naphtha blank showing near coincidence of an interfering C_2 band.

The CH series at 3628 Å is less intense; it interferes weakly with Fe 3719.9. Specificity factors are 0.2 and 8 for high and low dispersion.

c. *C_2 Bands.* Whenever CH bands are encountered in a given system, C_2 bands also are found and overlap with the CH bands at 4324 Å. The most intense C_2 series has a prominent bandhead at 5165 Å which degrades to the blue and extends to nearly 5000 Å. It interferes with BO_2 5180 seriously at low boron concentrations.

The least intense C_2 series extending from 5470 to 5636 Å also interferes

with BO$_2$ 5476 and Ba 5535.6. High-dispersion spectra showing OH interference with barium are given in Fig. 3.

Another C$_2$ series extends from 4685 to 4737 Å and interferes with
Sr 4607.3 and some lines of zinc. High- and low-dispersion spectra for C$_2$
and the zinc spectrum are available (6, 7).

    d. *Miscellaneous Bandheads.* Various other bands occur in flames
including some broad, intense H$_2$O bands in the red; the 9700-Å bandhead
interferes weakly with BaOH 8730.

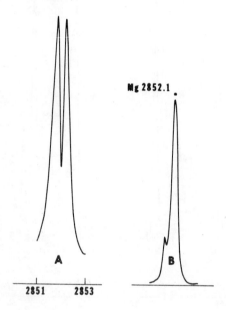

Fig. 4. High-dispersion spectra for Mg showing severe self-absorption. (A) 2000 μg/ml
Mg showing self-reversal and the appearance of two peaks 0.45 Å apart; (B) 100 μg/ml
Mg showing normal spectrum.

A very weak spectrum for the fourth positive series of CO bands extends
from the carbon line at 2478.6 Å, degrading to the blue and becoming
extremely faint at 2100 Å. With special flames, such as the nitrous oxide–
acetylene flame or cyanogen flames, CN band systems also occur.

5. *Self-Absorption*

Because it can influence intensity and the shape of calibration curves for
both flame emission and atomic absorption, self-absorption will be

considered here as a type of self spectral interference. For a definition and further details of self-absorption refer to Herrmann and Alkemade (*1*) and Dean (*5*). For certain elements, such as magnesium, sodium, and lead, self-absorption can become so severe that self-reversal occurs. This occurs at high concentrations; two peaks appear adjacent to each side of the wavelength normally observed. This is actually a severe broadening of the line with the appearance of self-reversal in the center (Fig. 4).

6. *Extraneous Light*

A unique type of interference from room lights could possibly be encountered when using extremely high amplification and wide slits or spectral bandwidths. For example, fluorescent lights contribute lines at 4358 and 4047 Å, probably Hg lines. The latter could interfere with Pb 4057.8. To eliminate this difficulty, turn out the lights directly above the instrument.

Internal scattering of radiation within an instrument (*stray light*) could also be considered a form of spectral interference. It is encountered when a large excess of an element with high sensitivity is involved. The outstanding example is sodium, with a relative intensity of 800,000 at 5890 Å (*1*). In such cases stray light is sometimes difficult to differentiate from a continuum (Section II. C.3) since they appear similar. Instrument manufacturers often quote stray light as being less than 0.1 %. In flame spectrometry even 0.01 % stray light could be serious. This would amount to a relative intensity of 80 for stray light from sodium. At this level of stray light, for the analysis of boron via BO_2 at 5180 Å (relative intensity equals 300), a sodium concentration $3\frac{1}{2}$ times the boron concentration would give a scattered light error of 100 %. (This is only a calculated estimate from the relative intensities (*1*) and should not be misconstrued as an accurate datum.)

D. ELIMINATION AND COMPENSATION OF SPECTRAL INTERFERENCES

1. *Instrumental Parameters*

Because certain instrumental parameters influence magnitudes of spectral interferences, they will now be briefly summarized.

Spectral dispersion is generally given as reciprocal linear dispersion in terms of Å/mm. For prism monochromators it is often given as half-intensity bandwidth or spectral bandwidth (twice the former) in terms of millimicrons per millimeter slit width. Large changes in dispersion have a profound influence on the degree of spectral interference.

Practical resolution (usually poorer than theoretical resolution) is defined as the difference in wavelengths for two lines which are just separated according to the Rayleigh criterion (16).

Mechanical slit width does not influence dispersion, but it does influence resolution. Narrow slit widths should be used to obtain the best resolution (least interference). The height and shape of the slit (curved for best results) also influence practical resolution and flux transmitting power. The low luminosity which is typical of flame sources makes it more difficult to use narrow slits; therefore, factors governing the use of narrow slits are important.

Flux transmitting power (F) indirectly influences spectral interference because high F aids the use of narrow slits. F is discussed by Jarrell (17) and in certain instruments is the factor which makes detection of low luminosity with multiplier phototubes far superior to photographic procedures.

Photodetectors are also a parameter governing the use of narrow slits. A good multiplier phototube of the proper type is far superior to a phototube.

2. Types of Instruments

Filter photometers are limited in use due to serious spectral interferences. They are generally employed only for the determinations of Na, K, Li, and Ca, and are incapable of resolving interferences such as Mn 4030.8 from Pb 4057.8. Photometers employing glass or gelatin filters have spectral bandwidths in the range 700–900 Å. Multilayer interference filters with spectral bandwidths in the range 120–180 Å are better. Dean (5) presents a good discussion on photometers and degrees of selectivity obtainable with them.

Low dispersion spectrometers are far superior to filter photometers for resolving spectral interferences; a Beckman DU spectrophotometer easily resolves Cu 3274.0 and Ag 3280.7 (6.7 Å apart). Dispersion for prism monochromators varies with wavelength (as much as 100-fold). Thus, a prism instrument may have good dispersion at low wavelengths but poor dispersion at high wavelengths. Jarrell (18) has compiled dispersion data for various quartz spectrographs. The Beckman DU monochromator, similar to a small quartz spectrograph, has a dispersion of 37 Å/mm, and a medium quartz spectrograph, 17 Å/mm at 3000 Å.

High dispersion spectrometers offer better possibilities of resolving spectral interferences. There is no definition in the literature which defines high dispersion or high resolution. High dispersion here will be defined as a dispersion of 10 Å/mm or better. In this case, some prism instruments will have high dispersion at low wavelengths but not at high wavelengths. Thus, a large quartz prism spectrograph could be considered a high-dispersion instrument below about 4000 Å. Some of the newer grating instruments, designed for use with either flame emission or atomic absorption techniques, have a dispersion of about 16 Å/mm and should be considered as borderline high-dispersion instruments. They are capable of resolving the manganese triplet (not resolved by a Beckman DU) and, therefore, Mn 4030.8 from Ga 4033.0 interference. Resolution of Pd 3404.6 from Co 3405.1 is borderline (specificity factor in Table 1 is 5 for low dispersion).

Few data concerning high dispersion flame spectrometry are available. Warren (*19*) gives some data obtained with a large quartz prism mono-

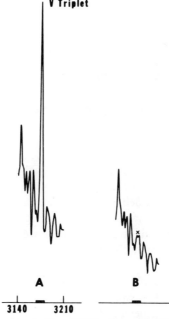

Fig. 5. Low-dispersion spectra for V and OH background. (A) 4000 μg/ml V in cleaner's naphtha showing the unresolved triplet (solid line at bottom indicates wavelength area of the equivalent high-dispersion spectra shown in Fig. 6); (B) cleaner's naphtha blank showing OH coinciding interference.

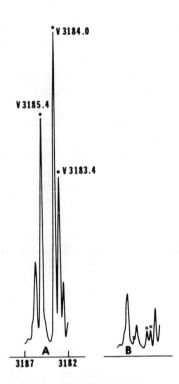

Fig. 6. High-dispersion spectra for V and OH background. (A) 3000 μg/ml V in cleaner's naphtha showing three well-resolved peaks for the triplet; (B) cleaner's naphtha blank showing coincidence of OH interference for the most sensitive V line.

chromator, which can only be considered a high-dispersion instrument at lower wavelengths (8 Å/mm for Mg 2852.1 and 12 Å/mm for Cu 3274.0 with a slit width of 10 μ). Buell (6) made an extensive study comparing high dispersion (4 Å/mm) to low dispersion (a Beckman DU spectrometer). Additional, unpublished data by Buell (10) are given in this section for various applications of high dispersion to the resolution of spectral interferences.

An outstanding example is the resolution of Cu 3274.0 from the OH bandhead at 3274.2 Å. Spectra for both high and low resolution are given in (6). With low dispersion the OH bands appear as a single, broad band which coincides with the copper line. With high dispersion the OH fine structure (vibration–rotation lines) is resolved from the copper line. The specificity factor is increased 90-fold in this example upon decreasing dispersion from about 35 Å/mm (a Beckman DU) to 4 Å/mm. Detection limits for Cu 3247.5 are low due to the interference of a coinciding OH line.

Another more complex example is the resolution of the vanadium triplet (3183.4, 3184.0, and 3185.4) and five OH lines which appear as one peak using low dispersion. The OH lines occur at about 3186.2, 3185.0, 3184.0, 3185.5, and 3182.9 Å. The detection limit is better for V 3185.4 than for the more sensitive line at 3184.0 Å due to exact coincidence of an OH line at 3184 Å. The specificity factors for V 3185.4 with low dispersion is 1350 mg/liter (for the unresolved triplet); with high dispersion it is 125 mg/liter. Low- and high-dispersion spectra are shown in Figs. 5 and 6.

Interference from C_2 and CH is encountered frequently. One example is the interference of Cr 4254.4 by CH. Low dispersion shows a large CH bandhead at about 4315 Å which degrades to the blue; the chromium line

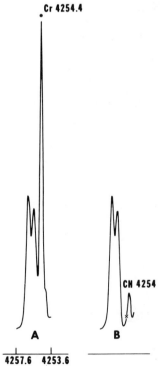

Fig. 7. High-dispersion spectra for Cr and CH background. (A) 8 μg/ml Cr in cleaner's naphtha; (B) cleaner's naphtha blank showing close proximity (about 0.3 Å away) of a small CH band.

appears on the side of this band. High dispersion resolves the fine structure of the CH band so that there is little interference with chromium from peaks at about 4256 and 4255 Å, although a small peak at about 4254.1 Å does interfere some. High-dispersion spectra for chromium and OH background are shown in Fig. 7.

Sr 4607.3 is interfered with by the C_2 bandhead. The difference between the main C_2 bands near 4685 Å for low and high dispersion is shown in (6). High-dispersion spectra in the strontium area are similar but of lower intensity and show (Fig. 8) that Sr 4607.3 is resolved from C_2 lines at about 4607 and 4608 Å. The interference is weak and the specificity factor measured for high dispersion is 0.025 mg/liter. With low dispersion the interference is more severe, as discussed in Section II. D. 5.

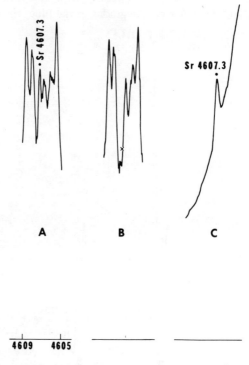

Fig. 8. (A) High-dispersion spectrum for 0.01 μg/ml Sr in cleaner's naphtha; (B) high-dispersion spectrum for a cleaner's naphtha blank showing close proximity and fine structure of C_2 background; (C) low-dispersion spectrum for 0.24 μg/ml Sr in cleaner's naphtha showing a small peak high on the steep slope of severe C_2 interference (not resolved).

A final example of the use of high dispersion to minimize spectral interference is given for the interference of calcium on barium. This example was selected because CaO radiation is such a common and severe interference for the most sensitive barium line at 5535.6 Å. Even with the use of high dispersion, C_2 also interferes mildly with this line, as shown in Fig. 3. The use of high dispersion for Ba 5535.6 increases the calcium interference specificity factor from about 0.1 to 3. Despite this gain, the most sensitive line for barium is the poorest to use in the presence of calcium and C_2 interference. The best line to use with high dispersion is the ion line at 4554.0 Å. The specificity factor for calcium interference is 400 and for C_2 interference is 0.4 mg/liter compared with 1.5 for Ba 5535.6. A complete discussion must consider the proper selection of a line for the dispersion used (See Section II. D. 5).

3. Modulation of Radiation

An instrumental technique based on modulating emission involves automatically alternating sample and blank radiation at a timed frequency. The technique is described by Herrmann, Lang, and Rüdiger (20). This compensates mainly for flame components and organic solvents. If a true blank were available (sample minus the analyte), interference from concomitants would be compensated for also. In practice, when preparing a blank solution, any omission of a concomitant which might contribute an unexpected interference would cause an error.

4. Correction for Background Radiation

A scanning technique was described for detecting interferences caused by overlap from broad bands or continuum (Section II. A). This technique, commonly known as the *base-line* method, can be used for correcting interferences where the background is level or has a uniformly changing slope. If the background has a small dip or hump concealed by the analyte line, an error will result using this technique. In this case a good method is to measure background at a wavelength predetermined to give an intensity equivalent to that found at the analyte wavelength. This technique has been applied to the determination of tetraethyl lead in gasoline (21). If such a nearby wavelength cannot be found, then an arbitrary wavelength can be used and a correction factor applied based on ratios. The correction factor is determined from the intensity ratios measured for a blank solution (containing the interferent) at the two wavelengths involved. This last technique can also be substituted for the

scanning base-line method when a recorder is not available. This ratio
technique can also be applied to corrections for a coinciding peak such as
shown in Fig. 1 for tin and OH. Since an additional, slightly larger OH
peak is close by, the ratio of the two OH peaks can be predetermined and
used to measure the magnitude of the OH peak which is hidden beneath
the tin radiation. This is actually a precalibration and measurement at two
wavelengths. This method is particularly suited to cases where there is a
variable interference caused by a known element which also can be determined by flame methods. Precalibration at a second wavelength can be at
a background point or for any line of the interferent. The correction can

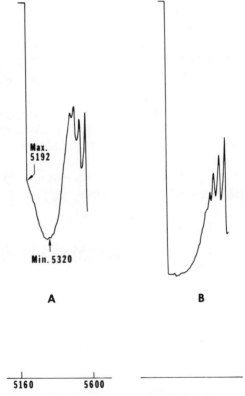

Fig. 9. Low-dispersion spectra for BO_2 and C_2 background demonstrating a scanning
technique and measurements at an arbitrary maximum and minimum to correct for
interference. (A) 20 μg/ml boron in gasoline showing points used for measurements;
(B) blank for gasoline showing C_2 background as a severe interference for determining
boron.

be made from graphs or an equation. The latter has been applied to a determination of boron in the presence of sodium-continuum interference (22).

In some cases measurement at an arbitrary minimum can be applied as a correction. Dean and Thompson did this in determining boron (23). In this example there was some loss in sensitivity because the minimum measured was partially caused by overlapping boron bands. This technique can be applied only where the minimum measured is equal to or larger than the true interference. In the case of strontium (Fig. 7) the lowest minimum adjacent to the strontium peak provides a good measure of the background. Spectra shown in Fig. 9 (also discussed in Section II. D. 7) illustrate a special application of this technique where a minimum and an arbitrary maximum are applied to determine traces of boron in gasoline in the presence of severe C_2 interference. The intersection of the sharply rising C_2 band and the lesser slope of the BO_2 band is used as the maximum reading representing BO_2 plus blank.

5. Selection of Analyte Wavelength

When interference occurs for one line of an element, an alternate line can often be used. As already indicated (Section II. D. 1), there is less interference from OH bands for Cu 3274.0 and V 3185.4 than for their most sensitive lines. Another example is the use of Ni (2320.0, 2321.4) to avoid the interferences from cobalt discussed in Section II. C.1.

Another example is Co 3873.1 where CH interference is strong (Section II. C.4, and Fig. 1). Even with high dispersion, interference is serious below 10 mg/liter; the specificity factor is 4 mg/liter. With high dispersion Co 3453.5 is more sensitive with a specificity factor of 1 mg/liter and a

TABLE 3

Relative Intensities for Cobalt

Co wavelength, Å	Relative intensity	
	Ref. (1)	High dispersion
3873.1	700	700
3526.8	460	1400
3502.3	500	1000
3453.5	480	1700

detection limit at least 10-fold better than for Co 3873.1. It is interesting to note the difference in relative intensities for high dispersion using an oxygen–hydrogen–naphtha flame compared with those given for cobalt in Ref. (*1*). A comparison is given in Table 3; the data indicate that sensitivity and specificity factors are better for the last three lines using high dispersion.

A final example is given for the interference of calcium on barium. Special measurements were made to illustrate the degree of interference for various barium lines. At low dispersion Ba 5535.6 is the most sensitive line but subject to severe interference from CaO bands. The BaOH 8730 band is best although it suffers from some CaO interference. The specificity factors measured for calcium and flame interferents (C_2 and H_2O) are

TABLE 4

Specificity Factors for the Interference of Calcium and Flame Background on Barium

	Low dispersion		High dispersion	
Wavelength	Ca interference	Flame interference[a]	Ca interference	Flame interference
BaOH 8730	25	19		
Ba 5535.6	0.1		3	1.5
Ba II 4554.0	11	47	400	0.4

[a] Background from H_2O or C_2 bands calculated as the mg/liter of Ba required to produce an intensity equivalent to the interference.

given in Table 4. The specificity factors for flame background must also be considered; these are 47 mg/liter for C_2 interference on Ba 4554.0 and 19 mg/liter for H_2O band interference on BaOH 8730.

At high dispersion things are quite different. As indicated in Section II. D.1, the best specificity factor for calcium interference on barium is obtained with the 4554.0-Å ion line, about 400, compared with 3 for Ba 5535.6 when spraying aqueous solutions into an oxygen–hydrogen flame. High dispersion provides little or no advantage for broad bands such as BaOH 8730. Since the calcium specificity factor for this line is about 25 (the best with low dispersion), the barium line becomes 16-fold better using high dispersion. Thus, we have an example of a combination of choice of lines and high dispersion to diminish calcium interference; a total of about 4000-fold compared with using the most sensitive barium line and low dispersion. Using high dispersion, the specificity factor for C_2 interference from organic solvents, Table 4, is also better for Ba 4554.0 (0.4 mg/liter) than for the more sensitive Ba 5535.6 line (1.5 mg/liter). This is because a prominent C_2 band at about 5535.4 Å contributes severe interferences at low barium concentrations.

6. *Choice of Flames and Solvents*

Certain parameters for flames used as spectral sources may influence spectral interferences. The relative intensity of various flame components and the degree of excitation produced for various elements (including the flame temperature and composition, which may contribute to over-excitation) must be considered. Flames containing no hydrocarbon content (hydrogen flames) can be employed to eliminate CH and C_2 interference. Although such interferences may be eliminated, the advantage gained is usually offset by lower excitation sensitivity for such flames. Some advantage may be provided by hydrogen flames for elements which require low excitation energies and which have sensitive lines located in regions relatively high in CH and C_2 radiation. An example is the determination of Sr 4067.3 using an oxygen–hydrogen flame with aqueous solutions or an oxygen–hydrogen–naphtha flame. In such cases the disper-

TABLE 5

Choice of Solvents.
Flame Spectrometric Factors for Strontium
Using High and Low Dispersion

Factor	Low dispersion		High dispersion	
	Water	Naphtha	Water	Naphtha
Specificity factor	0.06	0.8	0.06	0.025
Detection limit	0.01	0.05	0.01[a]	0.005

[a] Limited by noise.

sion of the instrument used is important. With a low-dispersion instrument aqueous solutions provide better specificity factors and detection limits. Although they provide less instensity, aqueous solutions contribute only a continuum background whereas naphtha contributes an intense, steeply sloped C_2 background (Fig. 8). With high-dispersion spectrometers, naphtha solutions are slightly better. Data are summarized in Table 5.

Hydrogen flames may also promote overexcitation of a few elements such as germanium and tin. For further details see Refs. (24) and (25) for flame emission and atomic absorption applications, respectively.

Flames providing higher temperatures or an overexcitation environment may also be useful. Radiation of metal oxide or hydroxide bands is often minimized in fuel-rich hydrocarbon flames. For example, an oxygen-acetylene flame should provide a better ratio of iron to MgOH interference. Greater sensitivity through overexcitation may be provided for elements requiring higher excitation energies. Buell (7), in several tables, lists enhancing factors for various elements which indicate degrees of over-excitation when this factor is greater than about 5. For example, enhancing factors of 30 and 5 are listed for Al 3961.5 and Ca 3968.5, respectively, indicating that interference of calcium on aluminum should be reduced about six-fold. Greater specificity might be offered by a rich acetylene flame or a premixed acetylene flame. References to flames providing over-excitation include (7, 24, 26–29). A sheathed burner (24) may also minimize certain interferences. For example, it appears to provide better interference ratio for BO_2 to C_2.

7. Other Methods

Use of limited areas in the flame (7, 8, 27, 27a, 30) masks all but a small area of the flame where either maximum emission or absorption occurs for the analyte. In emission flame spectrometry this technique lessens flame noise and minimizes interference from CH and C_2 which appears within and near the tip of the inner cone.

Suppression of unwanted ionic emission lines can be achieved through the use of radiation buffers—the addition to the test sample of a relatively high concentration of a second easily ionized element, but an element devoid of spectral interference at the analyte wavelength. Standards are treated similarly. The addition of high salt concentrations can cause difficulty with burner clogging and light scattering in absorption spectro-metry.

Sometimes the only way around a spectral interference is to separate the desired element(s) from the sample matrix. Chemical separation methods, such as liquid–liquid extraction and ion exchange, have found considerable use. Solvent extraction not only isolates the desired element(s) but often increases sensitivity by concentrating the test element and by enhancing the emission signal (5).

III. Atomic Absorption Spectrometry

In atomic absorprion spectrometry, spectral interferences may originate from two sources: (1) the light source, usually a hollow-cathode lamp, and (2) the device used to produce the population of ground state atoms, generally some type of flame.

The argon, neon, or helium used as the filler gas in a hollow cathode will emit its characteristic atomic line. Consequently, the filler gas must be chosen so as not to interfere with the emission lines of the element lining the interior of the lamp's cathode. Contaminants within the metal used to fabricate the hollow cathode will emit their characteristic lines; for example, copper may contaminate silver lamps, and calcium is often found in cerium lamps. Combination of elements in multielement lamps must be carefully chosen to avoid direct spectral interference and problems of selective volatility that could eventually cover the surface of one element with another. Fassel et al. (31) have recently studied line interferences.

Instances have been reported where the ionic line of an element interferes with the desired emission line from the hollow-cathode lamp. High-brightness lamps overcome this difficulty.

Spectral interferences originating from sample matrices or flame components can be largely eliminated by working with ac amplifiers and either interrupting the radiation signal electronically or mechanically with a chopper. Signals from the flame itself, not being modulated, are rejected by the ac amplifier. However, excessive emission from the flame or radiation from matrix elements can saturate the multiplier phototube and result in excessive instrument noise or permanent damage to the phototube.

IV. Atomic Fluorescence Spectrometry

Atomic fluorescence is the opposite of atomic absorption and is similar to molecular fluorescence (32). Although it has come into little use some comment on interferences are appropriate here. If an ac system, similar to that used for atomic absorption, is utilized, then the technique is remarkably free of spectral interferences. Because the light source used for irradiating ground state atoms in the flame is placed at a right angle to the optical path, even the interferences from hollow-cathode lamps encountered with atomic absorption are avoided. Scattered light is encountered as a spectral interference. The main source of error is self-absorption of the induced fluorescence by the sample. This can be minimized by working at at extreme dilutions. If a dc system is used then thermal emission from the analyte, concomitants, and flame components interfere.

REFERENCES

1. R. Herrmann and C. Th. J. Alkemade, *Chemical Analysis by Flame Photometry*, 2nd ed. Wiley (Interscience), New York, 1963.
2. G. R. Harrison, *Wavelength Tables*, Wiley, New York, 1939.
3. W. F. Meggers, C. H. Corliss, and B. F. Scribner, *N.B.S. Monograph 32*, Part I, Government Printing Office, Washington, D.C., 1961.
4. A. N. Zaïdel, V. K. Prokof'ev, and S. M. Raïskiï, *Tables of Spectrum Lines*, V. E. B. Verlag Technik, Berlin, 1955.
5. J. A. Dean, *Flame Photometry*, McGraw-Hill, New York, 1960.
6. B. E. Buell, *Anal. Chem.*, **38**, 1376 (1966).
7. B. E. Buell, *Anal Chem.*, **35**, 372 (1963).
8. B. E. Buell, *Anal. Chem.*, **34**, 635 (1962).
9. P. T. Gilbert, Jr., *Am. Soc. Testing Materials, Spec. Tech. Publ. 269*, 1960, pp. 73–155.
10. B. E. Buell, unpublished data.
11. V. A. Fassel, R. H. Curry, and R. N. Kniseley, *Spectrochim. Acta.*, **18**, 1127 (1962).
12. R. W. B. Pearse and A. G. Gaydon, *The Identification of Molecular Spectra*, 3rd ed., Wiley, New York, 1963.
13. C. G. James and T. M. Sugden, *Proc. Roy. Soc. (London)*, **A227**, 312 (1955).
14. A. G. Gaydon, *Spectroscopy of Flames*, Wiley, New York, 1957.
15. R. Mavrodineanu and H. Boiteux, *Flame Spectroscopy*, Wiley, New York, 1965.
16. Lord Rayleigh, "Wave Theory", in *Encyclopaedia Britannica*, 9th ed., Vol. XXIV, p. 1888 (cf. Ref. 17, p. 243).
17. R. F. Jarrell, in *Encyclopedia of Spectroscopy* (G. L. Clark, ed.), Reinhold, New York, 1960, p. 243.
18. R. F. Jarrell, in *Encyclopedia of Spectroscopy* (G. L. Clark, ed.), Reinhold, New York, 1960, p. 267.
19. R. L. Warren, *Analyst*, **90**, 549 (1965).
20. R. Herrmann, W. Lang, and K. Rüdiger, *Z. anal. Chem.*, **206**, 241 (1964).
21. B. E. Buell, *Am. Soc. Testing Materials, Spec. Tech. Publ. 269*, 1960, p. 157.
22. B. E. Buell, *Anal. Chem.*, **30**, 1514 (1958).
23. J. A. Dean and C. Thompson, *Anal. Chem.*, **27**, 42 (1955).
24. P. T. Gilbert, Jr., *Proceedings of the Xth Colloquium Spectroscopicum Internationale*, Spartan, Washington, D.C., 1963, pp. 171–215.

25. M. D. Amos, *Element*, (No. 14) Aztec Instruments, Inc. (see also No.'s 15 and 16).
26. M. D. Amos, Pittsburgh Conference on Analytical Chemistry and Applied Spectroscopy, Pittsburgh, Pa., March 5–10, 1967 (*Element*, No. 17).
27. J. A. Dean and W. J. Carnes, *Analyst*, **87,** 743 (1962).
27a. J. A. Dean and J. E. Adkins, *Analyst*, **91,** 709 (1966).
28. V. A. Fassel and D. W. Golightly, *Anal. Chem.*, **39,** 466 (1967).
29. A. P. D'Silva, R. N. Kniseley, and V. A. Fassel, *Anal. Chem.*, **36,** 1287 (1964).
30. C. S. Rann and A. N. Hambly, *Anal. Chem.*, **37,** 879 (1965).
31. V. A. Fassel, J. O. Rasmuson, and T. G. Cowley, *Spectrochim. Acta*, **23B,** 579 (1968).
32. J. W. Robinson, *Atomic Absorption Spectroscopy*, Marcel Dekker, New York, 1966.

10 Physical Interferences in Flame Emission and Absorption Methods

S. R. Koirtyohann

UNIVERSITY OF MISSOURI
COLUMBIA, MISSOURI

I. Introduction

Physical interferences may be defined as those effects which are caused by a physical property of the sample solution or which alter one of the physical processes involved in flame measurements. The physical processes of interest are aspiration, nebulization, transport of the spray to the flame, solvent evaporation, solute vaporization, and light scattering. The physical properties are viscosity, surface tension, vapor pressure, and temperature.

Unfortunately, it is seldom possible to alter any of these processes or properties without affecting one or more of the others, a fact which severely complicates the study of the phenomena. Another complicating factor is the incomplete separation between physical and chemical effects, especially in the areas of solute vaporization and the use of organic solvents.

Except for light scattering, the factors to be discussed change the atom population in the flame, and the behavior will be about the same in flame emission, atomic absorption, and atomic fluorescence. The type of flame will concern us more than the method of observation. The interference behavior is quite different in the total consumption (turbulent flame) burners than in the premix (chamber-type or laminar flow) burners. These differences will be considered in some detail.

II. Physical Processes

Before discussing interferences we should consider the various physical processes and the factors which are likely to alter them.

A. ASPIRATION

The driving force for aspiration is the pressure differential created by a high-velocity gas stream as it passes over the sample orifice. The gas velocities are high, usually supersonic, and the flow quite turbulent, making a quantitative mathematical description of the pressure drop impractical. The well-known Bernoulli equation which is used in more simple cases does not apply, although the same factors, i.e., the pressure and density (molecular weight) of the aspirating gas, are important. Aspirator construction is an important variable which is treated elsewhere in this series. Winefordner and Latz (1) found a nearly linear relationship between pressure differential at the orifice and aspirating gas pressure, and the importance of gas density can be demonstrated by operating an aspirator on hydrogen rather than oxygen or air. Much higher pressures are required, and none of the units tested in the author's laboratory gave satisfactory aspiration at any reasonable pressure with the lighter gas.

The primary forces opposing aspiration are hydrostatic head and viscosity. The former is usually kept reasonably constant and, since the aspirating force is much larger than the head, small variations do not affect the performance. Large variations in the level of the sample solution must be avoided, of course. Viscous resistance, the main force which limits aspiration rates, will be considered later.

Aspiration rates are about 1 ml/min for typical commercial total consumption burners and 3–10 ml/min for premixed flame burners where only a fraction of the aspirated solution reaches the flame. Flow rates outside this range can be provided by controlling the pressure over the surface of the sample solution (2, 3). Very accurate delivery volumes which do not depend on the variables associated with aspiration can be obtained by pumping the sample solution to the nebulizer. Motor-driven syringes (4, 5) and peristalsis pumps (6, 7) are commonly used. In certain automated flame equipment (Technicon Instruments Corp., Chauncey, N.Y.), a peristalsis pump is used for sample dilution and addition of reagents as well as delivery to the nebulizer. Pumps assure constant delivery of the sample to the nebulizer, but they add expense to the equipment and are somewhat inconvenient to operate. Pneumatic aspiration is still much more popular in analytical flame spectrometry.

B. NEBULIZATION

Nebulizer performance is probably the most important single variable in flame methods. All who work in the field should understand the factors which affect the process and be aware of the ways in which the final result can be changed. We will consider the mechanism of droplet formation, the performance of typical units, and the effect of solution properties on the performance. Because of their overwhelming popularity, only pneumatic nebulizers will be considered.

1. *Mechanism*

The mechanism of droplet formation will be covered only briefly. For a more complete discussion the reader should consult the original literature (8–10) or books by Dean (11) and Mavrodineanu and Boiteux (12). Nebulization proceeds by the following steps:

1. Formation of ligaments which are drawn out from the bulk of the solution by gas friction.
2. Collapse of the ligaments to form droplets.
3. Breakup of the larger droplets under the continued action of the high-velocity gas stream.

The formation of ligaments and their subsequent disruption are shown in photographs by Scheubel which are reproduced by Castleman (8). At high gas velocities, such as are usually used in flame nebulizers, the ligaments become less conspicuous and droplets appear to be torn directly from the bulk of the liquid, although small, short-lived ligaments probably exist. Some insight into the mechanism of ligament breakup can be gained from observing the formation of drops from relatively large liquid jets. Photographs (8, 9) show an initial necking down of the jet followed by separation of a drop which oscillates briefly between a flattened disk shape and an elongated cylinder. Frequently a much smaller satellite droplet forms from the thinnest portion of the necked down jet. Similar small droplets, formed as the ligaments break up in pneumatic nebulizers, probably play an important role in producing the very fine spray which is most useful in flame methods.

Very fine droplets can also be formed by the disruption of larger ones. Lane (10) has shown that a liquid drop subjected to a high-velocity air stream is flattened and then blown into a hollow bag which bursts, forming droplets of various sizes. The studies were conducted on relatively large drops (0.5–5.0 mm in diameter), but the equations describing the process indicate that drops as small as about 5 μ could be broken up by air at sonic velocities. Lane mentions but does not describe experiments which indicate that droplets larger than this can withstand such blasts. Extreme turbulence in a supersonic air stream, especially in the vicinity of an impact wall, has been shown by Hartmann et al. (13) in Schlieren photographs that are reproduced by Mavrodineanu (14). The improvement in nebulizer performance which is found when an impact wall is added (12, p. 104; 15) is undoubtedly due to droplet breakup caused by ultrasonic oscillations and by the turbulence near the wall.

2. Droplet Size Distribution

The following empirical equation relating the mean Sauter droplet diameter to solution properties was developed by Nukiyama and Tanasawa (16):

$$\frac{d}{d_0} = \frac{585}{v}\left(\frac{\sigma}{\rho}\right)^{1/2} + 597\left[\frac{\eta}{(\sigma\,\rho)^{\frac{1}{2}}}\right]^{0.45}\left(1000\frac{V_{\text{liq}}}{V_{\text{air}}}\right)^{1.5} \tag{1}$$

where d_0 is mean droplet diameter in microns, v is the velocity of air in m/sec, σ is the surface tension in dyn/cm, ρ is the density of the liquid in g/ml, η is the liquid viscosity in poises, and V_{liq} and V_{air} are volumes of the liquid and air. This widely cited equation was developed for small nebulizers operated on air.

When V_{air}/V_{liq} exceeds about 5000, the first term predominates and the mean droplet size is controlled by air velocity, surface tension, and density. In typical flame instruments this ratio is about 3000 and the second term cannot be neglected. The mean droplet diameter becomes independent of air velocity above about 350 m/sec, approaching about 20 μ for aqueous solutions.

The value of the equation is doubted by some (17), but it must be kept in mind that it was developed for a particular design of nebulizer and it should not be expected to apply rigorously to other types. In the author's opinion, its value is not in actually calculating droplet sizes but in showing the relative importance of the various parameters in nebulizer performance.

Measurement of droplet size distribution from nebulizers can be accomplished in several ways, all of which are beset by certain difficulties. The droplets are moving rapidly, and they can shatter, coalesce, evaporate, or condense during the measurement. A simple although tedious method of sizing was described by Dean and Carnes (18). They passed an MgO-coated microscope slide over the total consumption burner (flame off) and measured the diameter of the impressions formed by impact of the droplets using a microscope. A mean diameter of about 20 μ with a range from 5 to 65 μ was found when water was aspirated. About 10% of the solution volume was in droplets smaller than 20 μ. Results obtained in the author's laboratory (19) with a premixed burner using the same sizing method gave a mean diameter of 8.6 μ with a range from 4 to 20 μ. Mavrodineanu and Boiteux (12, p. 93) collected the droplets from the same type of burner on a microscope slide which had been coated with oil to retard evaporation. They found a mean diameter of 10 μ with very few droplets larger than 20 μ. Droplet size distributions for the two flame types, and also the change when an organic solvent with low surface tension is substituted for water, are shown in Fig. 1.

The results on premix burners agree with those of Dean and Carnes because droplets larger than about 20 μ are apparently lost in the spray chamber, accounting for about 90% of the aspirated volume. It is possible that the smallest droplets escape detection by being deflected around the slide with the air stream in these methods, but the good agreement between calculated and measured scattering losses found by Koirtyohann and Pickett (19) lends strong support to the reliability of the measurements. Willis (15), on the other hand, obtained a mean droplet diameter of about 1 μ using an adjustable nebulizer–spray chamber combination. He aspirated a solution of 0.5% methylene blue, evaporated the solvent, and collected the solute particles by a thermal precipitation method for microscopic sizing. An order of magnitude difference in droplet size cannot be explained by equipment variations between this and previous experiments. Additional research will be required to resolve the discrepancy.

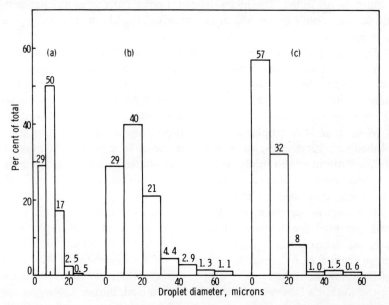

Fig. 1. Droplet size distributions. (*a*) Premix burner. (Reprinted from (*12*) by courtesy of Wiley.) (*b*) Total consumption burner aspirating water. (Reprinted from (*18*) by courtesy of American Chemical Society.) (*c*) Total consumption burner aspirating methyl isobutyl ketone. (Reprinted from (*18*) by courtesy of American Chemical Society.)

3. Effect of Solution Flow Rate on Nebulization

Equation (1) predicts a reduction in the mean droplet diameter with reduced sample flow. In premix burners, smaller droplets result in an increase in the fraction of the aspirated solution which reaches the flame. Willis (*15*) recently found that 15% of the sample solution reached the flame when the aspiration rate was 1 ml/min. This fraction dropped to 8% at 4 ml/min and to 5% at 8ml/min solution flow.

In total consumption burners, it is more difficult to evaluate changes in nebulizer performance with flow rate because of the rather severe lowering of the flame temperature at high sample flow. Emission intensities as a function of sample flow have been studied theoretically (20) and experimentally (21, 22) in several flames. At low sample flows, the intensity is proportional to the flow, but the curve reaches a maximum as the increased sample input is balanced by a reduction in flame temperature.

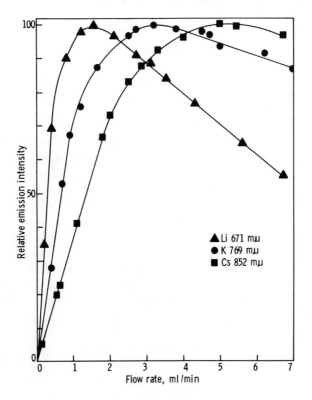

Fig. 2. Emission intensity at various solution flow rates in a total consumption flame. (Reprinted from (22) by courtesy of American Chemical Society.)

At higher flows the temperature effect predominates and intensities are reduced. The position of the maximum depends on the element and line used. Some of Foster and Hume's results (22) are shown in Fig. 2. These authors also found that the apparent rotational flame temperature of the oxygen–hydrogen flame decreased from 2643°K with no solution flowing to 2028°K with water being aspirated at the rate of 6.0 ml/min. The temperature change overshadows any variation in nebulizer performance.

Figure (2) shows that emission intensities are nearly independent of the solution flow rate when operating near the maximum in the curves, but may be critically dependent upon it at other flows.

C. TRANSPORT OF THE SOLUTION TO THE FLAME

In premix burners the nebulized sample solution must be carried to the flame following a tortuous path around baffles and through connecting tubing. With typical units, as mentioned in the previous section, about 90 % of the sample solution condenses in the spray chamber with only the finest droplets reaching the flame. A few years ago, because of the sample transport problem, internal standardization was believed to be required for accurate results from this type of burner (11, p. 13). The excellent success of atomic absorption spectroscopy with premixed flames has shown that the problems are not that severe. Indeed, the fact that spray droplets of relatively uniform size reach the flame often gives premixed flames a net advantage over the total consumption type.

The amount of sample reaching premixed flames depends on burner design, aspirating gas temperature, and solution vapor pressure as well as nebulizer performance. Baffles or flow spoilers are frequently placed in the spray chamber to assure adequate mixing of the combustion gases and their smooth delivery to the flame. Sample delivery to the flame is reduced somewhat, but the increased flame stability more than compensates for the loss with most burners. Evaporation reduces the size of the droplets in the spray chamber and increases the amount of sample solution transported to the flame. Preheating the nebulizing gas (23) or heating the spray chamber (24) increases the evaporation. In one commercial burner (Beckman Instruments, Inc., Fullerton, Calif.), the spray chamber is provided with heaters to evaporate most of the solvent. The gases are subsequently cooled to condense and remove the solvent, while allowing most of the fine droplets and/or salt crystals to pass into the flame. A substantial increase in sample transport is achieved without "flooding" the flame with solvent.

D. SOLVENT EVAPORATION IN THE FLAME

Unpublished experiments in the author's laboratory using a typical premix burner (Perkin-Elmer Model 290) show that most of the solvent is evaporated before reaching the flame. The burner was first heated by operating it for 30 min at the air and acetylene flows recommended by the manufacturer. The acetylene was then turned off and the light loss due to scattering by unevaporated droplets upon aspiration of distilled water was observed as a function of cooling time. The results are shown in Fig. 3. The scattering loss was quite small while the burner head was hot,

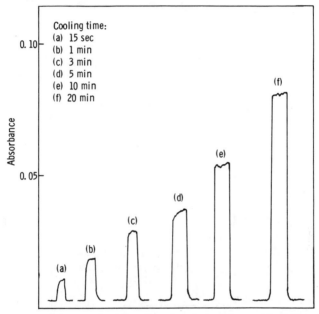

Fig. 3. Solvent scattering as a function of cooling time with a premixed flame burner.

but increased to about 10 times the initial value after 20 minutes of cooling. Similar results were obtained at wavelengths both longer and shorter than the 2852 Å used here. The water is apparently at least 90% evaporated prior to reaching the flame in this burner when the head is at its operating temperature. The result would be changed by water cooling the burner head, but droplets that are so readily evaporated could hardly resist very rapid vaporization at flame temperatures.

Parsons and Winefordner (25) have shown by light-scattering measurements that water evaporation is only 50–90% complete in the region of the total consumption flame that is normally viewed. The largest droplets pass through the entire flame without being vaporized. The evaporation behavior depends on the individual burner, nebulizer gas flow, fuel gas, and the height of the observation. Typical results are shown in Fig. 4. The dispersion efficiency is defined on the basis of scattered light intensity, and may be regarded as a measure of solvent evaporation. The height of the observation (time for evaporation) is seen to be an important variable. Unfortunately, observations high in the flame where evaporation is relatively complete usually show low emission sensitivity because of compound formation and low excitation efficiencies.

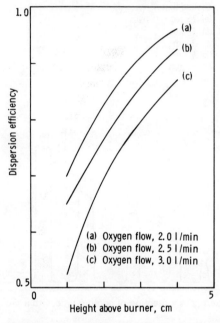

Fig. 4. Dispersion efficiency in a total consumption flame. (Reprinted from (*25*) by courtesy of American Chemical Society.)

E. Solute Vaporization in the Flame

After the solvent is evaporated from a given droplet, the remaining solid particle must be vaporized and decomposed before excitation or absorption can take place. The rate, the pathway, and the degree of completion of these processes depend on the chemical composition of the particle as well as its size and other physical properties. Thus we see that many of the so-called chemical interferences actually retard solute vaporization, a physical process. The well-known effect of phosphate on calcium atom populations, for example, involves a nonvolatile Ca–P–O compound.

In high-temperature, premixed flames formed with either nitrous oxide (26, 27), or oxygen (28), the effect disappears. In these burners, because only the small droplets are transported to a high-temperature flame, solute evaporation is driven to completion or nearly so in spite of the less favorable chemical state. Chemical interferences are considered elsewhere in this volume. The purpose here is not to debate the classification of these effects but to point out that no clean separation between physical and chemical interferences is possible.

Solute vaporization problems are obviously more severe with the total consumption type of nebulizer. Even if a volatile solvent is used to accelerate solvent vaporization, the solid particles coming from large solvent droplets will vaporize slowly and incompletely. This is clearly shown by the fact that phosphate interferes with calcium determinations in the total consumption burner with an oxygen–acetylene flame, in spite of the high temperature, unless releasing agents are added.

III. Physical Properties of the Solution

A. Viscosity

Viscosity is the primary force opposing aspiration. The well-known Poiseuille equation to describe viscous flow may be written in the form

$$\frac{V}{t} = \frac{\pi r^4 P}{8 \iota \eta} \tag{2}$$

where V is the solution volume in ml, t is the time in sec, r is the capillary radius in cm, P is the pressure in dyn/cm^2, ι is the capillary length in cm, and η is the viscosity coefficient. Equation (2) is strictly valid only when the liquid leaves the capillary with a small velocity and there is no turbulence. Winefordner and Latz (1) found that it was followed quite closely at low flow rates (high viscosities) but significant deviations were observed at higher flows.

Solution viscosity appears in Eq. (1) both directly and indirectly through its effect on aspiration rate. The latter is probably the more important. An increase in aspiration rate brought about by low viscosity will not necessarily produce a corresponding increase in emission or absorption signal, however. In premix burners the change in nebulizer performance tends to compensate for changes in flow rate with the amount of sample delivered to the flame remaining relatively constant (*15*). In nebulizer–burners the results depend on the position on the curves shown in Fig. 2. The signal may actually decrease with increasing solution flow.

In practical analytical solutions, errors due to viscosity changes can be avoided by running samples and standards in the same solvent system and by avoiding total acid or salt concentrations greater than about 0.5%. If more concentrated solutions must be used, standards matching the gross sample composition can be prepared or the method of standard additions used. It would be unwise for an analyst to attempt to apply a correction to his results based on measured sample viscosities.

B. Surface Tension

Large amounts of surface area are created during nebulization, and surface tension is one of the important variables in Eq. (1), as would be expected. Dean and Carnes (*18*) (Fig. 1) found that the fraction of solution volume in droplets less than 20 μ in diameter was nearly doubled when solutions of methyl isobutyl ketone or chloroform were nebulized and compared with water. The lower surface tension of the organic solvents undoubtedly made a major contribution to this change.

When using premix burners, the improvement in nebulizer performance brought about by lower surface tension may be partially offset by an increased tendency for the droplets to coalesce in the spray chamber. It has not yet been possible to isolate the effect of surface tension from that of other properties which are always changed when the solution composition is altered.

Surface tension is drastically reduced by low concentrations of detergents or other surface-active reagents, but in the total consumption type of nebulizer–burner this does not change the emission (*22*). Similar results were found, using premix burners in absorption, by Lockyer et al. (*29*) and Pungor and Mahr (*30*), although older reports (*11*, p. 12) had indicated an effect in this type of burner. These results appear to contradict Eq. (1) until one considers that much of the surface tension effect caused by detergents is due to accumulation of the material at the interface. No accumulation can take place during the vigorous agitation associated with aspiration and nebulization. The surface tension at the nebulizer tip is very different from that measured in the static solution. In order to alter nebulizer performance, the surface-active reagent must be present at a sufficiently high concentration to change the surface tension in spite of agitation. A major change in solvent or solution composition is required. Such changes can be exploited to gain sensitivity, but, so long as samples and standards are in the same solvent and the total solute concentration is kept low, analytical errors from this source are not very likely.

C. SOLUTION TEMPERATURE

Changes in solution temperature cause corresponding changes in viscosity and surface tension which, in turn, affect flame performance. Since the temperature is a frequently altered and easily measured solution

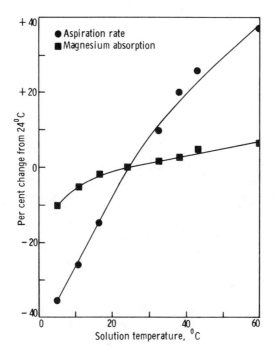

Fig. 5. Effect of solution temperature on aspiration rate and magnesium absorption in the premixed air–acetylene flame.

property, brief consideration of its effect seems in order. Foster and Hume (*22*) found rather large changes in aspiration rates but relatively minor variations in emission intensities from total consumption type of nebulizer burners as the solution temperature was changed. They were working near the peak of the emission intensity vs. aspiration rate curve, and with the large changes in flow rates, one would expect more change in intensity on other parts of the curve.

Experiments in the author's laboratory show that in premixed flames too, the effect of temperature on aspiration rates is much greater than on the final absorption response. The results are presented in Fig. 5. Nebulizer performance is apparently increased at the lower flow rates, as was found by Willis (15). These data show that, while solutions which have been heated or refrigerated must be brought to the same temperature as the standards prior to analysis, temperature variations of $\pm 4°C$ produce errors of only about 1 % near room temperature.

D. BULK MATRIX EFFECT

A reduction in signal is generally obtained when the sample solutions are very high in total solids, regardless of the test element or the nature of the matrix (though the severity of the effect changes with both). This so-called "solids effect" or "bulk matrix effect" is actually due to a combination of several factors. Concentrated solutions tend to be viscous and dense, thereby reducing aspiration rates and nebulizer efficiencies. Aspirator and nebulizer performance can be further reduced and made quite erratic by encrustation of salts around the orifices, especially with total consumption burners where there is a high rate of solvent evaporation near the openings. In both burner types, encrustation is more severe when organic solvents are used, again probably due to high evaporation rates. After solvent evaporation in the flame, the test element from a solution high in total solids may be imbedded in a large salt particle from which it cannot be vaporized quickly.

Errors may be avoided by dilution, standard additions, or standards which match the gross composition of the samples. Frequent aspiration of pure solvent helps to remove encrusted salts, but in severe cases dilution is required.

E. ORGANIC SOLVENTS

The advantages of using organic solvents in flame methods are well documented in the literature and in the recent books on the subject (11, 12). Detailed justification for their use is no longer required. At least a factor of 2 gain in signal can be obtained on nearly any determination in either flame type using mixtures of water and some miscible solvent such as acetone or the lower alcohols. The enhancement increases as the fraction of water decreases, but for practical analyses the final solution is usually 50–80% organic, and a portion of the sensitivity gain is often lost in dilution with the solvent. Depending on the sample type, however, dissolution of inorganic salts in water-free solvents can sometimes be used advantageously (31). Another method for bringing the element of interest into an all-organic medium for aspiration into the flame is to perform a liquid–liquid extraction of an appropriate metal chelate into an immiscible solvent. Chemical concentration and separation from interferences are provided along with the advantage of the organic solvent. In order to be useful, the extraction need not be specific (in fact, reagents which react with many metals are often preferred), but it should be complete and should reject the bulk of the sample matrix. The demands on the extraction are much less severe than they are if colorimetric measurement is used, for example, and the number of possible separations is limited only by the knowledge of the chemist. Chlorinated solvents should be avoided because they do not burn well when aspirated directly into the flame.

The reader can consult papers by Dean and co-workers (32–35), Willis (36, 37), Menis and Rains (38), and Mulford (39) for details on extractions. Our present attention should be directed toward answering why and how the organic solvents give their enhancement. The following factors are important:

1. Increased aspiration rates and nebulizer performance.
2. More rapid solvent evaporation.
3. Reduced quenching of the flame temperature.
4. More favorable environment for atom formation in the flame.

Allan (40) studied the use of organic solvents in the premixed air–acetylene flame and found that the atomic absorption enhancement factors were the same for copper, iron, manganese, zinc, and magnesium in a solvent containing 20% acetone and 20% isobutyl alcohol, and in methyl isobutyl ketone. He concluded that the enhancement was "due entirely to an increase in the amount of solution reaching the flame and to a temperature effect". The flame temperature is lower than when aqueous solutions are aspirated because the solvent replaces part of the acetylene in the combustion mixture with a less energetic fuel. The enhancement depended on the solvent and also the nebulizer which was used. Of about

12 water-immiscible solvents tested, Allan found that only esters and ketones behave satisfactorily in the premixed flame, although xylene (41), heptane, iso-octane, cyclohexane, and toluene (42) have been used more recently. Some of Allan's results are presented in Table 1.

TABLE 1

Enhancements of Copper Absorption by Organic Solvents in a Premixed Flame[a]

Solvent	Relative sensitivity
0.1N HCl	1.0
Methanol, 40%	1.7
Ethanol, 40%	1.7
Acetone, 40%	2.0
Acetone, 80%	3.5
Acetone, 20% plus isobutanol, 20%	2.35
Ethylamyl ketone	2.8
Methyl isobutyl ketone	3.9
Ethyl acetate	5.1

[a] Reprinted from (40) by courtesy of Pergamon Press.

The increased sample transport to the flame is brought about by improved nebulizer performance (Fig. 1) and increased evaporation of the volatile solvent in the spray chamber. Also, the fuel flow is reduced when the organic solvent is burned, thus reducing the dilution of the sample with flame gases.

Sample transport to the flame does not account for the absorption behavior in all cases. Lockyer et al. (29), using an air–coal gas flame, found enhancements that were different for each test element, and Strasheim and co-workers (43) recently found much greater enhancement for barium than for strontium using 80% ethanol as the solvent. Thus we conclude that much of the enhancement from organic solvents in premixed flames is due to better sample transport to the flame. Enhanced atom formation also contributes in low-temperature flames and for elements which tend to form stable compounds in the flame.

Enhancements due to organic solvents are generally larger and more variable from element to element in the total consumption nebulizer-burners. They range from about 2 for sodium in methanol to 100 or more for aluminium in methyl isobutyl ketone (11). Flame analysis of refractory metals is almost always done in organic solvents (*5, 31*). Smaller droplets of a more volatile solvent will evaporate more quickly and completely than water in the flame, allowing more time for sample decomposition and excitation. The rather severe quenching of the flame temperature when aqueous solutions are aspirated (*22*) is virtually absent with organic solvents (*11*, p. 60). The temperature with aspirated solvent is about the same as that of the dry flame, which is especially important in emission methods where these burners are usually applied. It is in this type of flame also that the chemical environment, particularly in the vicinity of an evaporated droplet, is most likely to be altered. The added fuel aids in formation of reduced carbon species which in turn helps to decompose metal oxides and make the atoms available for excitation or absorption (*44*).

Mixtures of organic solvents are sometimes preferable to a single solvent. Allan (*40*), for example, concluded that the most favorable water-miscible solvent for use in his apparatus was a mixture containing 20% acetone and 20% isobutyl alcohol. Rains (*45*) reports that using a total consumption burner, 10% glycerol added to acetone solutions improves precision without reducing the signal, while Sachdev et al. (*46*) found that addition of 20% oleic acid to alcohol or methyl isobutyl ketone solutions enhanced vanadium absorption in turbulent flames.

In summary, extractions into water-immiscible solvents are valuable regardless of the type of flame or the method of measurement. They provide chemical concentration, signal enhancement, and separation from interferences, usually simultaneously. In turbulent flame nebulizer–burners, water-miscible solvents provide worthwhile enhancements, but with premix burners the enhancement doesn't greatly exceed the extra dilution with the solvent except in special cases.

IV. Light Scattering

Light scattering by particles in the flame was first proposed by Willis (*47*) to explain small light losses which he had encountered due to matrix salts. This very plausible explanation was, for a time, used to account for virtually all light losses which were encountered in atomic absorption (*48; 49; 50*, p. 47), in spite of the fact that it was never experimentally verified. Koirtyohann and Pickett (*51*) demonstrated that molecular absorption rather than scattering was the cause for at least part of the light losses reported by Willis, and later these same authors (*19*) considered the light losses predicted by scattering theory. They measured the droplet size distribution on a typical commercial premix burner using the method of Dean and Carnes (*18*) and calculated the mean size of the solid particles formed on solvent evaporation assuming that:

1. One particle of specific gravity 2.5 formed from each droplet.
2. The solute was melted in the flame, forming spherical particles.
3. The solute was not vaporized at flame temperature.
4. The sample solution contained 1 % solute.

The mean droplet diameter was 8.6 μ, and the calculated mean solute particle diameter was 1.36 μ. Since the diameter is larger than the wavelengths used for atomic absorption, the Mie scattering theory must be used rather than the more familiar Rayleigh laws. Van de Hulst (*52*) gives a rather complete treatment of the mathematics of this theory, and some of his conclusions are applicable to atomic absorption. One is interested in the extinction or attenuation of the transmitted beam, not in its sidewise scattering, and needs to consider only the quantities:

$$S = \frac{\text{optical cross section of the particle for extinction}}{\text{geometric cross section of the particle}} \qquad (3)$$

$$X = 2\pi r / \lambda \qquad (4)$$

where r is the particle radius and λ the wavelength. S is a complex function of X; graphs and tables relating the two are given by Van de Hulst.

Using the mean particle diameter of 1.36 μ as the effective diameter, X ranges from about 6 to 20 for the wavelengths from 7000 to 2000Å. According to Van de Hulst, S is near 2 for these values of X, whether one considers nonabsorbing, totally reflecting, or opaque spheres. S seldom goes above 3 in this range of X values, and approaches 2 when a range of particle sizes is present and when X becomes large.

Using the mean droplet diameter and gas flow data, Koirtyohann and Pickett were able to calculate that about 5.9×10^3 particles were present in the light beam at a given time and that these had a geometric cross section of 8.5×10^{-5} cm². Since S is about 2 and the beam cross section was 0.1 cm², a light loss of 0.17 % at all wavelengths was predicted for the conditions assumed. The authors made no attempt to verify this small loss experimentally, but calculated and measured the larger scattering due to water droplets in the beam when the flame was not ignited. A scattering loss of 4.6 % of the incident radiation was predicted for the experimental conditions used. The measured losses varied from 3.9 to 5.1 % using wavelengths from 2138 to 7665Å and there appeared to be no wavelength dependence.

As mentioned previously, Willis (15), using a similar burner, found a mean droplet size about an order of magnitude smaller than was used in these calculations. Much larger scattering losses would be predicted if calculations were based on his droplet size. Rubeska and Moldan (53), however, measured the particle size in the aerosol leaving the flame and found a mean diameter of about 1 μ when the aspirated solution contained both aluminium and magnesium in concentrations of 1000 and 500 $\mu g/ml$, respectively. The value agrees quite well with that calculated by Koirtyohann and Pickett. Also, Elwell and Gidley (50, p. 47) reported light losses that were independent of wavelength when concentrated solutions of refractory metals were aspirated. There is considerable support for the conclusion that some mechanism other than scattering by particles in the flame must be responsible for much of the background absorption or light loss due to matrix salts often reported in atomic absorption. There are undoubtedly particles present in the flame with some samples, and these must scatter some light. Such scattering must be small, however, and must be approximately the same for all wavelengths. Molecular absorption probably accounts for most of the observed light losses. A correction for the light loss, regardless of its cause, can be made by measuring the absorbance at wavelengths adjacent to the resonance line using a continuous light source, and subtracting this from the measured absorbance at the resonance wavelength (54).

In flame emission measurements scattering need not be considered, although the presence of hot particles in the flame would increase the background, especially at long wavelengths, because of black body radiation. The background corrections that are commonly applied would include this radiation and it would cause no error. In atomic fluorescence, on the other hand, scattering can be quite important. Light from the primary source which is scattered from particles will appear as a signal which cannot be distinguished from that due to the presence of the test element if a monochromatic source is used. Continuous sources can be used in fluorescence (55, 56), and a wavelength scan then provides the necessary scattered background correction. Continuous sources do not yet provide sensitivities comparable with the best line sources for most elements. Theoretical treatment of the scattering is much more difficult in atomic fluorescence than in atomic absorption and its role in this very new analytical method is not yet known quantitatively. It is, however, one of the important factors which will limit the sensitivity attainable as more intense primary sources are developed.

REFERENCES

1. J. D. Winefordner and H. W. Latz, *Anal. Chem.*, **33,** 1727 (1961).
2. P. T. Gilbert, Jr., *A.S.T.M. Special Tech. Publ. 269,* 1959, p. 73.
3. K. Fuwa, R. E. Thiers, and B. L. Vallee, *Anal. Chem.*, **31,** 1419 (1959).
4. J. W. Robinson and R. J. Harris, *Anal. Chim. Acta,* **26,** 439 (1962).
5. R. K. Skogerboe, Ann T. Heybey, and G. H. Morrison, *Anal. Chem.*, **38,** 1821 (1966).
6. C. W. Gehrke, J. P. Ussary, and G. H. Kramer, *J. Assoc. Offic. Agric. Chemists,* **47,** 459 (1964).
7. B. Klein, J. H. Kaufman, and S. Morgenstern, *Clin. Chem.*, **13,** 388 (1967).
8. R. A. Castleman, *J. Res. Natl. Bur. Standards,* **6,** 369 (1961).
9. W. R. Marshall, *Chem. Eng. Progr. Monograph Ser.* **50,** No. 2 (1954).
10. W. R. Lane, *Ind. Eng. Chem.*, **43,** 1312 (1951).
11. J. A. Dean, *Flame Photometry,* McGraw-Hill, New York, 1960.
12. R. Mavrodineanu and H. Boiteux, *Flame Spectroscopy,* Wiley, New York, 1965.
13. J. Hartmann, P. V. Mathes, E. V. Mathes, and F. Lazarus, in *The Acoustic Air-jet Generator,* (G. E. Gad, ed.), Ingenir Vindenskabelige Skrifter No. 4, Kobenhavn, 1939.
14. R. Mavrodineanu, *Spectrochim. Acta,* **17,** 1016 (1961).
15. J. B. Willis, *Spectrochim. Acta,* **23A,** 811 (1967).
16. S. Nukiyama and Y. Tanasawa, Translation of reports 1 to 6, *Trans. Soc. Mech. Eng. Japan,* **4, 5, 6,** 1938–1940, by E. Hope. Available through the Defence Research Board, Dept. of National Defence, Ottawa, Canada.
17. J. Gretzinger and W. R. Marshall, *A.I.Ch.E. Journal,* **7,** 312 (1961).
18. J. A. Dean and W. J. Carnes, *Anal. Chem.*, **34,** 192 (1962).
19. S. R. Koirtyohann and E. E. Pickett, *Anal. Chem.*, **38,** 1087 (1966).
20. M. R. Baker and B. L. Vallee, *Anal. Chem.*, **31,** 2036 (1959).
21. K. Fuwa, R. E. Thiers, B. L. Vallee, and M. R. Baker, *Anal. Chem.*, **31,** 2039 (1959).
22. W. H. Foster and D. N. Hume, *Anal. Chem.*, **31,** 2028 (1959).
23. R. A. G. Rawson, *Analyst,* **91,** 630 (1966).
24. C. A. Dubbs, *Anal. Chem.*, **24,** 1654 (1952).
25. M. P. Parsons and J. D. Winefordner, *Anal. Chem.*, **38,** 1593 (1966).
26. J. B. Willis, *Nature,* **207,** 715 (1965).
27. E. E. Pickett and S. R. Koirtyohann, Midwest Regional ACS Meeting, Columbia, Missouri, November 1967.
28. V. A. Fassel, personal communication, 1967.
29. R. Lockyer, J. E. Scott, and S. Slade, *Nature,* **189,** 830 (1961).
30. E. Pungor and M. Mahr, *Talanta,* **10,** 537 (1963).
31. A. P. D'Silva, R. N. Kniseley, V. A. Fassel, R. H. Curry, and R. B. Meyers, *Anal. Chem.*, **36,** 532 (1964).
32. H. A. Bryan and J. A. Dean, *Anal. Chem.*, **29,** 1289 (1957).
33. J. A. Dean and C. Cain, *Anal. Chem.*, **29,** 530 (1957).
34. J. A. Dean and J. H. Lady, *Anal. Chem.*, **28,** 1887 (1956).
35. J. A. Dean and J. C. Simms, *Anal. Chem.*, **34,** 699 (1963).
36. J. B. Willis, *Nature,* **191,** 381 (1961).
37. J. B. Willis, *Anal. Chem.*, **34,** 614 (1962).

38. O. Menis and T. C. Rains, *Anal. Chem.*, **32**, 1837 (1962).

39. C. E. Mulford, *At. Absorption Newsletter*, **5**, 88 (1966).

40. J. E. Allan, *Spectrochim. Acta*, **17**, 467 (1961).

41. E. A. Means and D. Ratcliff, *At. Absorption Newsletter*, **4**, 174 (1965).

42. D. J. Trent, *At. Absorption Newsletter*, **4**, 348 (1965).

43. A. Strasheim, F. W. E. Strelow, and E. Norval, *J. So. African Chem. Institute*, **20**, 25 (1961).

44. V. A. Fassel, Eastern Analytical Symposium, New York, November, 1966.

45. T. C. Rains, personal communication, 1967.

46. S. L. Sachdev, J. W. Robinson, and P. W. West, *Anal. Chim. Acta*, **37**, 156 (1967).

47. J. B. Willis, in *Methods of Biochemical Analysis*, (D. Glick, ed.) Vol. XI, Wiley (Interscience), New York, 1963.

48. G. K. Billings, *At. Absorption Newsletter*, **4**, 357 (1965).

49. S. Sprague and W. Slavin, *At. Absorption Newsletter*, **5**, 9 (1966).

50. W. T. Elwell and J. A. F. Gidley, *Atomic-Absorption Spectrophotometry*, 2nd ed., Pergamon, New York, 1966.

51. S. R. Koirtyohann and E. E. Pickettt, *Anal. Chem.*, **38**, 585 (1966).

52. H. C. Van de Hulst, *Light Scattering by Small Particles*, Wiley, New York, 1957.

53. I. Rubeska and B. Moldan, *Anal. Chim. Acta*, **37**, 421 (1967).

54. S. R. Koirtyohann and E. E. Pickett, *Anal. Chem.*, **37**, 601 (1965).

55. Claude Veillon, J. M. Mansfield, M. L. Parsons, and J. D. Winefordner, *Anal. Chem.*, **38**, 204 (1966).

56. R. M. Dagnall, K. C. Thompson, and T. S. West, *Anal. Chim. Acta*, **36**, 269 (1966).

11 Chemical Interferences in the Vapor Phase

Ivan Rubeška

GEOLOGICAL SURVEY OF CZECHOSLOVAKIA
PRAGUE, CZECHOSLOVAKIA

I. Introduction

A. CLASSIFICATION

The terminology on interference effects is very rich and in no case uniform (*1–5*). The classification used by different authors may be widely divergent; thus it is necessary to define exactly what sort of interference effects are to be understood under the heading "chemical interferences in the vapor phase." Evidently these should include all processes which are taking place between the analyte and the interferent, both in a vaporized state, and which influence the signal reading of the analyte. However, the device of chemists from the good old times, "corpora reagunt nil nisi fluida," has long been abandoned, and in some particular cases it is possible that either the analyte or the interferent may not be actually evaporated and some mutual reactions on the surface of the finely dispersed aerosol particles still may take place. The term vapor phase interference might then include reactions between the gaseous and solid phases as well. It seems, therefore, advantageous to define the interferences which will be dealt with in this chapter by the experimental conditions under which they appear. We shall further consider chemical interferences which take place even if the analyte and interferent are introduced into the flame separately by twin nebulizers. Undoubtedly, dissociation and ionization processes in the flame are the most frequently occurring phenomena of this group. Excitation interferences also will be included.

B. The Flame as a Thermostat

From general thermodynamics it follows that knowing the values of the appropriate dissociation and ionization constants the particular interference effects should be susceptible to exact mathematical treatment and could thus be quantitatively enumerated. However, this is true only in exceptional cases and under special conditions. The flame as it is generally used for analytical work may be considered as being in thermal equilibrium only in a rather limited region, and even there the conditions depend not only on all preceding processes but on their rate as well. Thus, unless specially designed "shielded" or "sheathed" burners (6) are used, the flame properties are steadily changing along the axis, mostly by diffusion and/or entrainment of the surrounding atmosphere. The interference phenomena which may then be observed are strongly dependent on the height of observation, and contradictory results sometimes have been reported by different authors.

In the interconal gases several millimeters above the reaction zone, the flame gases, including the introduced sample, may be considered in thermal equilibrium. Consequently, all dissociation, ionization, or any other chemical reaction may be described by the appropriate equilibrium constants (7). The value of these constants naturally depends on the temperature, which is therefore of primary importance. For premixed flames the temperature of the interconal gases is well defined. However, for total consumption burners larger droplets are entering the flame and their evaporation causes temperature and concentration gradients in the observed region. The characterization of the equilibria by effective equilibrium constants is, therefore, only an approximation. Anyhow, it can be used for explaining the mechanisms of some of the interfering effects observed.

If, on the other hand, the measurements are performed near to or directly in the reaction zone where chemical equilibrium is not attained, the mechanism of the observed effects must be explained from kinetic considerations (8). Unfortunately, observations on these regions of flames so far are mostly confined to pure solutions, so that practically no information on possible interferences is available (9, 10).

C. Equilibria in Flames

The aerosol particles after entering the flame evaporate and the evaporated molecules (or atoms) are involved in further dissociation and ionization equilibria and may form new species with the different components of the flame gases. Simplifying somewhat the possible reactions in the flame gases, the processes taking place in flame spectrometry may be represented by Fig. 1. Predominantly spectra of free atoms are measured in analytical work. Molecular or ionic spectra are only seldom used. However, in both cases the concentration of the particular species is of interest.

Figure 1 does not give a complete description of the equilibria involved; there may be many further reactions and interrelations. Since one or two such equilibria are predominant, only these need to be considered from the analytical point of view.

The most important reactions are the dissociation of molecules

$$MX \rightleftarrows M + X, \qquad K_{MX} = \frac{p_M \, p_X}{p_{MX}} \qquad (1)$$

the formation of compounds with the flame components

$$M + Y \rightleftarrows MY, \qquad K_{MY} = \frac{p_M \, p_Y}{p_{MY}} \qquad (2)$$

and the ionization of atoms

$$M \rightleftharpoons M^+ + e^-, \qquad K_M = \frac{p_{M^+} \, p_{e^-}}{p_M} \tag{3}$$

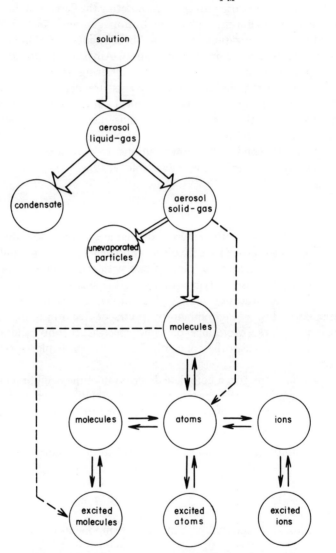

Fig. 1. Schematic process taking place in flame spectrometry. (For direct-sprayer burners several steps may be contracted into a single one.)

In these equations p is the partial pressure of the species indicated in the subscript. Formally there is no difference between the dissociation reaction (1) and the formation of compounds with the different flame components (2). However, it is advantageous to consider these separately. The partial pressure of the flame gas components is generally several orders of magnitude higher than the partial pressure of the particular element measured. It may, therefore, be considered constant and included in the equilibrium constant. Equation (2) is then simplified to express simply that the ratio of the dissociated and undissociated forms is constant.

$$K' = \frac{p_M}{p_{MY}} \tag{4}$$

The most important representatives of flame gas components forming compounds with the analyzed elements are oxygen, the hydroxyl radical, and hydrogen.

II. Total Atom Concentration

If the dissociation reaction does not involve a species present in the pure flame gases, the situation is somewhat more complicated because the partial pressure of the analyte and interferent are commensurable and the equilibrium state depends on the concentration level. For any theoretical treatment the so-called total atom concentration including the particular element in all its possible forms of existence is an important value.

The concentration of any species in the flame gases is most often given in atmospheres (less frequently in dynes per square centimeter) or in the number of the appropriate particles per unit volume. The two different values are related by equation

$$p = nkT \tag{5}$$

where p is the partial pressure in atm or dyn cm^{-2}, n the number of the particular species particles per unit volume (cm^{-3}), k the Boltzmann constant (1.365×10^{22} atm cm^3 deg^{-1} or 1.38×10^{-16} erg deg^{-1}, respectively), and T the absolute temperature (in degrees Kelvin). According to the units used, the equilibrium constants have different values. Further, we shall express the partial pressure in atmospheres.

Considering the reactions given in Fig. 1, the following equation for the total atom concentration evidently holds:

$$p_{\Sigma M} = p_{MX} + p_{MY} + p_M + p_{M^+} \tag{6}$$

Evidently $p_{\Sigma M}$ should be proportional to the molar concentration of the solution sprayed. The exact value, however, depends on a number of factors, including the volume of the solution introduced into the flame per time unit, the completeness of evaporation of the aerosol, the volume of the fuel and oxidant supplied per time unit, and the volume expansion of the gases due to the combustion reaction and the temperature increase. These factors differ, of course, according to the exact experimental arrangements. They are basically different for premixed flames with spray chambers and for turbulent flames from total consumption burners.

It is difficult to calculate the relation between the molar concentration of the element in the solution and its partial pressure in the flame gases. Not all the processes taking part may be quantitatively evaluated; therefore, when needed, this relation has been determined experimentally.

If the actual line shape emitted by the flame is known, the absolute concentration of free atoms in flame gases may be determined from the intersection of the two linear parts of its curve of growth (*11*). The measurement requires a shielded laminar flame. Sodium is most often used because in an air–acetylene flame it is completely atomized (*12*) and the appropriate Lorenz and Doppler widths of its resonance doublet are relatively precisely known. Although individual authors used quite different equipment, the relation actually found varied only within one order of magnitude (Table 1).

TABLE 1

Relation between the Molar Concentration in the Solution Sprayed C and the Total Atom Concentration in the Flame Gases for Premixed Air–Acetylene Flames

Relation reported	Ref.
$p_{\Sigma M} = C \times 2.5 \times 10^{-5}$	*11*
$p_{\Sigma M} = C \times 2 \times 10^{-4}$	*13*
$p_{\Sigma M} = C \times 2 \times 10^{-4}$	*14*
$p_{\Sigma M} = C \times 5.9 \times 10^{-5}$	*15*
$p_{\Sigma M} = C \times 1.2 \times 10^{-4}$	*16*

From the values reported in Table 1 the relation

$$p_{\Sigma M} = 10^{-4} C \tag{7}$$

where C is the molar concentration in the solution, may be accepted as a rough approximation.

For any calculations claiming higher precision, the exact relation between the molar concentration in the solution and the total atom concentration in the flame for the particular nebulizer–burner combination used should be determined experimentally. A relatively easy way to do this has been described by Alkemade (7).

The task of estimating the total atom concentration seems easier for total consumption burners. From the feed rate of the solution with known molar concentration, the fuel and oxidant flow, and the volume expansion of gases due to the combustion reaction and temperature increase, it should be possible to calculate the partial vapor pressure of the element exactly. However, with turbulent flames an undefined amount of air from the surrounding atmosphere is entrained and some water droplets may leave the flame unevaporated (17, 17a, 18) especially at higher aspiration rates. The relation

$$p_{\Sigma M} = 10^{-3}C \tag{8}$$

seems plausible, and very similar values have been employed by different authors for an oxygen–hydrogen flame (16, 19).

III. Dissociation Reactions with Flame Gas Components

A. COMPOUNDS FORMED IN FLAMES

Vapor phase interference effects observed in all flame spectrometric methods are a result of shifts in the various equilibria caused by the presence of the interferent. Initially, we shall deal only with dissociation equilibria involving flame gas components. As the flame gas composition is mainly determined by the ratio of the fuel and oxidant flows, as long as this flow ratio is kept constant these equilibria are relatively well stabilized and all interferences, if any, are only slight. Anyhow, the existence of such compounds in flames must be mentioned. For a review of possible compounds and their molecular spectra in flames see, for example, Ref. (20).

The least important from the analytical point of view is the formation of hydrides. The existence of hydrides has been confirmed for copper, thallium, gold, boron, aluminum, and indium. The copper hydride spectrum has been used for measuring flame profiles of atomic hydrogen (21).

Hydroxides of the type MOH are known to exist for the alkali metals, copper, manganese, gallium, indium, thallium, and possibly some rare earth elements. The most important are the alkali metal hydroxides. Their dissociation degree increases in the order Li < Cs < Rb < K < Na (*1*). In an air–acetylene flame it starts at about 20% dissociation for lithium and attains 100% for sodium (*12*). The exact values naturally depend on the composition of flame gases.

The compounds occurring most often are undoubtedly oxides. Their formation in flames limits the sensitivity of the so-called refractory elements, i.e., elements which cannot be observed in a common air–acetylene flame. For these elements the nitrous oxide–acetylene flame(*22*) or a strongly fuel-rich, oxygen–acetylene flame must be used (*23*).

Among elements forming predominantly oxides but which are still generally determined with the normal air–acetylene flame, the alkaline earth metals are an important group. Although their molecular spectrum is mostly due to hydroxides (*20*), it has been shown that they are predominantly present as oxides (*24*). The percent dissociation in an air–acetylene flame, according to Huldt and Lagerqvist (*25, 26*), are given in Table 2.

TABLE 2

Dissociation of Alkaline Earth Metal Oxides in a
Premixed Air–Acetylene Flame

Element	% Dissociation	
	Refs. (*25, 26*)	Ref. (*12*)
Mg	1.44	
Ca	8.55	4.7
Sr	19.6	11
Ba	0.8	0.21

The values found by Hinnov and Kohn (*12*) are about half as high. This is quite comprehensible because the degree of dissociation of oxides, and thus also the sensitivity of determination, depends on the exact flame gas composition.

B. INTERFERENCE EFFECTS DUE TO VARIATION IN THE FLAME GAS COMPOSITION

Gaseous oxides of most elements contain a single oxygen atom. The concentration of free metal atoms is, therefore, controlled by the relation

$$p_M = K_{MO} \frac{p_{MO}}{p_O} \tag{9}$$

where p_O is given by the fuel-to-oxidant flow ratio.

If, as is often the case, the vapor pressure of these refractory oxides is very low so that some unevaporated oxide particles are also present in the flame gases, p_{MO} is determined by the saturated vapor pressure and is, therefore, constant. The free atom vapor pressure then varies inversely with the oxygen atom pressure p_O. Using fuel-rich flames, where p_O is sufficiently low, free atoms of these refractory elements may be observed both in emission and absorption.

In Table 3 the variation of flame composition with varying fuel-to-oxidant flow ratios is given. The values were calculated by Lvov (27) for a total consumption burner using an oxygen–acetylene flame and spraying aqueous or ethanol solutions.

According to Lvov's conclusions, optimum reducing properties of the flame are achieved when the composition of the flame gases, including the solvent, has a carbon-to-oxygen ratio equal to one. Upon increasing the C/O ratio above this value, particles of solid carbon (soot) are formed but the reducing properties of the flame gases remain almost unchanged.

From Table 3 it also may be seen that upon replacing water by ethanol the partial pressure of the species O, OH, and H is not greatly influenced. Ethanol contains only two carbon atoms, and hydrogen is ineffective in producing a reducing flame. Evidence for this fact has been recently supported by the work of Skogerboe and co-workers (28) who were able to observe atomic spectra of some refractory elements in oxygen–hydrogen flames only when using forced aspiration of organic solutions containing carbon at above-normal rates.

Solvents with a higher ratio of carbon-to-oxygen atoms increase the reducing properties of flames more efficiently than ethanol. It should be remembered also that when using organic solvents the cooling effect due to the aspirated solution is decreased and a temperature rise takes place (29) which, for solvents with a carbon-to-oxygen ratio near unity, may be a more important factor (27). For premixed flames where the amount of solution introduced into the flame is smaller, the differences in flame gas composition when using aqueous and organic solvent solutions are even less significant.

From this reasoning it follows that if the gas flows and the solvent used are unchanged, no interferences of this kind should be expected. If any

TABLE 3

The Temperature and Composition of Flame Gases of an Oxyacetylene Flame with Varying Fuel Flows (27)

Gas flow (liter/min)		Temperature	Pressure, in atm									
Oxygen	Acetylene	°K	CO_2	CO	H_2O	H_2	O_2	OH	H	O	C	C_{solid}
Water												
2.8	5.5	2874	—	0.374	—	0.342	—	8.4×10^{-8}	0.055	8.2×10^{-9}	1.2×10^{-5}	0.229
	3.8	2876	—	0.526	—	0.355	—	1.1×10^{-7}	0.062	1.2×10^{-8}	1.6×10^{-5}	0.057
	2.8	3049	0.025	0.522	0.093	0.252	0.0004	0.012	0.093	0.0026	1.0×10^{-9}	—
	1.9	3164	0.081	0.406	0.201	0.128	0.014	0.054	0.092	0.023	4.2×10^{-10}	—
	1.4	3132	0.132	0.292	0.257	0.073	0.058	0.082	0.064	0.043	1.1×10^{-10}	—
	0.95	3023	0.177	0.169	0.300	0.038	0.147	0.090	0.033	0.047	1.2×10^{-11}	—
	0.7	2883	0.196	0.086	0.328	0.020	0.241	0.077	0.016	0.037	9.6×10^{-13}	—
Ethanol												
2.8	5.5	3013	—	0.310	—	0.309	—	9.5×10^{-8}	0.077	1.4×10^{-8}	4.5×10^{-5}	0.304
	3.8	3052	—	0.429	—	0.307	—	1.3×10^{-7}	0.095	2.4×10^{-8}	7.7×10^{-5}	0.169
	2.8	3084	—	0.552	—	0.306	—	1.7×10^{-7}	0.112	3.6×10^{-8}	1×10^{-4}	0.030
	1.9	3249	0.031	0.509	0.091	0.187	0.002	0.027	0.012	0.012	3.0×10^{-9}	—
	1.4	3288	0.066	0.429	0.146	0.199	0.018	0.062	0.123	0.038	1.3×10^{-9}	—
	0.95	3257	0.102	0.340	0.184	0.077	0.057	0.088	0.092	0.061	4.3×10^{-10}	—
	0.7	3214	0.126	0.272	0.203	0.056	0.103	0.099	0.070	0.073	1.7×10^{-10}	—

component present in the solution sprayed exhibits some interference, the explanation should be sought either in the condensed phase or evaporation processes.

C. Other Possible Interferences

The conclusions reached in the preceding paragraph do not hold exactly because, when working with flames used for routine analysis, the flame structure and the concentration gradients of the species H, OH, O cannot be disregarded. Flame profiles, i.e., axial distributions in the direction of the flame flow, are quite often reported. For analytical flames the radial distribution is also important; unfortunately, very little is actually known about this. One notable exception is the distribution of OH radicals in an air–acetylene flame with a 10-cm slot burner which was measured by Rann and Hambly (30).

Variations in the radial distribution are more likely to influence absorp-.tion measurements than emission measurements. The flame shape used in atomic absorption provides only a very limited region which may be assumed homogenous. Also the cooler outer parts of the flame are more likely to contribute to the absorption value measured than in emission, where excitation usually requiring high temperature is simultaneously needed.

An example of such an interference effect may be found with manganese in an air–acetylene flame. Belcher and Kinson (31) reported that chromium at a level of 2000 μg/ml enhanced manganese absorption, more so in a stoichiometric flame than in a reducing one. If a narrower light beam or a broader flame was used, this interference effect diminished. Similar observations were reported for the interference of silicon (32). It seems probable that chromium or silicon influenced the perpendicular gradient of oxygen atoms in the slot flame used.

The conclusion about the absence of interfering effects due to dissociation of compounds with flame gas components because of the stabilizing effect of the flame gas composition, also does not hold if the concentration of the particular species is commensurable with the concentration of the interfering element. This, however, is a very rare case and probably the only examples which may be found are some interference effects observed in the nitrous oxide–acetylene flame. The zone used for measurement of refractory elements, the so-called "red feather" (22), has an extremely low concentration of oxygen atoms. A further depletion of oxygen atoms by addition of other refractory elements should, therefore, be possible. However, it should be borne in mind that the red feather is a secondary reaction zone where some combustion reactions, probably with NO and OH (33), are still taking place, so that any considerations assuming an equilibrium state may be premature. Anyhow, Sachdev and co-workers (34) observed a considerable sensitivity enhancement for vanadium upon addition of aluminium or titanium in this flame. This effect was not due to suppression of the ionization of vanadium, because the enhancement attainable with alkali metals was only about half of the value found for aluminum and titanium. Similar enhancement by aluminum has been reported for titanium (35) and vice versa (35a) and by yttrium for some rare earths (36). In these latter cases, however, it cannot be decided what part of the enhancement was due to suppression of ionization and what part to dissociation shift, because the effect of alkali metals was not compared.

IV. Dissociation and Ionization Equilibria

A. ESTIMATION OF THE DEGREE OF DISSOCIATION AND IONIZATION

As an example of the equilibria in the flame when disregarding reactions with the flame gas components, consider what happens when an alkali halide is introduced into the flame. The following equilibria take place:

$$MX \rightleftharpoons M + X, \qquad K_p^d = \frac{p_M\, p_X}{p_{MX}} \tag{10}$$

$$M \rightleftharpoons M^+ + e^-, \qquad K_p^i = \frac{p_{M^+}\, p_{e^-}}{p_M} \tag{11}$$

$$X + e^- \rightleftharpoons X^-, \qquad (K_p)_X = \frac{p_X\, p_{e^-}}{p_{X^-}} \tag{12}$$

The three equations are further bound by the condition of electroneutrality

$$p_{M^+} = p_{e^-} + p_{X^-} \tag{13}$$

and a constant total concentration value of the metal and the halogen

$$p_{\Sigma M} = p_{MX} + p_M + p_{M^+} \tag{14}$$

$$p_{\Sigma M} = p_{MX} + p_X + p_{X^-} \tag{15}$$

From these equations the six variables p_{MX}, p_M, p_{M^+}, p_X, p_{X^-}, and p_{e^-} may be calculated. For an exact description the formation of metal hydroxides and the reaction of the halogen with hydrogen forming HX should be included, which would make the whole system even more complicated. From the analytical point of view it is, however, unnecessary to make these calculations. An analytical chemist is usually satisfied if he may roughly estimate the actual extent of dissociation or ionization. To do this, only the total atom concentration and the value of the particular equilibrium constant are necessary. Let us describe a very simplified calculation of the extent of dissociation, bearing in mind that analogous equations hold also for the ionization process.

If a single salt is introduced into the flame and the simplifying assump-

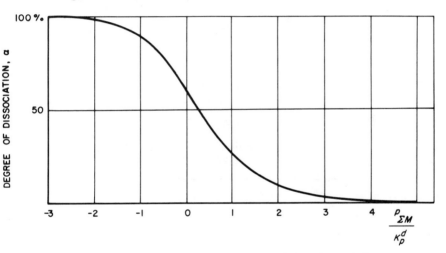

Fig. 2. Degree of dissociation, as a function of the ratio $p_{\Sigma M}/K_p^d$.

tion is made that the free metal concentration equals the free anion element concentration, i.e., $p_M = p_X$ is applied, the dissociation constant may be expressed as

$$K_p^d = \frac{p_M^2}{p_{\Sigma M} - p_M} \tag{16}$$

Introducing the degree of dissociation, $\alpha_d = P_M/P_{\Sigma M}$, and the expression $a = p_{\Sigma M}/K_p^d$, the equation

$$\alpha_d = \frac{(\sqrt{4a+1})-1}{2a} \tag{17}$$

may be derived for the degree of dissociation *(37)*. The function of Eq. (17) is graphically reproduced in Fig. 2, from which the degree of dissociation may be found for a given value of the parameter $p_{\Sigma M}/K_p^d$.

Dissociation constants of some alkali halides for the temperature of an air–acetylene flame (2500°K) and the air–coal gas flame (2000°K) are given in Tables 4 and 5. Using these values and Eq. (7) or (8) for estimating

TABLE 4

Dissociation Constants of Alkali Metal Halides in an
Air-Acetylene Flame (2500°K), in Atm

	Cl	Br	I
Na	2.2×10^{-4}	1.4×10^{-3}	3.2×10^{-2}
K	7.9×10^{-5}	5.4×10^{-4}	7.2×10^{-3}
Rb	4.7×10^{-5}	3.8×10^{-4}	5.8×10^{-3}
Cs	2.6×10^{-5}	2.3×10^{-4}	4.0×10^{-3}

TABLE 5

Dissociation Constants of Alkali Metal Halides
at $T = 2000°K$, in Atm

NaF	4.0×10^{-9}	RbF	4.0×10^{-9}
NaCl	6.3×10^{-6}	RbCl	6.3×10^{-6}
NaBr	1.1×10^{-4}	RbBr	4.0×10^{-5}
KCl	2.5×10^{-6}		

the total atom concentration, it may be seen that in an acetylene–air flame the dissociation of alkali halides is practically complete. In air–coal gas flames, on the other hand, when spraying $0.01M$ solutions of NaCl, the dissociation should be only about 75%. Actually the dissociation is higher, because in the presence of hydrogen part of the chlorine atoms form HCl and the dissociation reaction is shifted in favor of the dissociated species.

From Eq. (10) it is evident that upon increasing the concentration of the halogen atoms, whether by adding various salts or free acids to the solution sprayed, the equilibrium is shifted in favor of the undissociated salt and a decrease of free atoms may be observed. This evidently holds in the cooler flames where the dissociation might be incomplete, whereas in the hotter air–acetylene flame no great difference should be observed. However, it is well known that a depressive effect from acids may be observed even in this flame. To explain this interference, the ionization equilibrium must be taken into account.

Assuming complete dissociation of the particular salt and $p_{M^+} = p_{e^-}$, the ionization constant may be expressed as

$$K_p^i = \frac{p_{M^+}{}^2}{p_{\Sigma M} - p_{M^+}} \tag{18}$$

and a calculation analogous to Eqs. (16) and (17) may be carried through. The degree of ionization, $\alpha_i = p_{M^+}/p_{\Sigma M}$, may then be found also from a plot (similar to Fig. 2) of α_i against K_p^i. Ionization constants for the alkali and alkaline earth metals are given in Tables 7 and 8. Using these values it is found that slight ionization of the alkali metals takes place in the air–coal gas flame but it may be considerable in the air–acetylene flame.

The electron concentration of an unsalted air–acetylene flame is very low, below 10^{-8} atm (7, 38) or 3.6×10^{-8} atm (39), so that it may be neglected in comparison with electrons released by the alkali metal. Any addition of a further easily ionized element will thus increase the electron concentration and decrease the extent of ionization of the element measured. On the other hand, addition of strongly electronegative elements, as, for example, chlorine from hydrochloric acid, will shift the ionization equilibrium in favor of the ionized element. Two possible reactions have been considered. Either the cations are bound (40) according to the reaction

$$M^+ + X \rightleftharpoons MX^+ \tag{19}$$

or the electrons according to the reaction

$$e^- + X \rightleftharpoons X^- \tag{20}$$

The latter reaction seems more plausible because a decrease of the electron concentration with addition of halides has been observed by microwave attenuation measurements, and an enhancement of the ionic lines of alkaline earth metals has simultaneously been found (41) (Fig. 3). The first reaction would actually predict a decrease of the ionic species.

The effect of anions on the alkali metals may thus have different mechanisms according to the temperature of the flame used. In general, halogen anions influence the dissociation equilibrium in the cooler flames and the ionization equilibrium in the hotter air–acetylene flame.

B. Interference Effects of Acids and Anions

The effect of anions is most easily investigated by adding free acids to the solution sprayed. For alkali metals a depression is usually observed. The only exception is nitric acid because its decomposition product (NO)

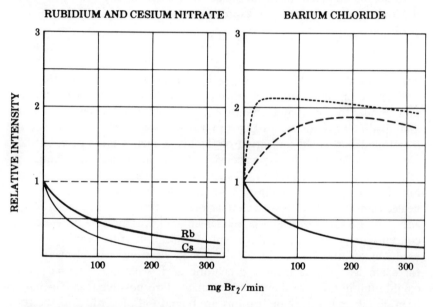

Fig. 3. The influence of bromine in an air–acetylene flame (*41*). *Full line:* microwave attenuation; *broken line:* electrical conductivity; *dotted line:* intensity of Ba II lines.

is already present in the flame gases from the air either used as oxidant or entrained. Its addition, therefore, has no influence on the reading.

The addition of acids can influence the aspiration rate, the nebulization, and thus alter the nebulizer yield—the percentage of the analyte that actually leaves the spray chamber as spray (*7*). This may be clearly seen from Table 6 where the effects of acids introduced jointly with the analyte and separately by two nebulizers are compared.

Evidently, sulfuric acid interferes less in the vapor phase than hydrochloric acid but depresses strongly the nebulizer yield. Phosphoric acid has a strong depressive effect on both processes.

With total consumption burners the vapor phase interference of acids is more pronounced, as may be expected because of the greater amount of solution introduced into the flame. On the other hand, the effect of acids on the nebulizer yield is smaller because coagulation in the spray chamber, which depends on the droplet size distribution, has no opportunity to occur (16).

The effect of acids on elements forming relatively stable oxides is much stronger than the effect on alkali metals. This, however, usually includes some condensed phase interferences, i.e., crystallization of salts with different thermal stability during evaporation of the solvent from the droplets.

TABLE 6

Comparison of the Effects of Acids on the Emission of Sodium in an Air–Acetylene Flame if Introduced Jointly and Separately (19). Concentration of Sodium, 23 μg/ml

Acid	Molar concentration	Galvanometer deflection	
		Jointly	Separately
HCl	2	83.5	88
H_2SO_4	2	73	93
H_3PO_4	1	66	82

The effect of acids on easily atomized elements such as copper, silver, gold, zinc, cadmium, mercury, thallium, antimony, and bismuth, is generally small. Usually no or only slight depression of the emission or absorption signal is observed and this generally might be explained by the influence of acids on the nebulization processes. Although some chlorides are formed, as revealed by their molecular spectra, it is doubtful that an interference mechanism takes place in the vapor phase unless, of course, the effect is simultaneously tried and confirmed with separate nebulization.

A somewhat more puzzling problem arises when an increase of the measured signal is observed, as has been reported for the determination of thallium by atomic absorption (42). In an air–propane flame, Na, K, Ca, Ba, Sr, Pb, Cu, Ni, Mg, Zn, Cd, Hg, Mn, Ag, Fe, Al, Cr, SO_4^{2-}, PO_4^{3-}, ClO_4^-, and NO_3^- all enhanced thallium absorption up to 20%. Because so many different compounds had a similar effect, this can hardly be explained by chemical equilibria in the flame. It is probably due to changes in the flame structure. The authors used a burner head with three rows of separate holes spaced about 2 mm apart. It seems possible that by addition of salt to the solution sprayed the individual flame cones are enlarged, less atmospheric air is entrained between the individual cones, and an enhancement is observed. Other authors found either no influence of acids (43) or a slight depression (44) by acids for thallium.

The elimination of interferences by acids or anions in analytical work is relatively easy. All samples may usually be prepared to contain a constant amount of the particular anions, or excessive acid may be added to make any possible variation of the anion content in the sample solutions negligible. The standard solutions should naturally have the same concentration of the anion as the samples.

C. Ionization in Flames

The ionization interference effects are probably the best understood of all the numerous interference effects taking part in flame spectrometric analyses. For the alkali metals, where the contribution of other reactions taking place in the flame gases may be neglected or relatively easily included into calculations on the mutual effect of the alkalis, the theoretical, i.e., calculated, and experimental values are generally in very good agreement (7, 37, 38).

Analogous to dissociation, the degree of ionization of a particular element increases with decreasing value of the expression $p_{\Sigma M}/K_M$, i.e., with decreasing concentration of the element in the solution sprayed. For values of $p_{\Sigma M}/K_M$ below 0.01 the ionization is almost complete, whereas for values above 1000 it is negligible. Using relations (7) or (8), the ionization may be estimated with a precision corresponding to the validity of these equations for the working conditions used. Values of ionization constants calculated according to the Saha equation for the alkali metals and the alkaline earth metals are given in Tables 7 and 8.

TABLE 7

Ionization Constants for Alkali Metals in an
Air–Coal Gas Flame (2000°K)

Element	K_p^i (atm)
Li	9.3×10^{-13}
Na	4.2×10^{-12}
K	4.7×10^{-10}
Rb	1.2×10^{-9}
Cs	6.3×10^{-9}

TABLE 8

Ionization Constants for Alkali Metals and Alkaline
Earth Metals at 2500°K

Element	K_p^i (atm)	Element	K_p^i (atm)
Li	1.48×10^{-9}	Cs	1.45×10^{-6}
Na	4.8×10^{-9}	Ca	1.9×10^{-10}
K	1.8×10^{-7}	Sr	1.35×10^{-9}
Rb	3.9×10^{-7}	Ba	1.26×10^{-8}

Thus, when spraying $10^{-3} M$ solutions, the ionization in premixed air–acetylene flames should be approximately 10% for lithium, 20% for sodium, 60% for potassium, 75% rubidium, and about 95% for cesium.

Because the extent of ionization decreases with increasing concentration of the particular element in the flame gases, it is generally smaller in turbulent flames from total consumption burners than in premixed flames of equal temperature (16). It also depends markedly on the aspiration rate, not only because of the concentration increase of the ionizable element in the flame gases but also because of the temperature fall due to the cooling effect of the solution sprayed into the flame (29). In Table 9 the percent ionization is given for sodium with an oxygen–hydrogen flame at different fuel flows and aspiration rates, according to Püschel el al. (18).

TABLE 9

Ionization Degree in an Oxygen–Hydrogen Flame (18).
Beckman Burner No. 4020. Oxygen Flow, 3.2 liters/min;
Na, 10 μg/ml

Hydrogen flow, liter/min	% Ionization		
	0.64 ml/min[a]	1.6 ml/min[a]	5.0 ml/min[a]
6.1	25.8	14.5	1.96
9.1	34.6	15.5	2.3
10.5	35.4	15.5	2.3
12.2	32.4	13.8	2.0
13.6	31.0	12.2	1.96
14.9	29.6	9.1	1.3

[a] Rate of aspiration.

Because the ionization depends on the concentration of the particular element, the working curves of elements undergoing ionization are not linear but exhibit a concave form with a bending away from the concentration axis (Fig. 4). This curvature is greater the lower the measured concentration and the larger the value of the ionization constant.

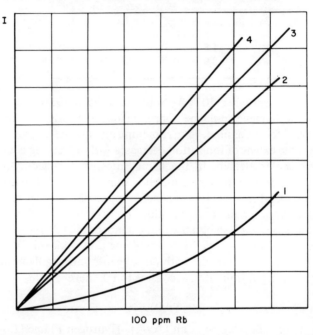

100 ppm Rb

Fig. 4. Working curves for rubidium with a premixed air–acetylene flame. Curve 1, no potassium; 2, 500; 3, 1000; 4, 2500 ppm of potassium.

The signal of the element measured is proportional to p_M unless, of course, some ionic lines or molecular spectra are measured, whereas the concentration in the solution determines $p_{\Sigma M}$. For very dilute solutions the ionization should be almost complete, and, using the assumption

$$p_{M^+} = p_{e^-}$$

the equation for working curves should have the form

$$p_M = \frac{(p_{\Sigma M})^2}{K_p^i} \qquad (21)$$

As one approaches zero concentration of analyte, the slope should tend to zero. This actually does not hold because the concentration of free electrons in unsalted flames is not negligible.

The upward curvature of working curves may be removed if the ionization of the element is suppressed either by using a low temperature flame or by increasing the electron pressure by addition of some easily ionizable element in excess. The curvature of working curves is also less, or completely absent, if the measurements are performed near the reaction zone where the electron concentration is in excess of the thermal equilibrium value (7, 8). This is clearly seen from Fig. 5, which records the enhance-

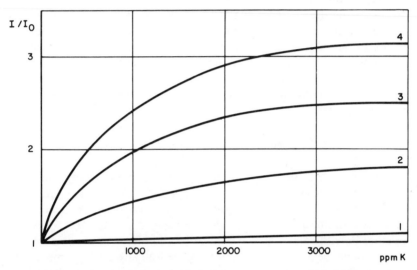

Fig. 5. Relative enhancement of rubidium emission by addition of potassium chloride at different heights in a premixed air–acetylene flame. Curve 1, 0; 2, 5 mm; 3, 15 mm; 4, 30 mm above burner head (45).

ment of rubidium emission at different heights in the flame upon addition of potassium (45).

Not much is known about the positive ions present in the reaction zone and the nearby regions, which must counterbalance the negative charge of free electrons. The ion H_3O^+ has been found by mass spectrometry to be the most prevalent positive ion in unsalted flames (8, 46). This species decays by recombination with electrons producing water and hydrogen. Ionization in flames has been found to be much weaker in pure hydrogen flames but increases if hydrocarbons are added. The reaction

$$HCO^+ + H_2O = H_3O^+ + CO \qquad (22)$$

is postulated to be responsible. The electron concentration is also higher in strongly fuel-rich flames where carbon particles are formed. These release electrons more readily than the flame gases (47).

These findings have no particular significance for analytical work. The reaction zone is not generally used for the determination of alkali metals or alkaline earth metals for which ionization in an air–acetylene flame is significant. However, the analytical chemist should be aware of these facts so that certain observations may be explained. For example, Willis (48) found by atomic absorption measurements that the ionization of potassium was smaller in a fuel-rich air–acetylene flame than in a lean one. By increasing the fuel flow, the flame profiles are somewhat elongated. If the path of the light beam through the flame is not changed, the measurements are actually performed nearer to the reaction zone where the excess electrons may partly suppress ionization. In addition, a temperature change may also play a role. In emission measurements, where the height of the flame column observed is generally much greater, the effect would probably be less.

D. IONIZATION INTERFERENCE EFFECTS AND THEIR ELIMINATION

If the analyte is partly or wholly ionized, interferences by substances releasing electrons in the flame must be expected. Whereas in air–acetylene, air–hydrogen, and oxygen–hydrogen flames both the alkali metals and alkaline earth metals are susceptible to ionization interferences (37, 49), in practice only the alkali metals need to be considered as possible interferents. Among the other elements, barium and lead also might be mentioned. Barium has a very low ionization energy, the value of its ionization constant lying between that for potassium and sodium. But due to formation of oxides in flames, barium is not as effective an interferent as sodium, although the greater part of the electrons is released by molecular ions $BaOH^+$ (6). Lead also is not ionized in atomic form but releases electrons through chemi-ionization according to the reaction

$$Pb + OH^* = PbOH^+ + e^- \tag{23}$$

where OH^* represents an excited hydroxyl radical (50). Both barium and lead will influence the signal of the analyte only if present in considerable excess of the analyte. For instance, a $0.1M$ solution of $Pb(NO_3)_2$ is about as effective as a $10^{-3}M$ solution of sodium (50). The greatest danger of possible interferences is undoubtedly due to alkali metals.

It is evident that any increase of the electron concentration in the flame

gases will shift the ionization equilibrium of the analyte in favor of non-
ionized atoms and an enhancement of the signal will be observed. The
greater the extent of the ionization, the greater the possible enhancement.
This may be seen in Fig. 6, where the relative enhancement of potassium

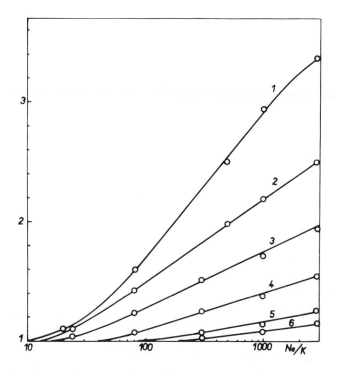

Fig. 6. Relative enhancement of potassium emission by addition of sodium chloride
in a premixed air–acetylene flame at different concentration levels. Curve 1, 5; 2, 10;
3, 20; 4, 40; 5, 70; 6, 100 ppm of potassium.

at different concentration levels (and also different percent ionization) by
addition of sodium is plotted. The highest enhancement is found for the
lowest potassium concentration.

The easiest way to eliminate possible ionization interference effects is
to stabilize the electron concentration in the flame gases at a relatively
high level by adding an easily ionizable element. The terms *deionizer* (5)
or *normalizer* (51) have been proposed for such additives. The deionizer
may be included in the solution sprayed or it may be introduced directly

into the flame by a separate nebulizer (45). In the latter case, all influences on the preceding processes—aspiration, nebulization, and evaporation—are eliminated. Because alkali salts are generally easily evaporated, these effects are rather small and the differences negligible (45).

Let us now consider what amounts of the deionizer should be added to eliminate the possible interference effects. Assuming that the electron concentration equals the sum of all the metallic ions, the following equation holds

$$p_{e^-} = p_{M^+,1} + p_{M^+,2} + p_{M^+,3} + \cdots \tag{24}$$

Inserting $p_{M^+} = p_{e^-}/(K_p^i)p_M$ from the particular ionization constant equations, it follows that

$$p_{e^-} = \sqrt{K_{M,1}^i \, p_{M,1} + K_{M,2} \, p_{M,2} + \cdots} \tag{25}$$

To ensure that ionization interference is eliminated, the product $(K_M^i)p_M$ of the deionizer must be so large that variation of the products for all other interferents is negligible, i.e., does not influence the value of the square root of the sum. The larger the ionization constant of the deionizer, the smaller the necessary amount. The heavier alkali metals are, therefore, most often used as deionizers.

When estimating the relative values of the individual products from the right-hand side of Eq. (23), molar concentrations in the solution sprayed may evidently be used for the calculation if necessary corrections for the possible formation of compounds or ionization are applied. For alkali metals, generally only the ionization of the deionizer must be considered.

The elimination of ionization interferences by adding deionizers has the further advantage that the signal of the analyte is simultaneously enhanced. It is, therefore, quite common to add such deionizers in considerable excess to suppress the ionization of the analyte completely. For the determination of lithium, sodium, and potassium the situation is favorable because cesium with the highest ionization constant may be used. Thus, Schuhknecht and Schinkel (52) proposed, in their universal method for the determination of Li, Na, and K, to add 5 g of CsCl per liter to suppress potential ionization interferences.

For the determination of rubidium and cesium, a complete suppression of ionization would often require too high a concentration of potassium. This may be clearly seen from Table 10, which shows the enhancement of cesium emission by addition of various amounts of alkali metals in a premixed air–acetylene flame (37).

TABLE 10

Relative Enhancement of Cesium Emission by Addition
of Different Alkali Metals

Molar concn of the added element	Cs 0.0001M solution			Cs 0.001M solution		
	Li	Na	K	Li	Na	K
0.0001	103	105	150	100	100	100
0.001	119	145	444	100	105	125
0.01	170	352	1200	100	107	195
0.1	340	765	1980	105	140	290
1.0	780	1270	2260	150	205	325

Therefore, when deteımining rubidium and cesium, potassium is simultaneously measured and then added to attain a relatively high but definite concentration level in the solution sprayed (53–56).

Ionization of many more elements takes place in flames with higher temperature. In the nitrous oxide–acetylene flame, with a temperature reaching about 3200°K, elements with ionization energies up to about 7 eV should be included. These elements must also be considered as possible interferents and deionizers. The percent ionization found by Amos and Willis for some elements is given in Table 11.

TABLE 11

Ionization in the Nitrous Oxide–Acetylene Flame (22)

Metal	Ionization energy, eV	Concn of the solution μg/ml	Ionization %
Be	9.32	2	0
Mg	7.64	2	6
Ca	6.11	5	43
Sr	5.69	5.5	84
Ba	5.21	30	88
Yb	6.2	15	20

The estimation of the ionization in a nitrous oxide–acetylene flame is not as simple as in the air–acetylene flame. The electron pressure of the unsalted flame is higher and may not be neglected compared with the electrons released by the introduced element. A confirmation may be found from the results reported by Amos and Willis (22) as well as Manning and Capacho-Delgado (57), who estimated the ionization of calcium and barium in a nitrous oxide–acetylene flame. When aspirating a 2 μg/ml solution of calcium, Manning and Capacho-Delgado found the ionization to be about 37%. Now the ionization constant of calcium at 3200°K is about 2×10^{-7} atm, and the 2 μg/ml solution equals a $5 \times 10^{-5} M$ concentration. Applying Eq. (7), a total atom concentration of 5×10^{-9} atm is found. From Fig. 2 the ionization of calcium under these conditions should be almost 100%. Manning and Capacho-Delgado assumed the electron pressure in the unsalted flame to be 10^{-6} atm. Electrons released by the calcium added are negligible and an agreement between the calculated and experimentally found values is attained. For a general method of calculating the extent of ionization when the electron pressure in pure flame gases is not negligible, see p. 542 of Ref. (21).

When working with the nitrous oxide–acetylene flame, addition of alkali salts for suppressing ionization and enhancing the sensitivity of determination, especially when pure solutions are aspirated, is frequently used (22). When analyzing solutions containing some other concomitants, their deionizing effect is sometimes sufficient. Thus Nesbitt (58), when determining magnesium in silicate rocks, found that the concentration of the other constituents present is high enough to suppress the ionization of magnesium completely. Magnesium has, however, a relatively high ionization energy and this situation might not hold for more easily ionized elements such as barium and aluminum.

V. Excitation Interferences

The third process which might influence the signal of the analyte in flames is equilibria between the excited and unexcited states of the species measured. Here again, the possible interferences depend on whether thermal equilibrium does exist or not.

Under conditions of thermal equilibrium, the occupational numbers of the various states are given by the Boltzmann law factor, i.e., defined by the energy of the particular state and the temperature. The actual mechanisms of excitation and de-excitation are completely irrelevant (46) and only temperature changes cause variations in the occupational numbers of the individual energy levels. Because the percentage of excited atoms is generally very small, it is evident that emission measurements will be influenced much more than absorption measurements.

The flame temperature depends primarily on the nature of the fuel and oxidant and on their relative flows. The solution aspirated may influence the final temperature only partly. For total consumption burners, where all the solution is introduced into the flame, this influence is stronger. Aqueous solutions have a marked cooling effect; the temperature fall depends on the amount of solution introduced (29, 59, 60). For organic solvents this cooling effect is always much smaller (Fig. 7).

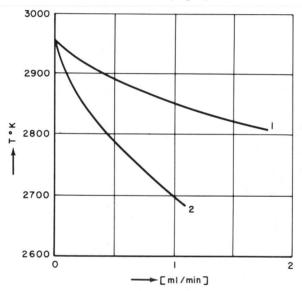

Fig. 7. Temperature decrease of an oxygen–hydrogen flame when aspirating methanol (curve 1) and aqueous solutions (curve 2). (Reprinted from Ref. (61) by courtesy of Springer Verlag.)

The flame emission of the element measured increases with its concentration in the flame but decreases with falling temperature because of the Boltzmann factor. These two contradictory effects determine an optimum aspiration rate with highest resulting emission (29), depending evidently on the excitation energy of the spectral line measured (Fig. 8).

With premixed flames the effect of the solvent on flame temperature is much smaller. By substituting water with an organic solvent, a slight temperature decrease may actually be observed (62, 63) in an air–acetylene flame because all common solvents have a smaller heat of combustion than acetylene. When working with spray chambers, organic solvents influence the nebulization and transportation processes so strongly that any effect of temperature variation in the flame is completely concealed. Of course, in analytical work the solvent composition may be kept un-

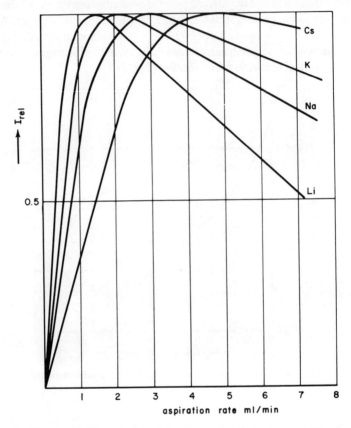

Fig. 8. Relative emission intensity of some alkali metals with increasing aspiration rates using an oxygen–hydrogen flame. (Reprinted from Ref. (*60*) by courtesy of the American Chemical Society.)

changed so that hardly any unexpected errors caused by these effects might be expected.

If, on the other hand, the measurements are performed in the reaction zone where the excitation may be suprathermal, the occupational numbers of the particular excited states can be influenced by the presence or absence of certain species participating in the particular exciting or quenching collisions or in chemiluminescence reactions with the element measured (46). Overexcitation has been found both in the premixed air–hydrogen (64) and air–acetylene flames (65) as well as in the turbulent flame with different gases (9, 10, 66–68). So far, little is known about the actual mechanism of the overexcitation and many different reactions have been proposed; for a review see Ref. (20), pp. 548–560.

In hydrogen flames chemiluminescent radiation has been explained by recombination reactions of hydrogen atoms, i.e.,

$$H + H + M \rightarrow H_2 + M^* \tag{26}$$

Hydrocarbon flames have been found much more effective in producing overexcitation. The most plausible reactions involve CH particles and may proceed according to the following schemes

$$CH + O + M \quad = CO + H + M^* \tag{27}$$

$$CH + OH + M = CO + H_2 + M^* \tag{28}$$

or

$$CH + O + M \quad = CHO + M^* \tag{29}$$

This mechanism explains the correlation found between overexcitation and ionization of unsalted flames (8), which is supposed to proceed according to the reaction

$$O + CH = HCO^+ + e^- \tag{30}$$

Because hydrocarbon flames are more effective, any addition of organic solvents to hydrogen flames might influence chemiluminescent radiation. A striking example was reported by Gilbert (9). By adding 11 vol % of isopropanol to the solution aspirated into an air–hydrogen flame, the emission of tin was doubled.

One type of overexcitation of atoms is caused mainly by collisions with overexcited molecules whereby the vibrational energy is transformed into electronic excitation energy. Molecules are also much more effective than atoms in quenching excited atoms. Therefore, when measuring atomic fluorescence, it may be advantageous to replace the air used for aspirating the sample solution by argon, thereby leaving the combustion to proceed only with entrained air. This may bring about enhancement of the fluorescence radiation.

By using argon instead of air with hydrogen, enhancement by a factor of 2 for silver and zinc, 10 for magnesium, and 20 for cobalt has been observed by Ellis and Demers (69). However, it is not clear what part of this enhancement is due to shifts in dissociation equilibria and what part is due to changes in the yield factor. An exact estimation of the relative merits would require simultaneous fluorescence and absorption measurements. The effect on fluorescence yield factors for some alkali metals of changing the flame gas composition was investigated by Hooymayers and Alkemade (70). With argon instead of nitrogen or carbon dioxide, the yield factor increased about 10 times.

Whatever the actual overexcitation or quenching reactions may be, all involve species which are components of the flame gases. Therefore, as in the case of dissociation interferences involving compounds with flame gases, these effects are not likely to produce errors in analytical work. All the critical parameters are easily kept constant during the measurements. What is more attractive is the possibility of enhancing the measured signals by choosing optimum conditions of fuel, oxidant, and solvent.

Before this chapter is concluded, one more point should be stressed. Interferences occurring in flame spectrometry measurements can seldom be ascribed to a single cause. Most interferents affect more than one process; this makes the explanation of their mechanism more complicated. The question whether the interference is due to processes in the vapor phase may be solved by comparing the effect when introducing the analyte and interferent jointly or separately by twin nebulizers. By refining the working technique of flame spectrometry—using split flames or long path absorption cells—new interferences so far unmentioned will probably be found. These, however, should belong to one of the classes described and the reader should be able to present a possible explanation and suggest a way to overcome them.

REFERENCES

1. R. Herrmann and C. Th. J. Alkemade, *Flammenphotometrie*, 2nd ed., Springer, Berlin, 1960, p. 53.
2. J. A. Dean, *Flame Photometry*, McGraw-Hill, New York, 1960, p. 168.
3. G. Pietzka and H. Chun, *Angew. Chem.*, **71**, 276 (1955).
4. S. Fukushima, *Mikrochim. Acta*, **1959**, p. 596.
5. P. T. Gilbert, Jr., in *Analysis Instrumentation-1964*, Plenum Press, New York, 1964.
6. F. W. Hofmann and H. Kohn, *J. Opt. Soc. Am.*, **51**, 512 (1961).
7. C. Th. J. Alkemade, *A Contribution to the Development and Understanding of Flame Photometry*, Ph.D. Thesis, Utrecht, 1954.
8. C. P. Fenimore, *Chemistry in Premixed Flames*, Pergamon, Oxford, 1964.

9. P. T. Gilbert, Jr., in *Proceedings Xth Colloquium Spectroscopicum Internationale* (E. R. Lippincott and M. Margoshes, eds.), Spartan, Washington, D.C., 1963, p. 171.

10. J. A. Dean and W. J. Carnes, *Analyst*, **87**, 743 (1962).

11. C. G. James and T. M. Sugden, *Proc. Roy. Soc. (London)*, **A227**, 312 (1955).

12. E. Hinnov and H. Kohn, *J. Opt. Soc. Am.*, **47**, 156 (1957).

13. E. Hinnov, *J. Opt. Soc. Am.*, **47**, 151 (1957).

14. N. S. Poluektov and M. P. Nikonova, *Zavodsk. Lab.*, **25**, 263 (1959).

15. N. S. Tchaj, *Opt. i Spectroskopiya*, **12**, 524 (1962).

16. J. Fischer and R. Kropp, *Glastech. Ber.*, **33**, 380 (1960).

17. J. D. Winefordner, C. T. Mansfield, and T. J. Vickers, *Anal. Chem.*, **35**, 1607 (1963).

17a. L. Simon, *Optik*, **19**, 621 (1962).

18. R. Püschel, L. Simon, and R. Herrmann, *Optik*, **21**, 441 (1964).

19. N. S. Poluektov, *Metody analiza po fotometrii plameni*, 2nd ed., Izdat. Khimia, Moskva, 1967.

20. R. Mavrodineanu and H. Boiteux, *Flame Spectroscopy*, Wiley, New York, 1965.

21. E. M. Bulewicz and T. M. Sugden, *Proceedings VIth Colloquium Spectroscopicum Internationale, Amsterdam, 1956*, Pergamon, London, 1957, p. 20.

22. M. D. Amos and J. B. Willis, *Spectrochim. Acta*, **22**, 1325 (1966).

23. V. A. Fassel and D. W. Golightly, *Anal. Chem.*, **39**, 466 (1967).

24. J. V. Vejc and L. V. Gurvitch, *Opt. i Spektroskopiya*, **2**, 274 (1957).

25. L. Huldt and A. Lagerqvist, *Arkiv Fysik*, **21**, 333 (1950).

26. L. Huldt, *Spectroscopic Investigation of the Electrical Arc and Acetylene-air Flame* (in German), Thesis, Uppsala, 1948.

27. B. V. Lvov, *Atomno-absorbcionnyj spektralnyj analiz*, Izd. Nauka, Moskva, 1966.

28. R. K. Skogerboe, Ann T. Heybey, and G. H. Morrison, *Anal. Chem.*, **38**, 1821 (1966).

29. M. R. Baker and B. L. Vallee, *Anal. Chem.*, **31**, 2036 (1959).

30. C. S. Rann and A. N. Hambly, *Anal. Chem.*, **37**, 879 (1965).

31. C. B. Belcher and K. Kinson, *Anal. Chim. Acta*, **30**, 483 (1964).

32. S. Sprague and W. Slavin, *At. Absorption Newsletter* [No. 23], 8 (1964).

33. G. F. Kirkbright, M. K. Peters and T. S. West, *Talanta*, **14**, 789 (1967).

34. S. L. Sachdev, J. W. Robinson, and P. W. West, *Anal. Chim. Acta*, **37**, 12 (1967).

35. J. B. Headridge and D. P. Hubbard, *Anal. Chim. Acta*, **37**, 151 (1967).

35a. T. V. Ramakrishna, P. W. West, and J. W. Robinson, *Anal. Chim. Acta*, **39**, 81 (1967).

36. R. J. Jaworowski, R. P. Weberling, and D. J. Bracco, *Anal. Chim. Acta*, **37**, 284 (1967).

37. N. S. Poluektov and R. A. Vitkun, *Zh. Analit. Khim.*, **16**, 260 (1961).

38. F. W. Hofmann, H. Kohn, and J. Schneider, *J. Opt. Soc. Am.*, **51**, 508 (1961).

39. A. I. Lyuty and V. S. Rossikhin, *Inzh. Fiz. Zh.*, *Akad. Nauk Belorussk. SSR*, **3**, 101 (1963).

40. N. S. Poluektov, *Zavodsk. Lab.*, **18**, 1069 (1962).

41. V. F. Zhitkevitch, A. I. Lyuty, N. A. Nesterko, V. S. Rossikhin, and I. L. Cikopa, *Izv. Vysshilch. Uchebn. Zaredenii, Fiz.*, [No. 2], 78 (1963).

42. W. A. Veenendaal and H. L. Polak, *Z. Anal. Chem.*, **223**, 17 (1966).

43. J. Malinowski, D. Dancewicz, and S. Szymczak, *Chem. Anal. (Warsaw)*, **6**, 183 (1961).

44. H. Bode and H. Fabian, *Z. Anal. Chem.*, **170**, 387 (1959).
45. Shouzow Fukushima, *Mikrochim. Acta*, **1960**, p. 332.
46. C. Th. J. Alkemade, in *Proceedings Xth Colloquium Spectroscopicum Internationale* (E. R. Lippincott and M. Margoshes, eds.), Spartan, Washington, D.C., 1963, p. 143.
47. K. E. Schuler and J. J. Weber, *Chem. Phys.*, **22**, 491 (1954).
48. J. B. Willis, *Spectrochim. Acta*, **16**, 551 (1960).
49. F. W. Hofmann and H. Kohn, *J. Opt. Soc. Am.*, **51**, 512 (1961).
50. C. Th. J. Alkemade, *Proceedings VIIIth Colloquium Spectroscopicum Internationale, Luzern, 1959*, R. H. Sauerländer, Aarau, 1960, p. 162.
51. J. Fischer and A. Doiwa, *Proceedings VIth Colloquium Spectroscopicum Internationale, Amsterdam, 1956*, Pergamon, London, 1957, p. 28.
52. W. Schuhknecht and H. Schinkel, *Z. Anal. Chem.*, **194**, 161 (1963).
53. J. A. Fabrikova, *Zh. Analit. Khim.*, **14**, 41 (1959).
54. J. A. Fabrikova, *Zh. Analit. Khim.*, **15**, 427 (1960).
55. T. E. Shellenberger, R. E. Pyke, D. E. Parrish, and W. G. Schrenk, *Anal. Chem.*, **32**, 210 (1960).
56. I. Rubeška and B. Moldan, *Collection Czech. Chem. Commun.*, **30**, 1731 (1965).
57. D. C. Manning and L. Capacho-Delgado, *Anal. Chim. Acta*, **36**, 312 (1966).
58. R. W. Nesbitt, *Anal. Chim. Acta*, **35**, 413 (1966).
59. K. Fuwa, R. E. Thiers, B. L. Vallee, and M. R. Baker, *Anal. Chem.*, **31**, 2039 (1959).
60. W. H. Foster, Jr., and D. N. Hume, *Anal. Chem.*, **31**, 2028 (1959).
61. S. Eckhard and A. Püschel, *Z. Anal. Chem.*, **172**, 334 (1960).
62. R. Avni and C. Th. J. Alkemade, *Mikrochim. Acta*, **1960**, 460.
63. J. Dvořák and V. Novobilský, *Acta Chim. Acad. Sci. Hung.*, **30**, 365 (1962).
64. P. J. Padley and T. M. Sugden, *Symp. Combust. 7th, London, Oxford, 1958*, Butterworths, London, 1959, p. 235.
65. V. F. Zhitkevitch, A. I. Ljutyj, N. A. Nesterko, V. S. Rossikhim, and I. L. Cikopa, *Opt. i Spektroskopiya*, **14**, 336 (1963).
66. J. A. Dean and J. C. Simms, *Anal. Chem.*, **35**, 699 (1963).
67. J. A. Dean and J. E. Adkins, Jr., *Analyst*, **91**, 709 (1966).
68. B. E. Buell, *Anal. Chem.*, **34**, 635 (1962).
69. D. W. Ellis and D. R. Demers, *Anal. Chem.*, **38**, 1943 (1966).
70. H. P. Hooymayers and C. Th. J. Alkemade, *J. Quant. Spectry. & Radiative Transfer*, **6**, 847 (1966).

12 Chemical Interferences in Condensed Phase

Theodore C. Rains

ANALYTICAL CHEMISTRY DIVISION
NATIONAL BUREAU OF STANDARDS
WASHINGTON, D.C.

I. Introduction

Chemical interferences do occur in varying degrees for all elements whether by flame emission, atomic absorption, or atomic fluorescence. Chemical interference is defined as any reaction which affects the analyte or element sought and which may occur in the vapor, solid, or liquid phase of the flame. Reactions occurring in the solid or liquid phase which suppress or enhance the dissociation of the molecular species into atomic vapor are referred to as condensed phase interferences. This interference is usually very troublesome but can be overcome by identifying the interferent and by the selection of the proper operating conditions. This chapter is devoted to the problem of chemical interferences in the condensed phase.

The condensed phase interference occurs when a concomitant (element, radical, or solute present in solution) inhibits the dissociation or excitation of the analyte. There is no published evidence to suggest that this type of interference is limited to only one of the three techniques (emission, absorption, or fluorescence). The various methods that are discussed here for eliminating condensed phase interference are just as effective in all three techniques, provided the same experimental conditions are used. This is because these methods are dependent on the production of free atoms or specific molecular species from the analyte. Condensed phase interference is often recognized by the occurrence of a sharp drop in the emission intensity or absorption, and then after a point of saturation the curve has a plateau as shown in Fig. 1. The location of the break in the curve is an indication of the stoichiometry of the refractory compound. This is especially apparent for phosphate and sulfate with alkaline earth metals. In the case of aluminum, the break is not very definite and no clear stoichiometric relation can be observed. This is probably due to the formation of a series of compounds or step-wise reactions at various heights within the flame. The literature is well documented with references to condensed phase interferences (*1–5*).

While many publications deal extensively with the effect of phosphate, sulfate, and aluminum on magnesium and calcium, it is of interest to note that there is mutual interference between many other elements which are known to form anions in the gaseous state. For example, mutual interference is reported between calcium and gallium or indium (*4*). Also, chromium, iron, silicon, and titanium are observed to suppress all the alkaline earth metals. In flame emission with an oxygen–hydrogen flame, the rare earth metals are subject to mutual interferences. The line spectra of europium and ytterbium are severely depressed by thorium and the other rare earth metals.

II. Mechanism of Interference

Molecular compounds dissociate at a rate that depends upon the flame temperature. If a relatively low flame temperature is used, a small proportion of the compound dissociates per unit volume or time; therefore, the number of free atoms available to emit or absorb radiation is limited. Several investigators (6, 7) have concluded that the evaporation rate of the droplet or aerosol particles may be the factor controlling the intensity in flame emission or atomic absorption by the analyte. This process is especially pronounced for the alkaline earth metals because the degree of dissociation of the monoxides shows a sharp decline above the reaction zone. The maximum sensitivity obtainable depends upon the kinetics of evaporation, size of droplets, and vapor tension of the compounds. The average droplet size will depend upon the type of nebulizer and solvent, while the vapor pressure will depend upon the compound formed during the vaporization and dissociation of the salt. Rubeška and Moldan (8) obtained strikingly different flame profiles for the alkaline earth metals in the presence of different anions. A similar flame profile for chloride and nitrate salts of calcium and strontium differed. The explanation given was that calcium and strontium form dehydrated chlorides which volatilize more easily than their respective monoxides formed from the nitrate. Although the oxides are formed, this reaction rate is evidently slower than the evaporation rate of the chloride. In the case of magnesium chloride, hydrogen chloride is released in the flame, giving rise to the monoxide in the same way as for magnesium nitrate (9).

The situation is further complicated by the fact that the metallic salts decompose into a variety of species, depending on flame conditions with competing equilibria such as (7)

$$M^o \leftarrow (MX)_s \rightarrow MO$$
$$\downarrow \qquad \updownarrow$$
$$MY \rightleftarrows M^o$$

where M = metal ion, X = anion, and Y = anion in flame gases. Since these reactions do not reach a state of equilibrium, the height or area within the flame will greatly affect the results. Now, if aluminum, titanium, or silicon is present as concomitant, it may react to form the oxide or very nonvolatile aluminates, silicates, or titanates. Therefore, the number of free atoms of the analyte is greatly reduced, thus decreasing the absorption or emission signal.

The mechanism of condensed phase interference is best studied with separated aspirators. By this technique, one can distinguish between an interference occurring in the flame gas or in the solid particle. Fukushima (10) studied the interference of aluminum, boron, phosphate, and sulfate with calcium in flame emission using separated aspirators and a burner with premixed gases. He concluded that the suppression of calcium radiation by these elements was caused by the slowness of the dissociation processes. Of the possible rate-controlling processes (see also Chapter 4) the one taking place in the gaseous phase seems the least probable. The suppression effect is probably due to the vaporization rate of calcium from a condensed phase to the gaseous state. The rate of vaporization is reduced by the addition of aluminum, boron, phosphate, and sulfate because of the formation of highly refractory mixed oxides. Fukushima's data indicate that maximum interference occurs at ratios of Ca/B, 1:2; Ca/P, 3:2; and Ca/S, 1:1. Elwell and Gidley (*11*) investigated magnesium by absorption and concluded that molecular binding must occur within the dried clotlet and not in the vapor state, confirming Fukushima's conclusion. Both investigators performed experiments using premixed gases and two nebulizers to introduce the cation and anion separately into the flame gases. Under these conditions, no condensed phase interference was observed.

Rubeška and Moldan (*8*) observed that the alkaline earth aluminate formed more readily in the presence of nitrates than in the presence of chlorides. This would indicate an intermediate step. The exact state of the oxide formed is debatable and has been postulated to be a series of compounds with the general formula $nMO \cdot mAl_2O_3$, where M is the alkaline earth metal. In an attempt to identify the composition of the oxide formed in a premixed air–acetylene flame with magnesium and aluminum, the particles were captured and their identity was determined by X-ray diffraction. In the presence of magnesium, a definite pattern of $MgO \cdot Al_2O_3$ was obtained. The pattern for calcium with aluminum was not distinct but indicated the compounds $3CaO \cdot 5Al_2O_3$, $5CaO \cdot 3Al_2O_3$, and $3CaO \cdot Al_2O_3$.

III. Occurrence of Condensed Phase Interference

For a given analyte a number of reactions may occur within the flame, depending upon the physical and chemical properties of the system. For example, the degree of dissociation of a molecular species within a flame will depend upon the temperature, the ratio of fuel to oxidant, the concentration of the analyte, the efficiency of the nebulizer, and the area or height under observation. Also, chemical interferences may occur in the presence of anions or cations due to the formation of stable or highly refractory compounds.

A. Effect of Anions

The suppressing effect of phosphate and sulfate ions on the alkaline earth metals has been proposed as a means of indirect determination of phosphate and sulfate (*12, 13*). These investigators are not in complete agreement on the extent of the suppression; however, this disagreement can be explained by differences in nebulizer type and flame conditions. The relative effects of various anions on the emission intensities of calcium and barium with a total consumption burner for an oxygen–acetylene and oxygen–hydrogen flame are shown in Figs. 1–3. The effects of sulfate and phosphate are less with the higher-temperature (oxygen–acetylene) flame than with the oxygen–hydrogen flame. The depression caused by the sulfate and phosphate was as expected, but few investigators have noted the effect of nitrate on calcium. The effect of phosphate on the alkaline earth metals depends on the form in which it is present. If it is present as diammonium hydrogen phosphate, the suppression is greater than in the presence of phosphoric acid. It is postulated that the increased adverse effect of diammonium hydrogen phosphate is due to its rapid conversion at high temperatures to pyrophosphoric acid (*16*). Pyrophosphoric acid is also produced when orthophosphoric acid is evaporated at elevated temperatures; but the reaction proceeds more readily when monohydrogen phosphate is present. By adjusting the acidity with a mineral acid to pH 0.5, this extreme suppression can be overcome. In an oxygen–hydrogen or oxygen–acetylene flame, H_3PO_4 above $0.01M$ apparently enhances calcium. Similar results are obtained for magnesium but not for strontium or barium. The enhancement must be due to the suppression of the monoxide formation of these two ions. The same general effects are observed in atomic absorption and atomic fluorescence, as in flame emission (*17, 18*).

Yofe and Finkelstein (*2*) investigated the effect of phosphate on calcium in flame emission with an oxygen–hydrogen flame. A suppression of the emission intensity of calcium was observed until a molar ratio (P/Ca) of 1 was reached, and then the intensity became constant to a molar ratio of 8 (the maximum investigated).

Tsuchihashi and Sekido (*19*) investigated the effect of phosphate on calcium and concluded that the suppression originated in the "gaseous phase." Margoshes and Vallee (*20*) attributed the suppression to formation of refractory oxides. To test their hypothesis they placed crystals of calcium compounds in the hottest part of a Meker burner using an air–natural gas flame and obtained only weak emission signals for those calcium compounds with high melting points. The emission intensities of

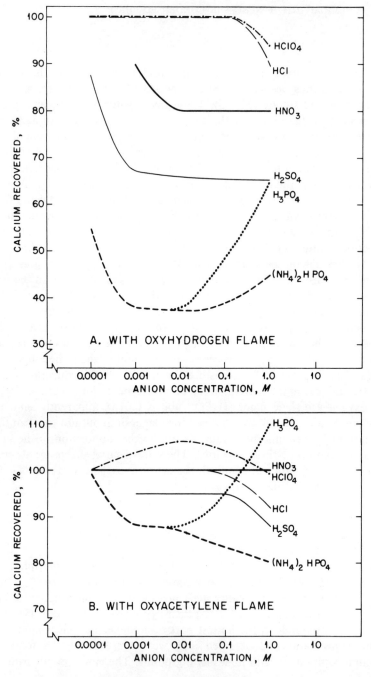

Fig. 1. Effects of various anions on the determination of calcium in emission. (Reprinted from (*14*), p. 367, by courtesy of *Talanta*.)

$CaCl_2$ and $Ca(NO_3)_2$ were strong and equal; $CaCl_2$ and $Ca(NO_3)_2$ have relatively low melting points, 772 and 561°C, respectively. The boiling point of $CaCl_2$ is 1600°C. In the presence of sulfate and phosphate, a marked decrease in intensity was observed; $CaSO_4$ and $Ca_3(PO_4)_2$ have melting points of 1450 and 1670°C, respectively. Since the boiling points of these compounds are not known, the values are probably quite high. Therefore, free calcium atoms are not available for excitation or absorption.

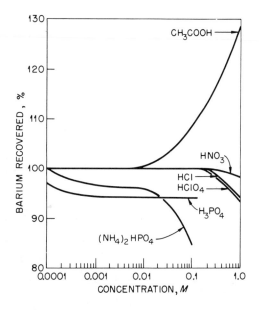

Fig. 2. Effects of anions on the recovery of barium in emission with oxygen–acetylene flame. Ba, 10 μg/ml; wavelength, 5536 Å; 0.5-m Ebert monochromator. (Reprinted from (*15*), p. 1726, by courtesy of American Chemical Society.)

B. Effect of Cations

The mutual interference of Al, Ti, and Si with the alkaline earth metals has been observed for many years. Some aspects of these interelement effects are discussed by several authors (*1, 21, 22*). As a rule, the interferences from Al, Ti, and Si are more troublesome than from phosphate and sulfate discussed previously. The exact mechanism taking place is not known. Dickson and Johnson (*23*) found that the depressive effect of aluminum on calcium absorption varied with the concomitants, magnitude of the suppression being in the order of $PO_4^{3-} > SO_4^{2-} > Cl^{1-} > NO_3^{1-} > ClO_4^{1-}$.

Mutual interference of cations is not limited to aluminum and the alkaline earth metals. Gilbert (24) has compiled a list of elements which cause a depression on various analytes due to the formation of mixed oxides of low volatility. This list includes B, Be, Cr, Fe, Mo, Si, Ti, U,

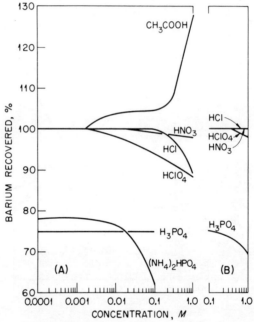

Fig. 3. Effects of anions on the recovery of barium in emission with oxygen–hydrogen flame. (A) Ba, 100 μg/ml; wavelength, 5536 Å; 0.5-m Ebert monochromator. (B) Ba, 100 μg/ml; wavelength, 5536 Å; Beckman DU spectrophotometer. (Reprinted from (15), p. 1726, by courtesy of American Chemical Society.)

V, W, and rare earth elements. Doty and Schrenk (4) observed interaction in flame emission with these pairs: Ca-B, Ca-Ga, Ca-In and Ca-Al. The typical knee or break associated with condensed phase interference was observed in all cases. Also, with an oxygen–acetylene flame at any given Al/Ca ratio, the aluminum suppression was significantly greater for the CaO band emission than for the calcium resonance line. However, with an oxygen–hydrogen flame the two curves were nearly superimposed. Rocchiccioli and Townshend (25) reported a 20% suppression of calcium by magnesium to a Mg/Ca ratio of 1, and then the absorption became constant. However, calcium was observed to enhance the absorption of magnesium. It was postulated that the following reaction occurs:

$$Ca_{(g)} + MgO_{(s)} \rightarrow Mg_{(g)} + CaO_{(s)} \tag{1}$$

Since CaO is more difficult to dissociate than MgO at 2000°K [$\Delta H_0 =$ -195 kcal/mole (8.5 eV) for CaO and -181 kcal/mole (7.9 eV) for MgO], this reaction would be thermodynamically possible. This reaction implies that the enhancement of magnesium atoms is at the expense of the free calcium atoms.

IV. Methods for Elimination or Control of Interferences

To eliminate or control condensed phase interferences it is essential that the various parameters associated with emission, absorption, or fluorescence be optimized. While the investigation of the various parameters may be a time-consuming process, in the final analysis, an improvement in sensitivity, precision, and accuracy will be obtained. By switching burners and oxidant–fuel conditions for various elements, improved results have been observed. It is a common practice to vary the height of observation at which measurements are taken (see Chapter 8) in the flame as well as the oxidant–fuel ratio for those elements which form stable oxides. The choice of solvent is important because it may affect the rate of nebulization, droplet size, and flame temperature. Often, it is essential that an additive be used. The additive may serve as a releasing or protecting agent for the analyte, and in many cases correction methods (see Section IV.G) must be applied to overcome certain types of interferences.

The means by which the sample is introduced into the flame will affect the type and degree of interference. The two basic types of burner design are the total consumption (sprayer) or diffusion burner and the premix or laminar flow burner. The function of the nebulizer–burner system is to produce the atomic vapor from the analyte in the sample solution. This process includes many steps, such as the dispersion of the solution in the form of small droplets, desolvation, decomposition of salt or oxide, formation of emitting vapor (atomization), excitation of the atom, and emission. The extent to which these steps occur within the flame will depend upon the analyte, matrix, type of nebulizer–burner, oxidant and fuel gases, and overexcitation effects.

A. Effect of Flame Temperature

The temperature of the flame plays a major role in the extent of interferences in flame emission and atomic absorption. When the flame temperature is altered by the concomitant, the processes within the flame gases will also be altered. Usually, in atomic absorption, small variations in flame temperature will have little effect, except in some cases where fuel-rich conditions are used. In flame emission, the rate of evaporation and the vapor pressure will be altered, changing the amount of species at equilibrium and the emission intensity. Temperatures and burning velocities for various gas mixtures are given in Table 2 of Chapter 6.

Many elements such as the alkali metals are fully dissociated in relatively cool flames such as argon (entrained air)–hydrogen or air–propane; others such as the alkaline earth metals require air–acetylene or oxygen–hydrogen, and others such as aluminum, silicon, and titanium require a fuel-rich nitrous oxide–acetylene. In absorption, the coolest flame that will produce maximum dissociation is usually best. If a high-temperature flame is used to overcome an interference, interference due to ionization may result. Ionization in high-temperature flames is especially prevalent with the alkali and alkaline earth metals. This type of interference is controlled by the addition of a cation having a similar or lower ionization potential than that of the analyte.

The temperature of a flame can be increased by preheating the gases, especially for the cooler types of flame. Rawson (26) used preheated air and natural gas in the determination of Mg, Cu, and Zn. Under his conditions, an increase in sensitivity was obtained, but the interference of phosphate and aluminum on magnesium was not prevented. However, preheated gases may be valuable for flame emission or atomic fluorescence.

Amos and Willis (27), Fassel and Golightly (28), and Manning (29) have shown that the performances of premixed oxygen–acetylene and nitrous oxide–acetylene flames are similar in terms of sensitivity and types of interference encountered. However, the premixed nitrous oxide–acetylene flame is usually safer.

B. Choice of Oxidant–Fuel

Many of the interferences due to the formation of refractory oxides can be overcome or minimized by the use of the proper oxidant–fuel system. Of the many oxidant–fuel systems used in flame emission, atomic absorption, or atomic fluorescence as shown in Table 1, fuel-rich conditions appear to be essential in the presence of refractory oxides.

TABLE 1

Oxidant–Fuel Conditions for Maximum Emission, Absorption, and Fluorescence

Analyte	Wavelength, Å	Type of burner	Oxidant–fuel Emission	Oxidant–fuel Absorption	Oxidant–fuel Fluorescence
Ag	3281	T	f-4		c
		P	a		
Al	3093	P		d-2	
	3962	T	e-4		
As	1937	T		c	
	2350	T	e-5		
Au	2676	T	f-4		f
	2428	P		a	
B	2497	P		d-2	
Ba	5536	P	d-3	d-2	
Be	2349	P		d-2	
		T			b
Bi	2231	P		a	
	3068	T			c
Ca	4227	T	f-6		b
		P		d-2	
Cd	2288	T			f
		P		a	
Co	2364	P		a	
	3427	T	f-4		
Cr	3579	P		a-2	
		T			b
	4254	P	d-2		
Cs	8521	P		a	
		T	f		
Cu	3248	P	d-2	a	
		T			c
Dy	4211	P		d-2	
	5730	T	f-4		
Er	4008	P		d-2	
	5040	T	f-4		
Eu	4594	P		d-2	
		T	f-4		
Fe	2483	P		a-2	
		T			b
	3720	T	f-4		
Ga	2874	P		a	
	4172	T	f		b
Gd	3684	P		d-2	
	4640	T	f-4		
Ge	2651	P	d-2	d-2	

359

TABLE 1 (*continued*)

Analyte	Wavelength, Å	Type of burner	Oxidant–fuel		
			Emission	Absorption	Fluorescence
Hf	2866	T			b
	3072	P	e-2	d-2	
Hg	2537	P		a	c
Ho	4163	P		d-2	
	5660	T	f-4		
In	3039	P		a	
	4511	T	f-4		
Ir	2850	P		a-1	
K	7665	T	f		
		P		a	
La	3928	P		d-2	
	7430	T	f-4		
Li	6708	P		a	
		T	f		
Lu	3312	P		d-2	
	4680	T	f-4		
Mg	2852	P	d-2	d-2	
		T			c
Mn	2795	P		a	c
	4031	P	d-2		
Mo	3133	P		a-2	
	3798	T			f
Na	5890	P		a	
		T	c		
Nb	4059	P	d-2	d-2	
Nd	4634	P		d-2	
	7000	T	f-4		
Ni	2320	P		a	
	2320	T			c
	3525	T	f-4		
Pb	2833	P		a	
	4058	T	f-4		c
Pd	2476	P		a-1	
	3635	T	f-4		
Pr	4951	P		d-2	
Pt	2659	P	d-2	a-1	
Rb	7800	P		a	
		T	f		
Re	3460	P	d-2	a	
Rh	3435	P		a-1	
	3692	P	e-5		
Ru	3499	P		a-1	
	3728	T	f-4		
Sb	2176	P		a	
	2311	T			b

TABLE 1 (*continued*)

Analyte	Wavelength, Å	Type of burner	Oxidant–fuel		
			Emission	Absorption	Fluorescence
Sc	2907	T			c
	3912	P		d-2	
	6070	T	f-4		
Se	1961	T		c	c
Si	2516	P		d-2	
Sm	4297	P		d-2	
	6520	T	f-4		
Sn	2246	P		b	
	2840	P	d-2		
Sr	4607	P		a-2	
		T	f-6		c
Ta	2715	P		d-2	
Tb	4326	P		d-2	
	5350	T	f-4		
Te	2143	P		a	
		T			c
Ti	3643	P		d-2	
	3949	T			c
	3999	P	d-2		
Tl	2768	P		a	
	3776	T	f-4		c
Tm	4094	P		d-2	
	4940	T	f-4		
U	3585	P		d-2	
	3812	T			b
V	3184	P		d-2	
	4379	P	d-2		
W	4008	P	d-2	d-2	
Y	4077	P		d-2	
	5970	T	f-4		
Yb	3988	P		d-2	
		T	f-4		
Zn	2139	P		a	
		T			c
Zr	3601	P	d-2	d-2	
		T			c

T = Total consumption;   P = Premix-laminar flow.

a = air–acetylene   1 = Fuel-lean
b = air–hydrogen   2 = Fuel-rich
c = argon–hydrogen   3 = Fuel-rich plus ionization suppressor
d = nitrous oxide–acetylene   4 = Organic solvent
e = oxygen–acetylene   5 = Reaction zone
f = oxygen–hydrogen   6 = Releasing agent

In selecting these oxidant–fuel conditions from the literature (*17, 27, 28, 30–33*) the criteria were maximum sensitivity with minimum interference. While only limited interference studies are reported in atomic fluorescence, a "cool" flame, argon (entrained air)–hydrogen, seems preferable for most elements. The nitrous oxide–acetylene flame which is used extensively in atomic absorption for elements that form refractory oxides has been used only briefly in flame emission. However, for many elements the sensitivity obtained with the nitrous oxide–acetylene flame in emission is as high as the sensitivities reported for the oxygen–hydrogen and oxygen–acetylene flames. The major advantage is the removal of many condensed phase interferences.

Kniseley et al. (*34*) have studied many refractory metals using the fuel-rich oxygen–acetylene flame. These workers have modified the Beckman total consumption (sprayer) burner into a premix type of burner which diminishes flame noise and gives increased sensitivity in flame emission for several elements. Also, the interference from many of the refractory oxides is reduced. However, for satisfactory operation, the aspirated solution has to be at least 50% ethanol or some other flammable solvent.

In atomic absorption, a burner with a premixed, fuel-rich, air–acetylene flame is used for many elements, as shown in Table 1. The fuel-rich condition gives an increase in absorption by minimizing the oxide formation and thus aids in the control of interferences. David (*35*) obtained absorption by molybdenum with a fuel-rich air–acetylene flame but no absorption with a stoichiometric mixture. Similarly, aluminum has been determined using a fuel-rich air–acetylene flame after extracting the aluminum 8-quinolinolate chelate with methyl isobutyl ketone. However, the use of a fuel-rich air–acetylene flame or an organic solvent will not remove many of the chemical interferences.

To overcome condensed phase interference, Amos and Willis (*27*) proposed the use of a nitrous oxide–acetylene flame. This mixture is capable of dissociating many of the refractory oxides. While many workers (*27, 36, 37*) recommend the nitrous oxide–acetylene flame, certain precautions in its use must be observed. Today, most commercial companies that manufacture burners will provide special nitrous oxide–acetylene burner heads, which are necessary for this fuel mixture, along with precautions in their use.

The nitrous oxide–acetylene flame will eliminate most of the condensed phase interference encountered with the alkaline earth metals. While its temperature is slightly lower than that of an oxygen–acetylene flame, one of its major advantages over the oxygen–acetylene flame is the lower burning velocity. The low burning velocity of the nitrous oxide–acetylene flame permits its use in the "premix" or slot burner. The major disadvantages of the nitrous oxide–acetylene flame are a loss of sensitivity due to ionization of easily excited atoms, need for safety precautions, and cost of the nitrous oxide. Loss of sensitivity due to ionization can be overcome by the addition of some easily ionizable elements such as cesium or potassium.

To overcome some of the objections of the nitrous oxide–acetylene flame, Fleming (36) proposed a system of flowmeters whereby the oxidants, air and nitrous oxide, can be mixed in any desired proportion. With this system, flame temperatures ranging from 2300°C, for air–acetylene, to 2955°C, for nitrous oxide–acetylene, are obtained. In a nitrous oxide–acetylene flame, a severe loss of sensitivity due to ionization is observed

TABLE 2

Absorbance of Various Flame Gases at 1937 Å

Burner	Oxidant–fuel	Absorbance
Premix[a]	Air-C_2H_2	1.350
	Air-H_2	0.960
	Ar-H_2	0.270
Total consumption[b]	O_2-H_2	0.700
	Air-H_2	0.290
	Ar-H_2	0.210

[a] Single pass.
[b] Three optical passes.

for many elements, especially the alkaline earth metals. By using a mixture of 23% nitrous oxide in air with a slightly fuel-rich flame, the interference of 2000 μg/ml of aluminum, titanium, or silicon in the analysis of 1 μg/ml of magnesium was eliminated. With this gas mixture, magnesium can be determined in the presence of several interfering ions using a single calibration curve prepared with standard solutions of magnesium.

Another factor in selecting the oxidant–fuel system is the flame background produced by the gas mixture. Emission with an oxygen–acetylene or oxygen–hydrogen flame in the presence of an organic solvent is affected by C_2 and CH band systems over large regions of the visible spectrum. An oxidant–fuel system which is known to produce an interfering band system in the region of the wavelength of the analyte should be avoided. These bands are less of a problem in atomic absorption, although they do produce a severe interference in some cases. For example, the resonance lines of arsenic, which are located at 1890, 1937, and 1972 Å, are severely affected by the flame gases. Various oxidant–fuel systems were tested and the most satisfactory system was an argon (entrained air)–hydrogen flame which produced the least absorption at a wavelength of 1937 Å, as shown in Table 2. However, many foreign ions cause severe interference.

Recently, the nitrous oxide–acetylene flame (*38*) was suggested for use in absorption of arsenic as a means of overcoming the effects of many refractory oxides. This system produces only a slightly higher background than the argon–hydrogen flame and only a slight loss of sensitivity for arsenic.

C. NEBULIZER–BURNER SYSTEMS

The ideal nebulizer would convert all the aspirated liquid into very fine drops (less than 1 μ in diameter). Even the best commercial nebulizers produce sprays in which not all the large droplets are removed before reaching the flame, thus tending to increase chemical interferences. Even the production of fine droplets will not eliminate all condensed phase interferences; however, it will minimize their effect. Willis (*39*) investigated the position of the capillary relative to the venturi and showed that its position determines the aspiration rate and droplet size distribution. The efficiency of the burner was improved by placing an impact bead in front of the nebulizer nozzle. The maximum absorbance of 5 μg/ml of copper was obtained when the bead was 0.5 mm from the nebulizer nozzle. Also, the interference of phosphate on calcium and aluminum on magnesium increased significantly as the aspiration rate was increased. Willis reported a slight reduction in interference with the use of the impact bead. Mavrodineanu and Boiteux (*40*) state that the function of the impact bead is twofold: to act as a mechanical separator and to aid in the production of fine droplets when the spray is projected with high velocity against its surface. The position of the impact bead is usually determined by the velocity of the air flow. In addition to the mechanical action, the bead is thought to act as a source of ultrasonic oscillation.

1. Total Consumption (Diffusion Sprayer) Burner

The total consumption burner, which has been used predominately in flame emission and atomic fluorescence, introduces *all* the droplets directly into the flame. Despite the high efficiency implied in the name, the actual efficiency of the total consumption burner for the production of free atoms is very low, due to a large and variable droplet size. The advantages of the sprayer burner are small area of flame, making it best suited for emission and fluorescence; complete safety in the use of combustible solvents; ease of cleaning; and high sensitivity for some applications. The major disadvantages of the sprayer burner are that gas flow must be carefully controlled to insure reproducible results, flame area is undesirably small for use in absorption, and there is a larger number of interferences. Many workers report interferences with total consumption burners not observed with burners using premixed gases. Fuwa et al. (*41*) found that phosphate suppressed the absorption of zinc with a total consumption burner using an air–hydrogen flame. With the same burner configuration, phosphate interfered with the determination of lead (*42*).

To overcome some of the objections to the diffusion burner, Gilbert (*43*) used a sheath to flow additional oxygen around the flame, thus preventing entrained nitrogen from cooling the lower portion of the flame. Many interferences are reduced because of the resulting higher temperatures, especially when organic solvents are used.

The oxygen-sheath principle has been applied in a slightly different way in the Chaffee–Keyes burner. The fuel (hydrogen or acetylene) is the nebulizing gas. The sample capillary tube is outside the burner and various sizes of capillary tubing can be interchanged. Loken et al. (*44*) reversed the oxygen and the acetylene gases in the determination of calcium in serum and urine. By reversing the gases, the sample is nebulized with the acetylene at a lower pressure, which decreased the flow rate without loss of sensitivity. This indicates the formation of finer droplets or perhaps an increase in flame temperature. Also, the interference of sulfate and phosphate is less.

2. Premixed Gas (Laminar Flow) Burner

The premixed gas or laminar flow burner is primarily used in atomic absorption. The sample is aspirated into a mixing chamber, which effectively separates the fine spray from the large droplets and mixes it with the gases. By this process only $1–10\%$ of the aspirated solution ever reaches the flame. However, the system using premixed gases suffers less from condensed phase interference because of smaller droplet size reaching the flame and because of the use of oxidant–fuel mixtures with lower burning velocities. Recently, West and co-workers (*45–48*) used this system in atomic fluorescence, and Pickett and Koirtyohann (37) used a premixed nitrous oxide–acetylene flame for emission.

3. Other Methods

Another method of producing atomic vapor for emission or absorption is with an electric furnace. Woodriff and Ramelow (49) used a high-temperature graphite-tube resistance furnace capable of reaching a temperature of 3000°C. The sample was aspirated into the furnace with argon gas. This system has proven to be especially satisfactory for the removal of condensed phase interferences and for the analysis of re-fractory oxides because the furnace operates in an inert atmosphere. This approach offers especially great potential for those elements that form refractory oxides in the conventional flame. The coupling of an ultrasonic nebulizer with a high-temperature furnace would undoubtedly permit the determination of trace elements in the presence of materials that form refractory oxides.

4. Droplet Size

The droplet size in emission and absorption is important since it affects the radiation and absorption of the analyte. The droplet diameter depends upon velocity of the aspirating gas, surface tension, and density of the liquid. Nukiyama and Tanasawa (50) showed that when the velocity of the nebulizing gas stream increased from 50 to 350 m/sec, the mean diameter of the droplet decreased from 65 to 10 μ. A further increase in the air speed failed to lower the droplet size.

Alkemade and Voorhuis (51) and Filcek (52) have reported that the droplet size is a factor in the interference of phosphate with the emission intensity of calcium. Filcek used different types of nebulizers in his study. The most interference occurred with the total consumption type, while a premix gas nebulizer with a baffle gave the least. The baffle was used to remove the larger particles with a slight loss of intensity.

The sensitivity lost due to the baffle can be recovered by heating the spray chamber. This removes the excess solvent and increases the per-centage of analyte reaching the flame.

Various techniques have been suggested for the production of fine particles. An approach which seems promising for emission or absorption is the use of an ultrasonic nebulizer (53–56). This system is reported to be capable of producing particles averaging less than 1 μ in size; however, at the present stage of development it is not as convenient to operate as the foregoing types of nebulizers. The advantages reported are production of uniform clotlets; low consumption of sample, and ability to aspirate highly concentrated solutions (e.g., saturated solution of brine).

D. FLAME REGION

When the interference by a concomitant is due to some rate process within the flame, the degree of interference may vary with the area or height of measurement within the flame. Dean and co-workers (57–59), Gibson et al. (7), and Buell (60) found that, in general, flame area of

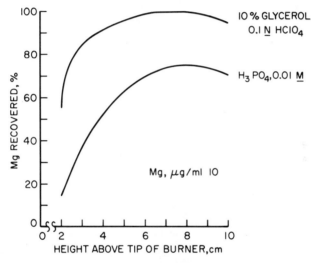

Fig. 4. Influence of phosphate and burner height on magnesium absorption. Zeiss total consumption burner, oxygen–hydrogen flame.

maximum emission is quite restricted when organic solvents are used or when operating with fuel-rich flames. Production of free atoms of the analyte is controlled by the rates of desolvation and vaporization of solute as it passes through the flame; longer retention times are required for the larger droplets. The interference from the more refractory oxides can be partially overcome by observing the flame further downstream in the outer mantle.

The effects of burner height with an oxygen–hydrogen flame and a total consumption burner are shown in Fig. 4. In this type of system the average diameter of the droplet is 15–20 μ (1), and the area of least interference, due to the high burning velocity of the gas mixture, is in the upper portion of the flame. Complete recovery of magnesium is obtained over the region 6–8 cm above the tip of burner with a solution containing 10% glycerol and $0.1M$ in $HClO_4$; however, the overall sensitivity is slightly reduced in this medium. In practice, this type of burner is seldom used in atomic absorption with a single optical pass because the light path of the flame is short. However, this burner system is frequently used with a multiple-pass (3 or 5) system or in the presence of organic solvents. The influence of

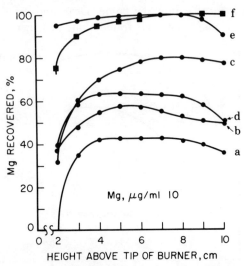

Fig. 5. Influence of aluminum and burner height on magnesium in absorption. Zeiss total consumption burner, oxygen–hydrogen flame. (*a*) Aluminum, 1.0 mg/ml, (*b*) aluminum, 1.0 mg/ml with lanthanum, 1.0 mg/ml, (*c*) aluminum, 1.0 mg/ml in 10 (v/v) % glycerol and $0.1M$ $HClO_4$, (*d*) aluminum, 0.1 mg/ml, (*e*) aluminum, 0.1 mg/ml with lanthanum, 1.0 mg/ml. (*f*) aluminum, 0.1 mg/ml in 10 (v/v) % glycerol and $0.1M$ $HClO_4$.

phosphate on magnesium is less in the upper region of the flame; the suppression of the magnesium in the presence of aluminum, on the other hand, is essentially constant over all the regions. The efficiency of glycerol and perchloric acid as releasing agents is increased, especially for aluminum when absorption measurements are taken in the region 6–10 cm above the top of the total consumption burner, as shown in Fig. 5.

Gibson et al. (7) studied the effect of sulfate on the emission intensity of calcium chloride as a function of burner height. Maximum suppression was observed near the region of maximum intensity for calcium, with a gradual decrease of suppression with increasing height. Thermodynamically, $CaCl_2$ and $CaSO_4$ should decompose at these flame temperatures; however, the decomposition step is rate controlled. Therefore, the rate of dissociation is greater with smaller clotlets.

The suppression of calcium due to sulfate in emission or absorption is relatively low in a premixed air–acetylene flame. This can be explained as follows: the droplet size of spray emerging from a premix nebulizer varies from 1 to 5 μ. Now the time the analyte remains in the flame gases is dependent on the particular gas flow required to produce a stable flame front. The flame front propagation rate for oxygen–hydrogen is 2000 cm/sec, which gives the particle a relatively short residence time in the flame. By contrast, the flame front propagation rate for air–acetylene is 160 cm/sec. This much lower burning velocity lengthens the residence time and therefore minimizes many of the condensed phase interferences.

E. ROLE OF ORGANIC SOLVENTS

Since the role of organic solvents will be discussed in detail in Volume II of this series, only a brief discussion of organic solvents and their effect on condensed phase interferences is appropriate. Many alcohols, ketones, and organic acids are used in flame emission and atomic absorption spectrometry. The enhancement in sensitivity obtained from these solvents ranges from 2 to 200, depending upon the element. This enhancement and the possibility of concentrating the solute through extraction techniques permit the analysis of lower concentrations; also, the interference from elements in the matrix is either minimized or removed. With the aid of fuel-rich flames and organic solvents, a number of elements that had been thought to be impossible to determine can be determined by emission or absorption methods. For example, Rains et al. (61) studied the complex spectra of the rare earth elements. Chelates of these elements with 2-thenoyltrifluoroacetone were extracted into methyl isobutyl ketone, and the flame emission spectrum was measured using an oxygen–hydrogen flame. The emission intensity was greatly enhanced by the organic medium; in many cases the enhancement was 100-fold as compared with aqueous solutions. However, under these operating conditions, no line spectra for Sc ,Y, La, Pr, Nd, Dy, or Ho were detected; only a few of the more intense lines for Sm, Tb, and Tm were observed. To elicit the atomic line spectra of the rare earth elements from an ethanol medium, one must use a fuel-rich oxygen–acetylene flame and observe the interconal zone (62). Similarly, analytically useful line spectra have been observed for many of the highly refractory metals such as Re, Ta, Ti, U, W, and Zr (63). These lines are not observed even under fuel-rich conditions from an aqueous medium.

Jaworowski et al. (64) compared the sensitivities of Al, Cr, Eu, Er, and Nd for nitrous oxide–acetylene, oxygen–acetylene, and air–acetylene flames for aqueous and 80% methanol solutions. The organic solvent nearly always improved the emission sensitivities of these elements. Sachdev et al. (65) compared the effects of some organic solvents on the absorption of vanadium. In every case, an improvement in sensitivity was obtained. A fatty acid, such as oleic acid, further improved the sensitivity when added to methyl isobutyl ketone solvent. The oleic acid decreased the feed rate about half, and a three-fold increase in absorption resulted. This enhancement of the absorption signal was attributed to an increased efficiency in the production of free atoms due to a decrease in droplet size. Similar results were obtained by the author for various elements by the addition of glycerol to acetone or methyl isobutyl ketone. The major advantage of organic solvents in emission or absorption is the elimination of the matrix effect or condensed phase interference by the use of selective solvent extraction techniques; this can be used effectively to preconcentrate the analyte.

F. Releasing and Protective Chelating Agents

Releasing and protective chelating agents are widely used in emission and absorption to eliminate the suppression of the analyte due to formation of involatile compounds. Releasing and protective chelating agents are defined as substances which, when added in sufficient quantity in the presence of an interferent, will restore the emission intensity or absorption of the analyte to its original value without interferent.

Releasing agents may be cations which preferentially combine with the interferent. Yofe and Finkelstein (2) demonstrated the efficiency of lanthanum for the restoration of the intensity of calcium in the presence of phosphate and sulfate. They postulated the reaction to be:

$$2CaCl_2 + 2H_3PO_4 + E = Ca_2P_2O_7 + 4HCl + H_2O \qquad (2)$$

and when lanthanum was introduced:

$$LaCl_3 + H_3PO_4 + E' = LaPO_4 + 3HCl \qquad (3)$$

where E and E' are heats of reaction. They deduced that the high heat of formation of lanthanum phosphate and its greater thermostability would make $E' > E$; therefore, the calcium chloride released would be free to dissociate at a much lower temperature. However, this would not explain the effectiveness of magnesium or beryllium in releasing calcium from sulfate because these sulfates have lower heats of formation than calcium sulfate. Dinnin (66) suggested that the releasing action is more of a mass action effect:

$$Ax + By = Ay + Bx \qquad (4)$$

where A = the analyte, B = high concentration of releasing agent, x = anion which forms a refractory compound, and y = anion which forms an easily dissociated compound. As the concentration of B is increased, the reaction will be forced toward Bx, thus leaving Ay free to dissociate at a lower temperature. This reaction alone will not explain why some cations will act as releasing agents and others will not. Since the process which occurs within the flame gases is rate controlled, as indicated by studies with low-velocity flames and variable height within the flame, the correct explanation is most likely a combination of the two mechanisms.

The analyst must choose one or a combination of releasing and/or chelating agents which will serve his purpose. In selecting the releasing and/or chelating agent, the following points should be considered: (1) background spectrum of releasing agent, (2) efficacy, (3) purity of releaser, and (4) cost. The reason that lanthanum has been so widely used as a releasing agent for the alkaline earth metals is that its lines and bands do not interfere with the resonance lines of the alkaline earths. Also, it can be obtained in high purity at a nominal cost. On the other hand, one certainly would not use calcium as a releasing agent for barium because the intense calcium band system is near the barium resonance line.

Strasheim and Wessels (67) used copper as a releasing agent in the determination of noble metals with an air–propane flame. Elements such as Sb, W, Co, Sn, and Ni sharply reduced the absorption by platinum; increasing concentrations of copper salts caused a sharp reduction, then an enhancement, and finally a constancy in the platinum absorption. Sulfuric acid caused a severe decrease in sensitivities for Pt, Pd, Rh, and Au, and mutual interferences were observed for Pt, Pd, Rh, Ru, and Au. In the determination of platinum, the addition of an oxygen acid such as H_2SO_4 or HNO_3 reduced the interference by the other noble metals.

David (68) found that phosphate, sulfate, aluminum, and silicate interfered in the analysis of calcium in plant materials by atomic absorption. He discussed the suppression of these interferences in detail and concluded that the most effective method is the addition of 6000 ppm of magnesium and 2% sulfuric acid. This suppressed the interference of 60 ppm of silica in the presence of 25 ppm of calcium. The calcium absorption depended on the ratio of fuel to air and varied with the observation height in the flame, being greatest adjacent to the base burner.

The manner in which chelates prevent condensed phase interferences, as well as serve as releasing agents, is not clearly understood. Compounds

TABLE 3

Releasing and Protective Chelating Agents Used
in Emission and Absorption

Reagent	Type	Interferent	Analyte	Ref.
La	Releaser	Al, Si, PO_4^{3-}, SO_4^{2-}	Mg, Ca	2, 23, 69–71
Sr	Releaser	Al, B, Te, Se, NO_3^{1-}, PO_4^{3-} SO_4^{2-}	Mg, Ca, Ba	11, 23, 66, 70 72, 73
Mg	Releaser	Al, Si, PO_4^{3-}, SO_4^{2-}	Ca	25
Ca	Releaser	Al, PO_4^{3-}	Mg, Sr	25, 74
Ba	Releaser	Al, Fe	Na, K, Mg	75
Nd, Sm, Y, Pr	Releaser	Al, PO_4^{3-}, SO_4^{2-}	Sr	66
Glycerol, HClO₄	Protector	Al, Fe, Th, rare earths Si, B, Cr, Ti, PO_4^{3-}, SO_4^{2-}	Mg, Ca, Sr, Ba	3, 14, 15
NH₄Cl	Protector	Al	Na, Cr	76
NH₄Cl	Protector	Sr, Ca, Ba, PO_4^{3-}, SO_4^{2-}	Mo	77
Ethylene glycol	Protector	PO_4^{3-}	Ca	14, 78
Mannitol	Protector	PO_4^{3-}	Ca	14
Dextrose, sucrose	Protector	PO_4^{3-}	Ca, Sr	4, 6, 14, 79
EDTA	Chelate	Se, Te, B, Al, Si, NO_3^{1-}, PO_4^{3-}, SO_4^{2-}	Mg, Ca	73, 80
8-Hydroxy-quinoline	Chelate	Al	Mg, Ca	81–83

such as ethylenediaminetetraacetic acid (EDTA) are known to form strong complexes with the alkaline earth metals and would preferentially complex the alkaline earth metals even in the presence of phosphate; however, the action of the simple sugars and glycerol has not been explained. A listing of releasing and protective chelating agents is given in Table 3.

The effects of phosphate on magnesium by flame emission, with and without releasing and protective chelating agents, are given in Fig. 6 (*17*). The glycerol with perchloric acid was found to be more effective than EDTA or lanthanum.

In a study of the effect of aluminum on magnesium by both emission and absorption, lanthanum was found to be more effective than glycerol or EDTA, as shown in Figs. 7 and 8 (*17*). Aluminum did not suppress the magnesium intensity when the weight ratio, lanthanum to aluminum, was at least 10:1. However, the high concentration of lanthanum required to release the magnesium when the aluminum concentration was greater

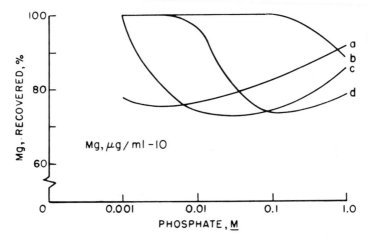

Fig. 6. Effects of phosphate on magnesium in emission with and without releasing agents. (*a*) H_3PO_4, (*b*) 10 (v/v)% glycerol, 0.1*M* $HClO_4$, (*c*) lanthanum, 1 mg/ml, (*d*) EDTA, 0.05*M*.

than 200 ppm clogged the burner. If, however, glycerol is used in conjunction with the lanthanum, a lanthanum-to-aluminum ratio of only 2:1 is necessary for complete release of magnesium. Similar results are obtained with the other alkaline earth metals. Also, the addition of a 10% solution of glycerol to the standard as well as to the unknown has the advantage of improving the burning characteristics and controlling the viscosity, thus increasing the accuracy of the method.

An excellent example of a protector is 8-hydroxyquinoline. Yanagisawa et al. (*83*) determined calcium in phosphoric acid by extracting the calcium 8-quinolinolate with methyl isobutyl ketone at pH 12.5–13.5. Various metal ions, which coextract at this pH and interfere in the absorption of calcium, were tested. Neither aluminum nor titanium showed interference with calcium at a 12:1 ratio. Larger ratios produced some suppression of the calcium absorption. The chelates formed are assumed to produce volatile compounds which are easily dissociated in the flame.

The releasing effect of lanthanum is facilitated by the addition of 8-hydroxyquinoline (8). Instead of requiring a 1% solution of lanthanum to overcome the suppression of aluminum, a 0.2% solution of lanthanum

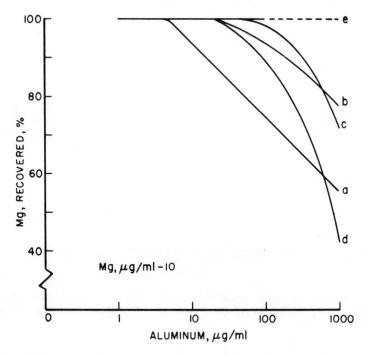

Fig. 7. Effects of aluminum on magnesium in emission with and without releasing agents. (*a*) Aluminum, (*b*) 10 (v/v) % glycerol, 0.1*M* HClO$_4$, (*c*) lanthanum, 1.0 mg/ml, (*d*) 0.05*M*, EDTA, (*e*) lanthanum, 10 mg/ml.

in 1% 8-hydroxyquinoline suffices. This corresponded to a La/Al molar ratio of 2. Similar results have been reported with a combination of EDTA and lanthanum (*84*).

The role of releasing agents differs with various burner systems. The effects of phosphate on magnesium by atomic absorption with three different burners, with and without releasing agents, are shown in Fig. 9. The suppression of magnesium is far greater with the total consumption burner (Fig. 9C) than with the laminar flow burners. As discussed previously, this is due to the high burning velocity of the oxygen–hydrogen flame and the larger droplet size produced by the total consumption burner. Also, a solution 10% in glycerol and $0.1M$ HClO$_4$ was more efficient than lanthanum in releasing magnesium. With the burners using

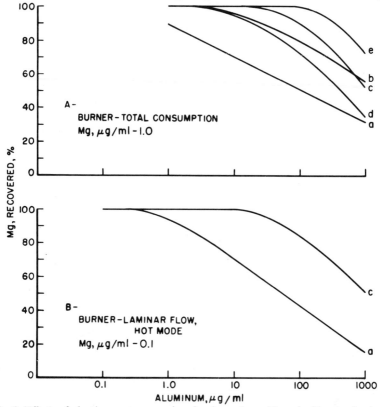

Fig. 8. Effects of aluminum on magnesium in absorption with and without releasing agents. (a) Aluminum, (b) 10 (v/v) % glycerol, $0.1M$ HClO$_4$, (c) lanthanum, 1 mg/ml, (d) EDTA, $0.05M$, (e) lanthanum, 1 mg/ml, 10 (v/v) % glycerol, $0.1M$ HClO$_4$.

premixed gases, phosphate added as H_3PO_4 is not a major interferent; however, $(NH_4)_2HPO_4$ or H_3PO_4 adjusted to pH 4–5 interferes strongly. In a solution containing glycerol [10 (v/v)%] and $0.1M$ in perchloric acid, recovery of 1 μg/ml of magnesium was complete in the presence of $0.05M$ phosphate. By increasing the acidity to pH 0.5, complete recovery was obtained up to $0.5M$ phosphate.

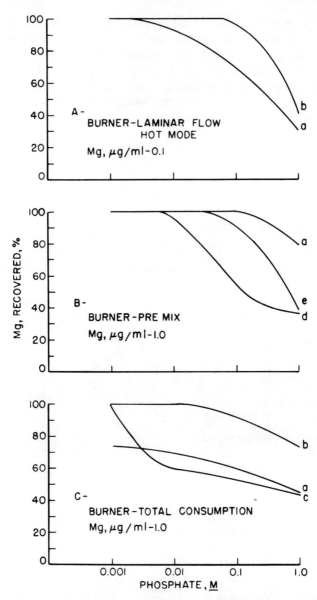

Fig. 9. Effects of phosphate on magnesium in absorption with three different burners. (A, B) Air–acetylene flame, (C) oxygen–hydrogen. (a) H_3PO_4, (b) 10 (v/v) % glycerol, 0.1M $HClO_4$, (c) lanthanum, 1 mg/ml, (d) $(NH_4)_2HPO_4$, (e) $(NH_4)_2HPO_4$, with 10 (v/v) % glycerol, 0.1M $HClO_4$.

David (*70*) found 1*N* ammonium chloride to be a protector for the determination of sodium, potassium, calcium, and magnesium in soils. Generally, in water solutions, the magnesium analysis suffers interference from phosphate, aluminate, silicate and sulfate, but only when these are present at much higher concentrations than the magnesium. In 1*N* ammonium chloride, silicate does not interfere in concentrations up to 15 times that of magnesium, and aluminum does not interfere in up to 10-fold concentration. The phosphate and sulfate interferences were not affected by the ammonium chloride. David reported that calcium protected magnesium from silica. The addition of 1500 ppm of strontium completely controlled the interference of phosphate and sulphate in the magnesium determination. Similar effects were noted in the calcium determination, but the interferences were more severe. Interference of phosphate was controlled with 1500 ppm of strontium even in concentrations five times that of the calcium.

G. Correction Method

If interference is still present after the use of releasing and protective chelating agents, often a correction method can be utilized. If the concomitant interferes with the analyte due to some chemical effect, the method of additions will correct for either depression or enhancement. If judiciously used, this technique will increase the precision and accuracy of flame methods. The two basic methods (single and multiple) of standard additions have a variety of names and will be described in detail in Volume II.

REFERENCES

1. J. A. Dean, *Flame Photometry*, McGraw-Hill, New York, 1960.
2. J. Yofe and R. Finkelstein, *Anal. Chim. Acta*, **19**, 166 (1958).
3. T. C. Rains, H. E. Zittel, and M. Ferguson, *Anal. Chem.*, **34**, 778 (1962).
4. M. E. Doty and W. G. Schrenk, in *Developments in Applied Spectroscopy* (J. E. Forrette and E. Lanterman, eds.), Vol. 3, Plenum Press, New York, 1964.
5. P. T. Gilbert, Jr., in *Symposium on Spectroscopy*, Am. Soc. Testing Materials, Spec. Tech. Publ. 269 (1960).
6. C. A. Baker and F. W. J. Garton, U.K. Atomic Energy Authority, *AERE-R-3490*, 1961.
7. J. H. Gibson, W. E. L. Grossman, and W. D. Cooke, *Anal. Chem.*, **35**, 266 (1963).
8. I. Rubeška and B. Moldan, *Anal. Chim. Acta*, **37**, 421 (1967).

9. C. Duval, *Inorganic Thermogravimetric Analysis*, 2nd ed., Elsevier, Amsterdam, 1963.
10. S. Fukushima, *Mikrochim. Acta*, **1959**, p. 596.
11. W. T. Elwell and J. A. F. Gidley, *Atomic Absorption Spectrophotometry*, 2nd ed., Pergamon Press, London, 1966.
12. W. M. Shaw, *Anal. Chem.*, **30**, 1682 (1958).
13. G. D. Christian and F. J. Feldman, *Anal. Chim. Acta*, **40**, 173 (1968).
14. T. C. Rains, H. E. Zittel, and M. Ferguson, *Talanta*, **10**, 367 (1963).
15. J. A. Dean, J. C. Burger, T. C. Rains, and H. E. Zittel, *Anal. Chem.*, **33**, 1722 (1961).
16. D. M. Yost and H. Russel, Jr., *Systematic Inorganic Chemistry*, Prentice-Hall, New York, 1944, pp. 224–233.
17. O. Menis, ed., *NBS Tech. Note 402*, 1966.
18. D. R. Demers and D. W. Ellis, *Anal. Chem.*, **40**, 860 (1968).
19. S. Tsuchihashi and E. Sekido, *J. Japan Chem. Soc.*, **78**, 1431 (1956).
20. M. Margoshes and B. L. Vallee, *Anal. Chem.*, **28**, 180 (1956).
21. R. Herrmann and C. T. J. Alkemade, *Chemical Analysis by Flame Photometry*, Wiley (Interscience), New York, 1963.
22. F. Burriel-Marti and J. Ramirez-Muñoz, *Flame Photometry*, Elsevier, Amsterdam, 1957.
23. R. E. Dickson and C. M. Johnson, *Appl. Spectry.*, **20**, 214 (1966).
24. P. T. Gilbert, Jr., *Analysis Instrumentation—1964, Proceedings of 10th National Analysis Instrumentation Symposium, San Francisco, June, 1964*, Plenum Press, New York, 1964.
25. C. Rocchiccioli and A. Townshend, *Anal. Chim. Acta*, **41**, 93 (1968).
26. R. A. G. Rawson, *Analyst*, **91**, 630 (1966).
27. M. D. Amos and J. B. Willis, *Spectrochim. Acta*, **22**, 1325 (1966).
28. V. A. Fassel and D. W. Golightly, *Anal. Chem.*, **39**, 466 (1967).
29. D. C. Manning, *At. Absorption Newsletter*, No. 24, September, 1964.
30. J. D. Winefordner, private communication, 1968.
31. W. Slavin, *Appl. Spectry.*, **20**, 281 (1966).
32. R. K. Skogerboe, A. T. Heybey, and G. H. Morrison, *Anal. Chem.*, **38**, 1821 (1966).
33. J. A. Dean, in *Developments in Applied Spectroscopy*, (J. E. Forrette and E. Lanterman, eds.), Vol. 3, Plenum Press, New York, 1964.
34. R. N. Kniseley, A. P. D'Silva, and V. A. Fassel, *Anal. Chem.*, **35**, 910 (1963)).
35. D. J. David, *Analyst*, **86**, 730 (1961).
36. H. D. Fleming, *Spectrochim. Acta*, **23B**, 207 (1967).
37. E. E. Pickett and S. R. Koirtyohann, *Spectrochim. Acta*, **23B**, 235 (1968).
38. L. P. Morgenthaler, private communication, 1968.
39. J. B. Willis, *Spectrochim. Acta*, **23B**, 811 (1967).
40. R. Mavrodineanu and H. Boiteux, *Flame Spectroscopy*, Wiley, New York, 1965.
41. K. Fuwa, P. Pulido, R. McKay, and B. L. Vallee, *Anal. Chem.*, **36**, 2407 (1964).
42. S. R. Koirtyohann and C. Feldman, in *Developments in Applied Spectroscopy* (J. E. Forrette and E. Lanterman, eds.), Vol. 3, Plenum Press, New York, 1964.
43. P. T. Gilbert, Jr., *Proceedings Xth Colloquium Spectroscopicum Internationale*, Spartan, Washington, D.C., 1963, p. 271.
44. H. F. Loken, J. S. Teal, and E. Eisenberg, *Anal. Chem.*, **35**, 875 (1963).
45. T. S. West, *Trace Characterization, Chemical and Physical*, (W. W. Meinke and B. F. Scribner, eds.), NBS Monograph No. 100, Washington, D.C., 1967.

46. R. M. Dagnall, T. S. West, and P. Young, *Talanta*, **13**, 803 (1966).
47. R. M. Dagnall, K. C. Thompson, and T. S. West, *Talanta*, **14**, 557 (1967).
48. R. M. Dagnall, K. C. Thompson, and T. S. West, *Anal. Chim. Acta*, **36**, 269 (1966).
49. R. Woodriff and G. Ramelow, *Proceedings XIIIth Colloquium Spectroscopicum Internationale*, A. Hilger, London, 1968, p. 283.
50. S. Nukiyama and Y. Tanasawa, *Trans. Soc. Mech. Engrs. Japan*, 4, 5, and 6 (1938–40). Translation by E. Hope, available through the Defence Research Board, Department of National Defense, Ottawa, Canada.
51. C. T. J. Alkemade and M. H. Voorhuis, *Z. Anal. Chem.*, **163**, 91 (1958).
52. M. Filcek, *Z. Pflanzenernaehr. Dueng. Bodenk.*, **85**, 112 (1959).
53. C. D. West and D. N. Hune, *Anal. Chem.*, **36**, 412 (1964).
54. R. H. Wendt and V. A. Fassel, *Anal. Chem.*, **37**, 920 (1965).
55. H. Dunken, G. Pforr, W. Mikkeleit, and K. Geller, *Z. Chem.*, **3**, 196 (1963).
56. H. C. Hoare, R. A. Mostyn, and B. T. N. Newland, *Anal. Chim. Acta*, **40**, 181 (1968).
57. J. A. Dean and W. J. Carnes, *Analyst*, **87**, 743 (1962).
58. J. A. Dean and J. C. Simms, *Anal. Chem.*, **35**, 699 (1963).
59. J. A. Dean and J. E. Adkins, Jr., *Analyst*, **91**, 709 (1966).
60. B. E. Buell, *Anal. Chem.*, **35**, 372 (1963).
61. T. C. Rains, H. P. House, and O. Menis, *Anal. Chim. Acta*, **22**, 315 (1960).
62. V. A. Fassel, R. H. Curry, and R. N. Kniseley, *Spectrochim. Acta*, **18**, 1127 (1962).
63. A. P. D'Silva, R. N. Kniseley, and V. A. Fassel, *Anal. Chem.*, **36**, 1287 (1964).
64. R. J. Jaworowski, R. P. Weberling, and D. J. Bracco, *Anal. Chim. Acta*, **37**, 284 (1967).
65. S. L. Sachdev, J. W. Robinson, and P. W. West, *Anal. Chim. Acta*, **37**, 156 (1967).
66. J. I. Dinnin, *Anal. Chem.*, **32**, 1475 (1960).
67. A. Strasheim and G. J. Wessels, *Appl. Spectry.*, **17**, 65 (1963).
68. D. J. David, *Analyst*, **84**, 536 (1959).
69. C. H. Williams, *Anal. Chim. Acta*, **22**, 163 (1960).
70. D. J. David, *Analyst*, **85**, 495 (1960).
71. C. B. Belcher and K. A. Brooks, *Anal. Chim. Acta*, **29**, 202 (1963).
72. R. L. Mitchell and I. M. Robertson, *J. Soc. Chem. Ind. (London)*, **55**, 269T (1936).
73. T. V. Ramakrishna, J. W. Robinson, and P. W. West, *Anal. Chim. Acta*, **36**, 57 (1966).
74. J. A. Brabson and W. D. Wilhide, *Anal. Chem.*, **26**, 1060 (1954).
75. W. Schmidt, K. Konopicky, and M. Baum, *Tonind.-Ztg. Keram. Rundschau*, **87**, 157 (1963); *CA* **59**, 9325.
76. L. Barnes, Jr., *Anal. Chem.*, **38**, 1085 (1966).
77. D. J. David, *Analyst*, **93**, 79 (1968).
78. M. E. Doty, Thesis, Kansas State Univ., Manhattan, 1963; *Dissertation Abstr.*, **24.** 1367 (1963).
79. M. J. Pro and A. P. Mathers, *J. Assoc. Offic. Agr. Chemist*, **37**, 945 (1954).
80. A. C. West and W. D. Cooke, *Anal. Chem.*, **32**, 1471 (1960).
81. G. B. Marshall and T. S. West, *Talanta*, **14**, 823 (1967).
82. F. J. Wallace, *Analyst*, **88**, 259 (1963).
83. M. Yanagisawa, M. Suzuki, and T. Takeuchi, *Talanta*, **14**, 933 (1967).
84. P. B. Adams and W. O. Passmore, *Anal. Chem.*, **38**, 630 (1966).

13 Accuracy and Precision

R. K. Skogerboe

DEPARTMENT OF CHEMISTRY
CORNELL UNIVERSITY
ITHACA, NEW YORK

I. Introduction

The judgment of an analytical chemist is ultimately made on his ability to produce a reliable result. Error—or the absence of it—is inferred by the term reliable and this obviously depends on the choice of the right method of analysis and on exercising good analytical technique. Accuracy and precision, sensitivity, scope, selectivity, and sampling and standards requirements are the paramount criteria considered in the selection of the appropriate analysis method. Nearly all of these characteristics show interrelationships to some degree; these will become apparent as the basic aspects of each are treated in the appropriate places throughout. It is the purpose of this chapter to define pertinent terms; demonstrate practical methods for the recognition, evaluation, and specification of errors; discuss means by which errors can be minimized; present examples relating to these problems; and attempt to provide some degree of standardization in handling these problems.

II. Types of Error

An evaluation of errors is implicit in any analysis simply because it is impossible to make explicit statements about the analysis without the evaluation. It is paradoxical, however, that the analytical chemist typically receives only a superficial training in the concepts and techniques required for the documentation of the validity of his analysis. As a result, a variety of ambiguous statements about errors and the concepts thereof are common. In an attempt to reduce this problem, let us begin by defining *error* as simply a deviation from the true value or result. In general, analysts are concerned with two types of error: systematic and random.

A. Random Errors

Random errors, which are always present in any measurement, are characterized by a symmetric dispersion of deviations from the true result described by the "normal distribution." The three primary properties of this distribution are demonstrated in Fig. 1 wherein the true value μ occurs most frequently, the errors are directionally inconsistent (random), and the dimensional geometry of the curve is determined by the precision or repeatability of the analysis. The true standard deviation σ is the modulus of precision which defines the sharpness of the frequency curve, e.g., Figs. 1a and 1b represent methods of good and poor precision, respectively. In the absence of systematic errors, the normal distribution function predicts that 68, 95, and 99% of all measurements will lie within the intervals $\mu \pm \sigma$, $\mu \pm 2\sigma$, and $\mu \pm 3\sigma$, respectively.

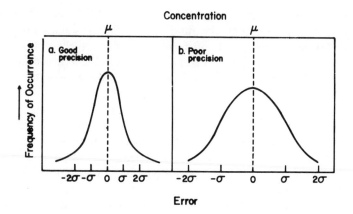

Fig. 1. Normal distribution (systematic errors absent).

B. SYSTEMATIC ERRORS

Unlike random errors, systematic (or determinate) errors do not neces-sarily exist. They are characterized by unidirectional deviations from the true result. In other words, the analysis is most frequently biased in the same direction, as shown in Fig. 2 where $\bar{C}$ is the most frequent measured

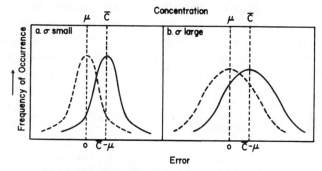

Fig. 2. The effect of systematic errors on accuracy.

result. As a direct consequence, the difference, $\bar{C} - \mu$, defines the average inaccuracy in the result originating from systematic errors. Hence, the average concentration $\bar{C}$ is an unbiased estimator of μ in the absence of systematic errors (*1–3*).

Accuracy, then, refers to the reliability of the result and is determined by the magnitudes of both the random and the systematic errors. Recalling that the reproducibility of the result depends solely on the random errors, we can now formulate a distinction between the terms accuracy and precision. Precision implies and, in fact, limits the accuracy of the measurement *if and only if systematic errors are absent*. Results cannot be specified as accurate unless both types of error are small; this produces a dual problem for the analyst if he is to make objective accuracy statements about his analysis. The possible coexistence of both error categories, coupled with the fact that the true concentration is rarely known, complicates the matter even further. If we consider the isolation and estimation of the magnitude of systematic errors with reference to Fig. 2, it is apparent that the reliability of this process depends on the relative magnitudes of the two types of error. In essence, small determinate errors are difficult to detect in the presence of larger random errors. To discuss this problem in depth, it is desirable to consider the overall process of analysis and the origins of errors.

III. Sources of Error

Most analytical processes can be conveniently divided into three general steps or phases—sampling, pretreatment, and measurement (*4, 5*). Both types of error can originate in the execution of each step and these will be reflected in the final result. The present discussion shall be restricted solely to random errors and referred to the breakdown of the analytical process presented in Fig. 3.

A. RANDOM CONTRIBUTIONS

The overall analysis error is estimated by the standard deviation, s_t, the magnitude of which is determined by the errors accumulating at each phase. Because variances (s^2) are additive, this estimate is given by

$$s_t = (s_s^2 + s_c^2 + s_m^2)^{1/2} \tag{1}$$

where the subscripts s, c, and m refer to the sampling, pretreatment, and measurement steps, respectively. The errors associated with the last two

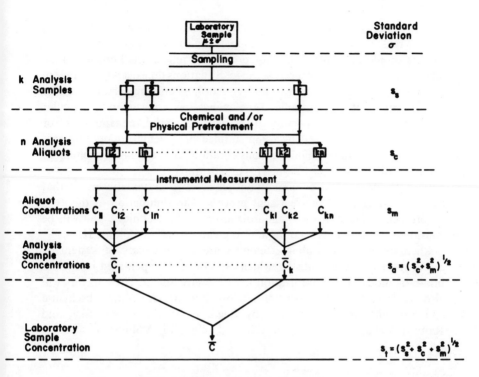

Fig. 3. Schematic of the analytical process.

steps are also conveniently referred to as the analysis error, s_a, which is determined by

$$s_a = (s_c^2 + s_m^2)^{1/2} \qquad (2)$$

The overall average concentration, $\bar{C}$, and the overall standard deviation, s_t, are estimators of the true concentration and standard deviation of the laboratory sample, respectively. Each analysis sample also has a true concentration and standard deviation which are estimated by $\bar{C}_i$ and s_a, respectively, because both the pretreatment and the measurement steps contribute random errors to this result.

B. TYPICAL SYSTEMATIC ERRORS

Systematic errors, too, can accumulate at each analysis step. The analytical literature generally implies (if it does not explicitly state), that random sampling eliminates systematic errors at the sampling stage. It is for this reason that the laboratory sample is specified in Fig. 3 and analysis reports should also specify this for protection, unless it is known that the laboratory sample was properly selected. Situations do exist where random sampling is not the best approach if reduction of sampling errors of either type is important. For example, if the analyte has localized in a particular stratum or recognizable portion of the matrix material, the sampling error can frequently be reduced by using statified or systematic sampling procedures. For a more definitive consideration of these latter techniques and their advantages, see Laitinen (6) or Cochran (2).

Loss of the analyte or contamination are two systematic errors that can occur during the pretreatment process. The elimination of this type of problem relates to the standardization of the technique and will be considered in following sections and in greater detail in Volume II.

Chemical and physical interferences are prime causes of systematic errors at the measurement step, which can also be compensated by appropriate methods of standardization and/or pretreatment. These factors will also be covered at the proper point below. For further detailed discussion and examples, see the chapters by Buell, Koirtyohann, Rubeška, and Rains in Volume I and those by Ellis and Schrenk in Volume II.

IV. Methods for the Evaluation of Errors

A. EVALUATION OF PRECISION

The schematic in Fig. 3 outlines the approach to evaluating the respective random error contributions, i.e., the analysis-of-variance (ANOVA) (1, 3–6). When several sources of error are involved, ANOVA becomes rather complicated. Fortunately, this breakdown is relatively simple and we shall use it to illustrate the principles involved. More complicated situations can be handled by an extension of this format. In the breakdown, k samples are taken from the laboratory sample and each is treated chemically and/or physically (weighed, dissolved, fused, diluted, etc.) in preparation for measuring the amount of analyte. Subsequently, n measurements are made on each sample solution and these are used to compute the average concentration for each, $\bar{C}_i$, and the overall average concentration, $\bar{C}$. The former estimates the concentration of the ith sample and the latter estimates that of the laboratory sample.

To illustrate, consider the data presented in Table 1. A single crystal of KCl was cleaved into six sections of approximately 200 mg each, dissolved, and analyzed for Li by flame emission. Four measurements were made on each sample solution at random. An examination of the average concentrations for each sample immediately implies heterogeneous distribution of the Li, and it is the purpose of the ANOVA to objectively evaluate this implication, i.e.: Is sampling error significant in comparison to the other errors present?

TABLE 1

Data for Analysis of Variance ($\mu g/g$ Li in KCl)

Measurement No.	Sample No.						
	$i = 1$	$i = 2$	$i = 3$	$i = 4$	$i = 5$	$i = 6$	
$j = 1$	27.8	30.8	31.3	31.6	34.5	34.2	
$j = 2$	28.1	29.1	33.7	28.2	34.4	33.7	
$j = 3$	30.2	27.7	34.2	30.2	34.4	35.2	
$i = 4$	28.3	31.8	33.4	33.5	34.2	35.9	
Average of ith sample	28.6	29.9	33.1	30.9	34.4	34.7	Overall average 31.9

Table 1 is a one-way classification with equal numbers such that a total number of $N = nk = 24$ observations are grouped into k classes of n measurements each. Thus, there are two assignable sources of variations, the sampling error and the random errors inherent in the flame measurement. The pretreatment contribution was not isolated because experience has shown that it is generally less than 0.1 % for this type of treatment and would thus be essentially negligible (7).

1. Overall Variation

If the overall average of the N measurements is $\bar{C}$ and if $\bar{C}_i$ is the average of the n observations on the ith sample, the total sum of squares, SST, can be obtained by summing the squares of each individual deviation from the overall average (6), i.e.,

$$\text{SST} = \sum_{ij} (C_{ij} - \bar{C})^2 = \sum_{ij} (C_{ij} - \bar{C}_i)^2 + n \sum_i (\bar{C}_i - \bar{C})^2 \qquad (3)$$

If a calculator is to be used, the following identity can be applied to simplify the calculation

$$SST = \sum_{ij} (C_{ij} - \bar{C})^2 \equiv \sum_{ij} (C_{ij})^2 - \frac{(\sum_{ij} C_{ij})^2}{N} \tag{4}$$

2. Measurement Variation

Because each sample solution is homogeneous, the repetitive measurements on each reflect only the random measurement errors of the method as determined by the first term on the right side of Eq. (3). Hence, the measurement sum of squares, SSM, is obtained by summing within each sample the squares of the deviations from that sample average and subsequently summing over all the samples, i.e.,

$$SSM = \sum_{ij} (C_{ij} - \bar{C}_i)^2 \equiv \sum_{ij} (C_{ij})^2 - \frac{\sum_i(\sum_j C_{ij})^2}{n} \tag{5}$$

Summing over all samples provides a pooled estimate of SSM (1, 4–6) which is more reliable than that calculated for any one sample alone because of the larger number of degrees of freedom involved.

3. Sampling Variations

The sum of squares of sampling, SSS, is given by the last term of Eq. (3) and is obtained by summing the squares of the deviations of the sample averages from the overall average, i.e.,

$$SSS = n \sum_i (\bar{C}_i - \bar{C})^2 \equiv \sum_i \frac{(\sum_j C_{ij})^2}{n} - \frac{(\sum_{ij} C_{ij})^2}{N} \tag{6}$$

When different numbers of measurements are made on each sample, however, the following weighted sum of squares must be computed

$$SSS = \sum_i n_i (\bar{C}_i - \bar{C})^2 \tag{7}$$

Equation (3) then reduces to

$$SST = SSM + SSS \tag{8}$$

so one of the terms can be determined by subtraction after computation of the other two (4, 6).

The analysis of variance on the Table 1 data is presented in Table 2, wherein the method of computing the respective variance terms is outlined.

TABLE 2
Analysis of Variance (from Table 1)

Source of error	Sum of squares	Degrees of freedom	Variance	F_c	$_{0.95}F_{(5,\ 18)}$
Sampling	SSS = 127.78	$k-1 = 5$	$s_s^2 = \dfrac{SSS}{5} = 25.56$	$\dfrac{25.56}{2.02} = 12.7$	3.4
Measure-ment	SSM = 36.33	$N-k = 18$	$s_m^2 = \dfrac{SSM}{18} = 2.02$		
Total	SST = 164.11	$N-1 = 23$	$s_t^2 = \dfrac{SST}{23} = 7.13$		

The number of degrees of freedom, like the sum of squares, is additive. To determine if the sampling error is significant in comparison to the measurement error, we compute the statistic

$$F_c = \frac{\text{larger variance}}{\text{smaller variance}} \tag{9}$$

This value is compared with one from standard tables for the confidence level required and the appropriate degrees of freedom, e.g., $_{0.95}F_{(5,\ 18)}$ is the value given for the 95% confidence level and the subscripts 5 and 18 are the degrees of freedom designated by the numerator and denominator, respectively (3, 6). Because F_c is greater than the tabulated value, we are 95% confident that the sampling error is significantly greater than the measurement error and a means for reducing the sampling contribution is desirable. (See discussion of confidence limits below.) Before proceeding to this, however, it is most advantageous to consider the detection of systematic errors.

B. Accuracy Evaluation

As previously stated, the accuracy of an analysis is determined by the magnitude of systematic and random errors. Failure to resolve the analytical signal from some extraneous signal originating from the sample or to make adequate blank compensation and chemical interferences are common systematic errors. The ability to evaluate accuracy depends largely on the sensitivity of the analysis method.

1. *Sensitivity*

Analytical sensitivity, as used herein, refers to the ability to discern a small change in concentration or amount of the analyte (*5, 8, 9*). Because the reproducibility and the magnitude of the signal measured limit this capability, it is necessary to consider the measurement process in greater detail.

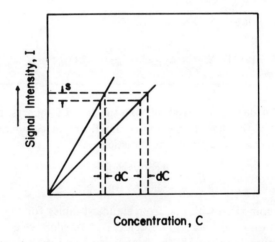

Concentration, C

Fig. 4. The effect of curve slope on concentrational sensitivity at constant measurement precision.

All instrumental measurements can be categorized into two general classes (*5, 9*). When signal reduction methods such as atomic absorption are used, the 100% signal level is defined with a blank and the amount of analyte is inferred from the reduction in signal caused by its presence. Signal increase methods such as flame emission deduce the analyte concentration from the intensity of the signal it emits. In either category, the final result is determined by the ability to reliably measure the difference between the analytical signal and the blank, background, and/or electronic noise signal(s). Both the extraneous (blank) and the analysis signals exhibit simultaneous fluctuations determining the reproducibility with which the signal differences can be measured. Because this repeatability generally varies with signal magnitude, the relationship between signal intensity and the amount of the analyte must be considered. Referring to Fig. 4, a larger signal change per unit concentration, provided that the measurement precision does not become proportionately worse, intuitively implies greater sensitivity. This concept is satisfied in a mathematical definition proposed by Mandel and Stiehler (*10*) and adopted by Skogerboe et al. (*5, 8*) and Ramírez-Muñoz (*11*). The sensitivity, γ, is defined by

$$\gamma = (dI/dC)s = m/s \tag{10}$$

where I = analytical signal intensity, C = concentration, and s = the standard deviation of the signal measurement. The term is thus derived in reciprocal concentration units. Figure 5 illustrates the dependency of

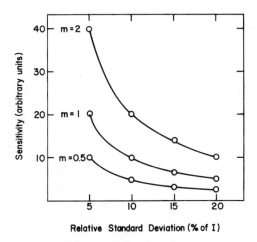

Fig. 5. Sensitivity as a function of curve slope and measurement precision.

sensitivity on the slope and signal measurement precision as defined by Eq. (10). The fact that the best sensitivity is obtained at maximum signal-minimum fluctuation is also consistent with the signal-to-noise ratio concepts common to electronics, emission spectrography, radiochemistry, etc.

Considering this definition and the situation depicted in Figs. 1 and 2, it becomes apparent that the detection of systematic errors and the concomitant specification of accuracy depend on the sensitivity of the method used. The actual means for evaluating accuracy are essentially limited to empirical methods.

2. *Empirical Methods*

Since instrumental analyses are generally calibrated with synthetic standards or with samples and standards analyzed by independent methods reasonably good determinate error corrections can be obtained. The approach assumes that the concentrations of the standards are known with a high degree of confidence and that the general compositions and the preparative histories of the samples and standards are similar or have been converted to a common state. The utilization of solution samples for flame emission and absorption places these techniques at an advantage from the standpoints of standard preparation and preparative history destruction. Comparisons between independent laboratories and methods are also of value provided that adequate controls are exercised and the statistical approach for the objective evaluation of the data is used. The method of standard additions is easily applied to flame methods and offers useful solutions to the problem in many instances. The paper by Beukelman and Lord (*12*) should be consulted for an apt discussion of the use of this method, its advantages, limitations, and problems, Youden (*13*) has presented a rapid technique for estimating inaccuracy. In its simplest form, two samples are analyzed and then equal amounts of each are combined to make a third sample. The concentration of the latter is given by

$$C_{12} = \tfrac{1}{2}(C_1 + C_2) \tag{11}$$

where the C_i designate the respective concentrations. The difference between the measured value of C_{12} and its calculated value serves as an estimate of the inaccuracy of the results. Of course, these values must deviate by an amount greater than the standard deviation of the method to be regarded as significant (*1, 3*). When a matrix, interelement, or spectral interference effect is suspected for a particular sample, the magnitude of the effect can be estimated by combining the interferent in various weight ratios with a sample for which the effect is absent (or its magnitude known) for analysis. The explicit requirements that the source of systematic error be absent or that the magnitude of its contribution be known are prime limitations for this technique.

It is worthwhile to note at this point that the one-way classification system (Table 1) and the associated analysis of variance can be used to evaluate accuracy as mentioned earlier. For example, the comparison of results obtained by different laboratories, methods, or analysts is frequently required. Substitution of laboratories, analysts, or methods for the samples is all that is required if the samples involved are homogeneous.

The sampling variance becomes the variance between laboratories and the measurement error is replaced by the error within a laboratory. If the material is heterogeneous, at least a two-way classification and treatment are required (*1, 3, 6, 14*). The objective determination of significant differences (inaccuracies) is discussed in the next section.

3. *Specification of Accuracy*

It should be understood that even though we give a numerical value to accuracy, it is not usually possible to precisely state what the error of a particular result is. It is nearly meaningless to state a nominal figure having little practical significance, so the accuracy is best given in terms of limits, $\pm x$, which indicate that the error will be less than x in a specific percentage of instances. This concept refers to the term *confidence limits* which are based on probability theory. Confidence limits are calculated from the standard deviation of the method and "confidence constants" for the appropriate error distribution. The average analysis result, $\bar{C}$, is an estimator of the true concentration, μ. A statement of accuracy indicates how likely it is that $\bar{C}$ is close to μ. Making use of the t distribution, the following probability statement can be made:

$$\left[\bar{C} - \frac{s}{(n)^{1/2}} t_{(1-\alpha/2)(n-1)} < \mu < \bar{C} + \frac{s}{(n)^{1/2}} t_{(1-\alpha/2)(n-1)} \right] = 100(1-\alpha)$$

(12)

where $100(1-\alpha)$ is the percentage confidence level required, n is the number of analyses used to compute $\bar{C}$ and s, and $t_{(1-\alpha/2)(n-1)}$ is a numerical quantity extracted from standard tables (*1, 3*). The above statement is read as follows: The probability that the interval

$$\bar{C} \pm \frac{s}{(n)^{1/2}} t_{(1-\alpha/2)(n-1)}$$

will include the true concentration, μ, is equal to $1-\alpha$. For random samples obtained from a normal population, it can be said that we are $100(1-\alpha)$ percent confident that the true concentration will be within these limits. The t distribution is applied because the values of t are adjusted to compensate for the smaller numbers of measurements normally used in analysis. As n increases, the value of t approaches the values of the confidence constants of the normal distribution.

Given an estimate of the standard deviation of a method, confidence limit techniques can be used to compute the number of measurements (or samples) needed to specify a concentration within certain required limits at a particular confidence level (*1, 2*). Confidence concepts are also useful in determining if apparent differences are actually significant.

4. *Comparison of Methods or Results*

When two or more methods, sets of results, analysts, or laboratories are compared there may be two general purposes in mind, depending on the situation or the requirements. To demonstrate, we shall consider the application to analysis results. Extension to the other possible applications is obvious. In the first case, the question may be: Is there a significant difference between the average concentrations measured by methods 1 and 2, i e., is $\bar{C}_1 \neq \bar{C}_2$? To answer, compute (*3*)

$$t' = \frac{\bar{C}_1 - \bar{C}_2}{\left(\dfrac{s_1^2}{n_1} + \dfrac{s_2^2}{n_2}\right)^{1/2}} \tag{13}$$

and answer affirmatively if

$$t' \leq -(w_1 t_1 + w_2 t_2)/(w_1 + w_2) \tag{14}$$

or if

$$t' \leq (w_1 t_1 + w_2 t_2)/(w_1 + w_2) \tag{15}$$

where s_i and n_i indicate the respective standard deviations and numbers of measurement,

$$w_1 = s_1^2/n_1, \quad w_2 = s_2^2/n_2, \quad t_1 = t_{(1 - \alpha/2)(n_1 - 1)}, \quad t_2 = t_{(1 - \alpha/2)(n_2 - 1)}$$

Acceptance for the case of t' falling outside the stated limits indicates that the two results are different at the $100(1 - \alpha)$ percentage confidence level. Otherwise, they are the same at that confidence level. The previously mentioned effect of poor precision on the ability to detect inaccuracies and/or significant differences is apparent in Eqs. (13–15).

Given the fact that two methods produce equivalent results, it may also be of interest to determine if one is more precise (and accurate) than the other, i.e., does $s_1^2 = s_2^2$? For this test compute the F-ratio defined by Eq. (9) and reject if (*3*)

$$F \geq F_{(1 - \alpha/2)(n_1 - 1, n_2 - 1)} \tag{16}$$

As in the previous example, rejection specifies that one method is less precise than the other at the indicated confidence level. For a more comprehensive discussion of this type of hypothesis testing, see Chapter 7 in Ostle (3) and others (1, 2, 6, 14).

The question which most obviously follows an evaluation of errors is: What can be done to reduce or eliminate them?

V. Reduction of Errors

Again, it is convenient to consider the two types of errors separately in discussing means for their minimization. Random errors can be reduced by either statistical or chemical, physical, and instrumental means. Only the latter techniques are applicable to the reduction of systematic errors, although the objectivity of the statistical approach is required for their evaluation and/or correction.

A. STATISTICAL REDUCTION OF RANDOM ERRORS

In theory, the standard deviation of the average of n samples or measurements is determined by

$$s_a = s/(n)^{1/2} \tag{17}$$

where s is the standard deviation of a single measurement (1, 4). Replication effectively decreases the standard deviation of the average, but a point of diminishing improvement is reached at approximately $n = 10$ because of the square root relationship. This reduction can be obtained by replication at any one phase of the analysis and is frequently used for this purpose. The advisability of repeating operations at any point in the analytical process is highly dependent on the relative magnitudes of the error terms comprising the overall precision estimates. In view of this, the argument for a definitive evaluation of the distribution of errors among analysis stages is obvious.

1. *Measurement Step*

In flame emission and absorption the measurement error is principally determined by the stability of the electronic system, the flame, and the delivery of the sample solution to the flame. It is popularly accepted that the last two are the primary contributors. Still, these contributions can be reduced to a degree by repeat measurements. Some recent instrumental developments actually take advantage of statistical concepts and are thus considered in this section.

Digital read-out accessories designed to improve measurement precision by replication are marketed by several instrument manufacturers. A scale–expansion capability, which will be discussed, is a design feature available on a number of these accessories, and some of these units can be used for both emission and absorption read-out. In general, the units can automatically take 1, 4, 8, or 16 separate readings of the sample and compute the average before digital display. An experimental comparison of this mode of averaging at a low signal level was made in the author's laboratory with a Perkin-Elmer DCR–2 set for a 2-sec time constant. The following relative standard deviations were observed for 1, 4, 8, and 16 readings, respectively: 2.5, 1.8, 1.7, and 1.7%. Similar results were observed for several systems. In essence, the improvement in precision is still limited by the stability of the flame and sample delivery systems as well as the electronic noise level. Improvement can be obtained by increasing the time constant so the read-out effectively "sees" less fluctuation.

Electronic integration or counting methods to average out variations have not been used to any degree in flame methods. A solid state integrator applicable to these methods has been described (15). If scanning of the line signal is to be used, the unit samples the background (or blank signal) on one side of the line and averages it over five time constant intervals. This value is automatically subtracted from the line signal during the integration of the area under the peak and the net area is displayed on an electronic counter. The unit, as used in the laboratory, was set for a 1-sec time constant and the gain was adjusted to produce 6000 counts/min per 10-mV signal. A further increase in the signal per unit area may be readily obtained by increasing the gain or reducing the scan rate. Continuous integration of the signal over a period of time can be obtained by setting on the peak to be' measured. A comparison with measuring the peak height with a recorder is presented in Table 3.

The data were obtained for the flame spectrophotometric analysis of gold. The relative standard deviation values given were computed from four successive measurements via each technique. Although some improvement in the precision is realized by integrating while scanning the peak in comparison to the recorder height measurement, it is apparent that the improvement is limited by the reproducibility of the scanning drive system. A most striking improvement occurs when the integration is carried out setting on the peak (for 1 min in this case). As previously reported for other applications (15) the precision closely approximates the $\sqrt{N}$ where N is the number of counts. Recalling the sensitivity concept, it is apparent that a smaller change in concentration can most readily be determined with the latter method. The ability to increase the precision by increasing the total number of counts (longer integration periods) is

TABLE 3

A Comparison of Electronic Integration Versus Recorder Measurements
for Signal Intensity

Concn of gold, μg/ml	Peak height, mV	Peak area (counts) (scanning 2 Å/min)	Peak height (counts/min) (sitting on line)
0			$4,200 \pm 2.1\%$
0.7	$0.68 \pm 18.3\%$	$38 \pm 15.7\%$	$4,582 \pm 1.4\%$
1	$0.80 \pm 15.0\%$	$46 \pm 17.1\%$	$4,673 \pm 1.5\%$
2	$1.5 \pm 13.2\%$	$93 \pm 7.1\%$	$4,727 \pm 1.5\%$
4.9	$3.6 \pm 8.2\%$	$249 \pm 9.8\%$	$6,100 \pm 0.9\%$
10	$7.1 \pm 4.8\%$	$509 \pm 3.9\%$	$17,800 \pm 0.8\%$

an attractive possibility with this system. The ability to measure to ± 0.1 or better will not necessarily reduce a $\pm 5\text{--}10\%$ inherent variation in the emission source to that level, however.

2. Sampling Step

In addition to replication, the sampling error can be reduced by taking larger samples, or by mixing to obtain homogeneity. The approach chosen will be dictated by the analysis requirements and by the preference of the analyst, but it is worthwhile to examine the respective aspects associated with each.

a. *Homogeneity.* For practical reasons a homogeneous material must be defined as one in which the unit defining segregation (or heterogeneity) is considerably smaller than the analysis sample (5). The grain and the particle may be the units determining segregation of a trace element from the matrix in solid and particulate matter, respectively; whereas the atom, ion, or molecule may be the defining units in solutions. In other words, a homogeneous material is one for which the probability of including the same number of trace element units in a particular sample size approaches unity. For samples having small units of definition, such as solutions, it is relatively easy to obtain the required probability for nearly any sample size. As the defining unit size increases, however, the sample size required to maintain unit probability increases also. In essence, the observed sampling error becomes greater as sample size decreases. Figure 6 presents

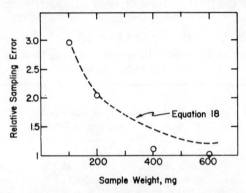

Fig. 6. The effect of sample weight on observed sampling error.

actual data demonstrating that a good approximation of the effect on sampling error, as expressed by the standard deviation, is given by

$$s_j = \frac{s_i}{(w_j/w_i)^{1/2}} \tag{18}$$

where w refers to sample weight and i and j refer to samples of different size. If the number of samples of both sizes are not the same, Eq. (18) must be modified to compensate for the effect of replication expressed in Eq. (17) to obtain

$$s_j = \frac{s_i}{(w_j/w_i)^{1/2} (n_j/n_i)^{1/2}} \tag{19}$$

Obviously, when the value of the sampling standard deviation is known for one size, these relationships can be used to compute the size required to reduce the standard deviation of sampling to a particular value.

   b. *Mixing.* In view of the foregoing discussion, a reduction in the sizes of the defining units of segregation is implicit in mixing to obtain homogeneity. Unless reduction in the unit sizes is accomplished, mixing will not increase the probability of drawing equal numbers of analyte units in any one sample size. The exception to this, of course, is the case where the analyte has become localized in a particular stratum of the matrix. At any rate, mixing solid samples always raises the valid question: How do we know when homogeneity is obtained? The answer can only be obtained by experimental evaluation. Consider, however, the effect of mixing on materials composed of discrete, essentially uniform sampling units, e.g., pills (6).

An analytical method has an inherent measurement error estimated by the standard deviation, s_m, for a single measurement and a sampling error estimated by s_s, for a single sample. The overall standard deviation for one measurement on one sample is given by

$$s_t = (s_m^2 + s_s^2)^{1/2} \tag{20}$$

If n samples are analyzed once each, the standard deviation of the overall average concentration is estimated by

$$s_t = \left(\frac{s_m^2 + s_s^2}{n}\right)^{1/2} \tag{21}$$

When n samples are well mixed and divided into n parts before analysis, the composition is averaged and the sampling standard deviation is reduced according to Eq. (17). If one sample is analyzed from this batch, the standard deviation is

$$s_t = \left(s_m^2 + \frac{s_s^2}{n}\right)^{1/2} \tag{22}$$

Finally, if n samples are analyzed after mixing, the estimate is given by

$$s_t = \left(\frac{s_m^2}{n} + \frac{s_s^2}{n^2}\right)^{1/2} \tag{23}$$

In essence, by mixing the samples before analysis, a more precise result is obtained than by analyzing the same number separately and averaging the result. Although mixing is a physical method of reducing error, it has been included in this section because of the above interrelationships.

The analyst using flame emission or absorption can readily take advantage of using larger samples and of mixing obtained by dissolution of samples to reduce sampling errors. These techniques are also amenable to the determination of the degree of heterogeneous distribution of impurity elements in many instances. This latter capability is becoming increasingly important in solid state physics as well as other disciplines. In this respect it is fortunate that the concentrations of individual analysis samples can frequently be estimated with better precision than the bulk concentration of the laboratory sample because of the contribution of the sampling error to the latter.

B. Chemical, Physical, and Instrumental Reduction of Errors

Recalling the definition of sensitivity given above, it is possible to generalize and say that anything which increases sensitivity decreases error. Certainly this statement is not inviolate, but the exceptions are limited.

1. *Flame-Nebulization Regulation*

A prominent source of variability—instability in the flame—can be improved through the use of highly accurate ($\pm 1\%$) flow meters for regulating the gas flows delivered to the burner. The detection of small changes in burner characteristics caused by clogging or salt deposition on the orifice and the ability to adjust carefully and reproducibly the gas flows to the optimum values are features realized through the use of good flow meters (*5, 8*).

Independently controlling the sample delivery with an infusion pump is a technique routinely used to good advantage in the author's laboratory (*8*). For example, 10 successive absorption measurements on a zinc solution —allowing the burner to perform its own delivery-nebulization function— produced a relative standard deviation of the average absorbance of 1.2%. When the burner was fed at exactly the same rate by an infusion pump, the same average absorbance was obtained but the relative standard deviation was reduced to 0.3%. This latter value very closely approximates the limiting instrumental stability, which was found to be 0.25% by measuring an equivalent absorption signal produced by a screen without the burner in operation. Optimization of the sample feed rate at a level above that obtainable by normal sample feed methods increased the zinc absorption by a factor of 3 without a deleterious effect on the precision.

2. *Optimization*

As Parsons and Winefordner (*16*), Mandel (*14*), and the author (*17*) have indicated, the sensitivity concept provides a useful criterion for the selection of optimum instrumental, physical, and chemical conditions for analysis. In the majority of instances the relationship between signal intensity and some controlling variable passes through a maximum, as shown in Fig. 7. Obviously, the choice of the level of the variable x which maximizes the intensity is desirable in two respects. First, the slope is maximized, and second, because there is usually an inherent limit to the degree with which x can be regulated (e.g., $\Delta x = \pm 2\%$), the best signal reproducibility is most frequently obtained on the plateau, as demonstrated in the figure. Regardless of the measurement parameter used to indicate optimization, the selection of the appropriate settings for the

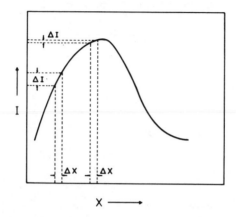

Fig. 7. Improved signal measurement precision through optimization.

many variables in an analytical method presents a formidable problem summarized by the following questions:

a. What variables influence the selected measurement parameter? (Can any of these be ignored?)
b. Which variables are interdependent?
c. What is the best combination of variable levels? (Are there others?)
d. What degree of regulation is required for each variable?

Statistically designed experiments provide the only really acceptable answers to these problems. For a good introduction to the concepts and capabilities of experimental design, the reader is referred to the books by Cochran and Cox (*18*) and Davies (*19*). For examples of applications of these techniques to spectroscopic problems, the papers by Parsons and Winefordner (*16*), Grant (*20*), Cellier and Stace (*21*), and the author (*17*) should be consulted.

Figure 8 presents an example of the increase in the analytical signal that can be realized by optimizing the sample feed rate with an infusion pump on a slot-type burner in atomic absorption. In this case the absorbance of an ethanol solution of chromium was increased by more than a factor of 2 in comparison to that obtained at the normal burner feed rate (3.0 ml/min). The increase has consistently been observed for a wide variety of systems investigated in the author's laboratory. It is also accompanied by an improved measurement precision.

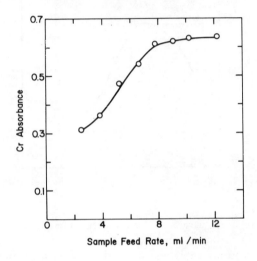

Fig. 8. Typical effect of sample feed rate on an atomic absorption measurement.

3. *Increasing the Signal-to-Noise Ratio*

Given optimum analysis conditions, scale expansion or precision spectrophotometric techniques are frequently used to reduce the error in reading the analytical signal. This effectively amounts to amplifying (or suppressing) the signal by electronic means so that its intensity level lies in a region for which the measurement error is minimum—the sensitivity is increased. The sensitivity of an instrument cannot, of course, be increased without limit merely by increasing amplification. Even when stray light signals have been reduced to a negligible level, there is an inherent random fluctuation (noise) in an instrument which results from the discrete nature of the charges in a nonmetallic medium (shot noise), and the random movement of charged particles (thermal noise). These fluctuations are always present at some level and usually present the ultimate limitation on the sensitivity of the instrument. It is also common in spectrophotometry to consider the related term—*dark current* of the photomultiplier.

The dark current originates from current leakage through insulators, thermionic emissions from the photocathode, and currents due to non-propagating gas discharges and optical feedback at higher voltages. Since the magnitude of the dark current fluctuations generally depends on the magnitude of the dark current itself, it is desirable to keep the latter as small as possible. This factor also generally limits the ultimate degree of amplification. There are a number of relatively simple expedients for reducing these noise contributions.

a. *Noise Reduction.* The main consideration in selecting a photomultiplier tube is that it must have a high photosensitivity (gain) coupled with a low dark current. Photomultipliers of a given type can vary over wide ranges in this respect. For example, the EMI 6255B and 6256B photomultiplers are equivalent in spectral response and overall sensitivity but their average dark currents are specified at 150×10^{-9} and 10×10^{-9}A respectively.

A lower theoretical level for the thermal noise is given quantitatively by (*22, 23*).

$$\bar{E}_{rms} = (4RkT\,\Delta F)^{1/2} \tag{24}$$

where $\bar{E}_{rms}$ is the root mean square value of the noise voltage, R is the resistance of the element, k is Boltzmann's constant, T is the absolute temperature, and ΔF is the bandwidth of the circuit.

The maximum shot-effect noise is given by

$$E_{rms} = (2qiR_L^2\,\Delta F)^{1/2} \tag{25}$$

where q is the charge on each charge carrier (electron), i is the total current through the circuit, and R_L is the value of the load resistor.

The methods for reducing noise are all suggested by Eq. (24) and (25). Keeping the resistance of the critical circuit elements low forces a compromise between high input resistance and low noise. Cooling the photomultiplier tube by electromechanical means is a technique that has been used to good advantage to reduce photomultiplier dark current, particularly in gamma and scintillation spectrophotometry. Units designed for use in other areas of spectrophotometry are commercially available. It is possible to reduce the dark current and its fluctuations by 2–3 orders of magnitude or more by cooling the photomultiplier tube to $-25°C$.

The absolute magnitude of the shot noise is proportional to the square root of the primary current (dark current plus photocurrent) emitted from the photocathode, and the relative noise is inversely proportional to the square root of the current (22, 24). In other words, a large signal is least affected by noise. Shot and dark current noise both cover a large range of frequencies but only a limited bandwidth. An ac amplifier passes only a portion of this range, dF. Producers of spectrophotometers have used ac amplification systems extensively for this reason. Most recently, two distinct design approaches to this means for eliminating noise have emerged: A narrow-band ac amplifier is followed by a rectifier and then a dc read-out system; or an ac amplifier (possibly wide-band) is followed by a phase-sensitive rectifier or lock-in amplifier and then a dc read-out (24). In the former, the amplitude of the dark current noise component transmitted by the system replaces the zero by an amount proportional to $(\Delta F)^{1/2}$. A noise component is superimposed on this reading. In the latter design, the phase and frequency of the phase-sensitive system must correspond to that of the interrupted signal. The zero displacement does not occur here, and the read-out remains proportional to the signal even at the smallest levels. The dark current and amplifier noise fluctuations are still present; however, their magnitudes are proportional to $(\Delta F)^{1/2}$. In the ultimate limit for either system, the signal-to-noise ratio can be increased by decreasing ΔF or by using a longer time constant to "smooth out" the noise fluctuations; there are practical limitations to both possibilities.

b. *Scale Expansion.* The precision spectrophotometric (or scale-expansion) technique is generally used to eliminate the dependence of error in concentration upon the errors made in measurement. In the usual theoretical treatment of this subject, it is assumed that the measurement error is constant throughout the range at a value such as 1 % of full scale. In view of the preceding discussion, it is apparent that this assumption, while informative, rarely represents a practical situation. Blaidel and Meloche (25) have presented a more practical evaluation of the use of this technique for systems wherein the standard deviation of measurement varies with the magnitude of the analytical signal. As might be anticipated, the scale ranges for minimum concentration error are highly dependent on this last relationship. Mandel (14) has applied the sensitivity concept given above to the evaluation of this problem with similar results. Either of these treatments can be used to calculate the sample dilution or preconcentration factors required to minimize concentration errors. See also the practical experimental evaluation given by Weir and Kofluk (7) and the application of precision spectrophotometric techniques in conjunction with measurement replication reported by Menis and Rains (26).

4. *Internal Standardization*

Perhaps the most widely accepted means for reducing errors is the use of the internal standard principle devised by Gerlach in 1925 (*27*). By monitoring the signal intensities of the analyte and the internal standard element (chosen to have properties similar to those of the analyte), variations due to changes in the atomization, nebulization, and measurement processes can be reduced or cancelled. The best utilization of this method in flame emission or absorption is realized only when the signals are measured simultaneously. If sequential signal readings are taken, random variations are not necessarily reduced, and systematic variations such as changes in the instrumental sensitivity, sample nebulization, and atomization may occur which would not necessarily be cancelled. Truly dual-beam, photomultiplier read-out systems for flame emission and absorption which permit simultaneous measurements have only recently become commercially available (*28*). By using strontium as the internal standard for the determination of calcium by atomic absorption, Smith (*28*) observed relative standard deviations in the 0.2–0.4% range for 20 successive measurements. This closely approaches what appear to be the present instrumental limits (*7*).

A nearly ideal application of the internal standard method in flame emission has recently been reported (*29*). The method, which involves measuring the intensity ratios of multiplet pairs, as a function of concentration, actually employs the element as its own internal standard. Among the advantages demonstrated for the systems studied are: prominent reductions in the dependence on flame conditions, ionization equilibria, and solvent effects; and elimination or reduction of solute vaporization interferences. This approach is equally applicable to atomic absorption and, if used with a truly dual-beam system, should produce highly precise results.

Because the application of any analysis technique is governed to a large extent by the analytical sensitivity, a large portion of the preceeding discussion has been devoted to this concept. We have not directly considered the closely related, but distinct, term detection limit or other factors involved in choosing the analysis method to be used.

VI. Selection of the Analysis Method

A. DETECTION LIMITS

The detection capability of a method is of prime importance for many analysis problems. A variety of definitions have been proposed for this term but the most generally acceptable verbal definition appears to be: the minimum concentration that can be detected at a particular confidence level (5, 8, 9, 11, 30, 31). This capability for any technique is generally determined by the species of interest, the matrix in which it is present, and the identities and levels of other trace or minor species present in the samples. In essence, the detection limit may define the applicability of a technique, the sample size required, and the chemical and/or physical pretreatment methods used in the analysis process.

In spite of the general acceptance of the above verbal definition, the agreement degenerates in the formulation of a mathematical definition for detection limit. Much of the argument originates from the erroneous assumption that the detection of low concentrations is strictly limited by the signal-to-background ratio. It is well documented, however, that the limiting factor is the ratio of the analytical signal to the statistical fluctuations in the background (or blank) signal (30–32). In retrospect, it is apparent that this is exactly what the sensitivity definition given above measures.

At, or near, the detection limit the magnitudes of the analytical signal, I, and its standard deviation, s, approach the magnitudes of the background (blank, or noise signal), I_b, and the background fluctuation, s_b, respectively (5, 8, 9). The minimum signal change that can be differentiated is given by

$$dI_m = I - I_b \equiv s = s_b \tag{26}$$

If we wish to objectively associate a particular confidence level with dI_m, it is necessary to introduce the appropriate value of the t statistic, i.e.,

$$dI_m = st_{(1 - \alpha)(n - 1)} \tag{27}$$

where the value of t depends on the number of measurements, n, used to compute s and the $100(1 - \alpha)$ percentage confidence level required. The concentration associated with dI_m is readily determined from the analytical curve. For a linear curve:

$$I = mC + I_b \tag{28}$$

where m is the slope and C the concentration. Substitution into Eq. (27) produces the following expression for the minimum concentration:

$$C_m = \frac{dI_m}{m} = \frac{st_{(1 - \alpha)(n - 1)}}{m} \tag{29}$$

On substitution of Eq. (10) this reduces to

$$C_m = \frac{t_{(1 - \alpha)(n - 1)}}{\gamma} \tag{30}$$

This definition is entirely consistent with another popular definition, i.e., the concentration which gives rise to a signal equal to twice the standard deviation of the blank fluctuations (32). The use of "twice" in the latter refers to a large number of measurements (normal distribution) while the use of t permits a calculation based on fewer measurements (30, 31).

Equation (30) effectively defines the minimum determinable change in concentration at any level if the slope and the standard deviation for that level are used to determine γ. Thus, it can be used to define terms such as determination limits or minimum working concentrations suggested by others (11). It must be emphasized that, even though detection limits are carefully measured and defined, they are still somewhat nebulous quantities (33). They depend both on the mode of data acquisition and the characteristics of the instrumentation used. A factor of 2–3 uncertainty in the values can be anticipated.

The full realization of the potentialities of an analysis technique can, in many cases, be achieved only by coupling the technique with preconcentrations and separations to remove or minimize the persisting possibility of interferences or to provide adequate analyte for the measurement to be used. These analysis operations constitute the pretreatment step and may be accomplished by various physical or chemical methods.

B. Physical and Chemical Pretreatment

The sample characteristics, the measurement technique employed, and physical capabilities of the instrumental system determine the specific requirements for preconcentration and separation. Many methods provide some degree of physical resolution which can be adjusted to minimize interferences. For example, spectral interferences can be reduced by increasing the resolution of the instrument, and solute-vaporization interferences can be obviated by choosing the proper flame for atomization and/or excitation (34).

Sample pretreatment may also be required to convert the analyte to a form most appropriate for the measurement. In atomic emission or absorption, for example, the treatment may be chosen such that the analyte is obtained in a chemical form suitable for dissolution in, or extraction into, an organic solvent. The pretreatment step may also include some means for homogenization when necessary. Whatever the reason for the operation, extreme care must be taken to avoid contamination or loss of the analyte, particularly at the trace concentration levels. These problems have been treated extensively in a number of papers (35–38). Wherever possible, the minimum of pretreatment is preferable and direct methods of analysis should be selected if applicable to the problem.

A variety of chemical separation methods are available, but the most universally applicable ones are: ion exchange, solvent extraction, chromatography, electrodeposition, volatilization, precipitation, and coprecipitation. Preconcentration by sample ashing is used extensively, and the recently developed method of low-temperature dry-ashing appears particularly promising (39). Zone melting and selective evaporation are two popular physical methods for solid samples.

There are two important terms relating to this discussion which should be defined. One is the recovery or yield (R_A) of the analyte A and the other is the separation factor ($S_{B/A}$) for the unwanted constituent B with respect to the analyte. The definitions are:

$$R \text{ (in percent)} = 100 Q_A / Q_A^0 \tag{31}$$

and

$$S_{B/A} = \frac{Q_B/Q_A}{Q_B^0/Q_A^0} \tag{32}$$

where Q_A^0 is the amount of A in the sample, Q_B^0 the amount of B in the sample, Q_A is the quantity of A after separation, and Q_B the amount of B after separation (5).

The concentration or enrichment factor of A, when B is the matrix, is given by the reciprocal of Eq. (32). In the ideal case, $R_A = 100\%$ and $S_{B/A} = 0$. When the limits of detection are known, the appropriate method of separation and/or preconcentration and the sample size can be selected by applying Eq. (31) and (32). Whenever pretreatment is used, it is advisable to process standards and blanks with the samples to avoid a variety of errors.

C. SCOPE AND SELECTIVITY

Other characteristics which are important in the selection or comparison of analysis methods are scope, selectivity, cost, and time (5, 9).

Several facets are associated with the term analytical scope; most of these directly or indirectly influence other characteristics. A method of large scope permits the simultaneous determination of many species, is accurate and sensitive, requires minimal pretreatment operations (direct analysis), is interference-free (selective), uses simple and readily available standards and calibration procedures, accepts samples of diverse form and composition, provides results which are easy to obtain and interpret, and minimizes the cost-time function (5).

There are countless examples demonstrating the inseparability of these considerations. A direct analysis suggests high selectivity but may impose more stringent requirements on the choice of standards should interference exist. The greater scope of a multielement technique may minimize the cost–time function but be less selective than a single-element technique. Nonselective methods may require separations which are subject to loss and contamination and may also increase the time–cost gains associated with the multielement aspect. Frequently, sensitivity or accuracy is sacrificed in favor of another gain within the aspects of scope. No single technique is a panacea for all problems, but one offering a fair degree of versatility is generally preferred. The final choice of an analysis method is reached through a series of compromises which are governed by the analysis requirements, the intended use of the results, and the other practical considerations mentioned.

The preceding survey of the sources, methods of evaluation, and techniques for minimizing errors has, of necessity, been general in many respects. More extensive treatments of each topic will be found in the appropriate chapters. Good introductory statistical background may be obtained by referring to any of several references (1, 3, 4, 14, 31, 40, 41).

There is an increasing awareness of the value of statistics in analytical chemistry. Even so, the general literature of analysis shows a lack of uniformity with regard to statements about accuracy and precision. A statement such as: "The relative standard deviation was found to be $\pm 8\%$ and it is assumed that the accuracy is equivalent . . ." is nearly meaningless unless the method of determining the precision is definitely stated and an objective comparison of the results with other independent results has been made. In this sense, an evaluation of all three phases of the analysis will be beneficial in reducing confusion and in establishing the accuracy of the method.

REFERENCES

1. W. J. Youdon, *Statistical Methods for Chemists*, Wiley, New York, 1951.
2. W. G. Cochran, *Sampling Techniques*, Wiley, New York, 1963.
3. B. Ostle, *Statistics in Research*, Iowa State Univ. Press, Ames, 1963.
4. A. B. Calder, *Anal. Chem.*, **36**, (No. 9) 25A (1964).
5. R. K. Skogerboe and G. H. Morrison, in *Treatise on Analytical Chemistry* (I. M. Kolthoff and P. Elving, eds.), Part I, Wiley (Interscience), New York, in press.
6. H. A. Laitinen, *Chemical Analysis*, McGraw-Hill, New York, 1960.
7. D. R. Weir and R. P. Kofluk, *At. Absorption Newsletter*, **6**, 24 (1967).
8. R. K. Skogerboe, A. T. Heybey, and G. H. Morrison, *Anal. Chem.*, **38**, 1821 (1966).
9. G. H. Morrison and R. K. Skogerboe, in *Trace Analysis: Physical Methods* (G. H. Morrison, ed.), Wiley (Interscience), New York, 1965.
10. J. Mandel and R. D. Stiehler, *J. Res. Natl. Bur. Std.*, **A53**, 155 (1954).
11. J. Ramírez-Muñoz, *Talanta*, **13**, 87 (1966).
12. T. E. Beukelman and S. S. Lord, Jr., *Appl. Spectry.*, **14**, 12 (1962).
13. W. J. Youden, *Ind. Eng. Chem., Anal. Ed.*, **19**, 943 (1947).
14. J. Mandel, *Statistical Analysis of Experimental Data*, Wiley (Interscience), New York, 1964.
15. R. K. Skogerboe, W. L. Harrington, and G. H. Morrison, *Anal. Chem.*, **38**, 1408 (1966).
16. M. L. Parsons and J. D. Winefordner, *Appl. Spectry.*, **21**, 368 (1967).
17. R. K. Skogerboe, in *Developments in Applied Spectroscopy* (W. Baer and E. L. Grove, eds.), Plenum, New York, in press.
18. W. G. Cochran and G. M. Cox, *Experimental Design*, Wiley, New York, 1960.
19. O. L. Davies, *Design and Analysis of Industrial Experiments*, Hafner, New York, 1960.
20. C. L. Grant, *Can. Spectry.*, **47**, (1963).
21. K. M. Cellier and H. C. T. Stace, *Appl. Spectry.*, **20**, 26 (1966).
22. H. V. Malmstadt, C. G. Enke, and E. C. Toren, Jr., *Electronics for Scientists*, Benjamin, New York, 1963.
23. E. J. Bair, *Introduction to Chemical Instrumentation*, McGraw-Hill, New York, 1962.
24. R. Herrmann and C. T. J. Alkemade, *Chemical Analysis by Flame Photometry* Wiley (Interscience), New York, 1963.
25. W. J. Blaidel and V. W. Meloche, *Elementary Quantitative Analysis*, Harper and Row, New York, 1963, p. 878.
26. T. C. Rains, in *N.B.S. Tech. Note 424* (O. Menis, ed.) 1967.
27. W. Gerlach, *Z. anorg. allg. Chem.*, **142**, 383 (1925).
28. S. B. Smith, Company Report, Instrumentation Laboratory, Inc., Watertown, Mass., 1966.
29. R. K. Skogerboe, R. Todd, and G. H. Morrison, *Anal. Chem.*, **40**, 2 (1968).
30. H. Kaiser and H. Specker, *Z. anal. Chem.*, **149**, 46 (1955).
31. H. Kaiser, *Z. anal. Chem.*, **216**, 80 (1966).
32. V. A. Fassel and D. W. Golightly, *Anal. Chem.*, **39**, 466 (1967).
33. W. Slavin, *Appl. Spectry.*, **20**, 281 (1966).
34. V. G. Mossotti and M. Duggan, *Applied Optics*, **7**, 1325 (1968).
35. T. T. Gorsuch, *Analyst*, **84**, 135 (1959).

36. A. Mizuike, in *Trace Analysis: Physical Methods* (G. H. Morrison, ed.), Wiley (Interscience), New York, 1965.
37. J. Stary; *Solvent Extraction of Metal Chelates*, Pergamon, New York, 1965.
38. *U.S. Atomic Energy Comm. Repts. Nucl. Sci. Series, NAS-NS*, Washington, D.C.
39. C. E. Gleit, *Am. J. Med. Electronics*, **2**, 112 (1963).
40. M. G. Natrella, *Experimental Statistics, Nat. Bur. Std. (U.S.), Handbook*, **91**, 1963.
41. F. J. Linnig and J. Mandel, *Anal. Chem.*, **36**, (No. 13), 25A (1964).

Author Index

Numbers in parentheses are reference numbers and indicate that an author's work is referred to although his name is not cited in the text. Numbers in italics show the page on which the complete reference is cited.

A

Adams, P. B., 374(84), *379*
Adkins, J. E., 290(27a), *293*, 345(67), *348*, 367(59), *379*
Aime, C. P., 39(10, 11), *48*
Alkemade, C. T. J., 8, 9, 13, *22*, 88(25), *98*, 103(5, 6), 105(12), 106(15), 107(18), 110(5, 6), 111(18), 112(5, 6), 113(5, 6, 36), 114(6, 36, 39), 115(39), 116(42, 18), 117(18), 119(18), 123(58), 124(18), 126(6, 18), 128(18), 130(70), 131(70, 71), 132(70), 138(6, 18), 139(18, 83), 140(84), 141(84), 142(18), 143(83, 84), 146(90), 147(96), *148*, 168, 177(53), 179(62), *186*, 217(1), 219(4), 220(5), *238*, 250, *265*, 268, 279, 288(1), *292*, 317(1), 319(7), 323, 331(7), 332(7), 334(7), 337(7, 46), 338(50), 342(46), 343(62), 345(46), 346, *346*, *348*, 355 (21), 366, *378*, *379*, 404(24), *410*
Allan, J. E., 7, 10, 12, *21*, *23*, 309, 310(40), 311, *315*
Amos, M. D., 94(46), *99*, 134(77), 135(78), *150*, 194(12), 199(12), 200(12), *210*, 290(25, 26), *293*, 324(22), 327(22), 341(22), 342(22), *347*, 358, 362(27), *378*
Anderson, C. H., 236(23), *239*
Asaba, T., 169, *186*
Avery, W. H., 261(19), 262, *265*
Avni, R., 105(12), *148*, 343(62), *348*

B

Baily, S. M., 236(24), *239*
Bair, E. J., 403(23), *410*

Baker, M. R., 204(33), 206, *210*, 249(4), 254(4), 256(4, 13), *265*, 301(20, 21), *314*, 325(29), 335(29), 343(29, 59), *347*, *348*, 351(6), 372(6), *377*
Baldwin, R. R., 155(4), *185*
Balmer, J. J., 51, *98*
Barber, C. R., 228(17), *239*
Barnes, Jr., L., 372(76), *379*
Barnes, R. B., 6, *21*
Barthel, C., 204(42), *211*
Bartholomay, A. F., 204(31), 206, *210*
Bartholomé, E., 191(4), *209*
Bascombe, K. N., 158(11), *185*
Bauer, S. H., 165(33), *186*
Baum, E., 6, *21*, 372(75), *379*
Becker, D. A., 46(21), *48*, 191(9), *210*
Beckmann, E., 4, *20*
Belcher, C. B., 327, *347*, 372(71), *379*
Bell, E. E., 204(36), *210*
Bell, G., 253(10), *265*
Belles, F. E., 168, 169, *186*
Berkowitz, J., 180(68), *187*
Berry, J. W., 6, *21*, 209, *211*
Beukelman, T. E., 392, *410*
Billings, G. K., 311(48), *315*
Blaidel, W. J., 404, *410*
Bleckrode, R., 93(44), *99*
Bode, H., 334(44), *348*
Bohr, N., 53, *98*
Boiteux, H., 86(20), *98*, 103(7), 113(7), 116(7), 119(7), 126(7), 127(7), 138(7), 141(7), *148*, 179(61), *187*, 190(3), 192(3), 200(3), *207*, *211*, 274, *292*, 297 299, 308(12), *314*, 323(20), 324(20), 345 (20), *347*, 364, *378*
Bonne, U., 160(24), *186*

413

Subject Index

A

Absorbance, factors controlling, 246–252
  flame profiles of, 242–245, 250–251, 255–256, 258, 262
Absorption, integrated, 250
Absorption flame methods, 28, 34–36; *see also* Atomic absorption
Absorption line, selection of, 359–361
Absorption path, long tube, 11
Absorption spectra, 50
Absorption transitions of spectral lines, 70
Accuracy, 18, 384
  comparison of methods, 394–395
  empirical method for, 392–393
  evaluation of, 389–395
  reduction of errors
    instrumental, 400–405
    statistical, 395–399
Acetone, influence on flame temperature, 236
Acetylene, oxidation of, 92–94, 160
Acetylene flames, 95–97, 160, 195, 199–201
  burning velocity of (table), 191
  emission features of, 274–278
  temperature of (table), 191; *see also* Air-, Nitrous oxide-, Oxygen-
Acid concentration, interference from, 332–334, 353
Addition method, 377
Adiabatic flame temperature, 171–175
Aerosol particles, 102–103, 319
  effect on absorption, 249
  formation of, 6–7, 108–111
  vaporization of, 102–116, 304–305, 350–357
Agricultural and plant materials, analysis of, 9
Air–acetylene flame, 199
  atomic distribution in, 243–244
  burning velocity of, 191
  composition of, 233
  hydroxyl radical in, 262
  interferences from, 358
  oxygen influence in, 236
  spectrum of, 274–278
  temperature of, 173, 191, 218, 233–236
Air–hydrocarbon flame, *see* Hydrocarbon flames
Air–hydrogen flame
  burning velocity of, 191
  composition of, 86–88, 154, 172, 233
  emission features, 86–92
  interference in, 358
  reaction of gases in, 84–86, 154
  reaction zone of, 153
  temperature of, 172, (table) 191, 233–235
Air pressure, influence on droplet size, 300–302
Air–propane flame, temperature of, 234–235
Alcohol flame, 2
Alkali metal halides, dissociation constants of (table), 330
Alkali metal hydroxides, 117, 324
  bond energies, 182
  heats of formation (table), 91
Alkali metals, 5
  emission intensity and aspiration rate, 344
  energy levels of, 52, 55–57
  heats of formation (table), 91
  ionization of, 130–133, 334–342
  ionization constants (table), 334–335
  quenching cross sections of (table), 140
  radial probability—electron density distribution function, 63–64
  reversal temperatures of (table), 323
  selection rules for, 67
  spectra of, 58, 75
  term system, 52, 56